A Fan
for All
Seasons

A Fan for All Seasons

Laurence Marks

LITTLE, BROWN AND COMPANY

A *Little, Brown* Book

First published in Great Britain in 1999
by Little, Brown and Company

Copyright © Laurence Marks 1999

The moral right of the author has been asserted.

A CIP catalogue record for this book
is available from the British Library.

ISBN: 0 316 84945 6

Typeset in Palatino by M Rules
Printed and bound in Great Britain
by Clays Ltd, St Ives plc

Little, Brown & Company (UK)
Brettenham House
Lancaster Place
London WC2E 7EN

All Arsenal fans are eternal optimists. They say we can still win the Premiership title if we win seven out of the last four games.

I should like to dedicate this book to David Dein, the Arsenal vice-chairman, whom I believe has done more than anyone to make the Arsenal a team we are proud to support, and a club we are proud to belong to . . . Oh, and for bringing Arsene Wenger to Highbury.

The dedication extends too, to the members of the Crescit Club, who gather before each home game to put right the wrongs of team selection and club policy – though never better than those who are paid to do so.

Andrew Arends
Ed Bishop
Cindy Blake
Melvyn Bragg
Maurice Gran
Anthony Holden
Ben Holden
Joe Holden
Sam Holden
Colin Hughes
Sarah Panath
and
Alan Samson

Introduction

I once asked my favourite of all diarists, Tony Benn, 'What do you think makes a good diary?' He poured me a large mug of tea, and while we puffed our pipes, filling the room with what resembled an old-fashioned London fog, he replied, 'Diaries are distinct from memoirs. Political memoirs are usually written in retirement and tend to recall such triumphs as can be imagined and conveniently forget the failures. The media, in contrast, can tell you what to think today and reflect with time, disdainfully excluding those who fall outside their spectrum of permissible opinion. Historians, who are usually not involved in the events they describe at all, can bask in the afterglow of hindsight, and present their own (highly personal) interpretation of those events.

'The diarist, however, writes a nightly confession in which mistakes are recorded before they are recognised as such and when predictions of the future are yet to be verified. For this reason, diaries have an important part to play in providing raw material for those who wish to interrogate posthumously those who have played some part in the period of history they may wish to study.'

The period I wish to study is the reign of Arsene Wenger as it affected me, an Arsenal supporter through and through. To be able to do this through the benefit of the notes that I made at the time, without correction, means that I am not being wise after the event. Our memories inevitably play tricks with us, but a diarist can turn to a time in his/her life and be exact in knowing his/her thoughts at that given moment. Unlike millions of football supporters, no matter which team they support, I suppose I am able to recall events that I would swear never at all happened were I to be recalling them today.

At the start of the 1996–97 season, could we Gooners really have wanted Frank Clark as the new Arsenal manager instead of an unknown quantity called Arsene Wenger? Well, apparently we did. I had forgotten that fact. But there it was, in the pages of my diary! A mistake that was recorded before it was recognised as such.

LM

Monday, 12 August 1996

The season begins on Saturday and both Maurice [Gran] and I find it extremely odd that Arsenal have not ventured into the market for players, particularly as it is so obvious that they are more than a little deficient in the midfield department, not to mention strike force. I wouldn't mind placing a little wager that Bruce Rioch, the Arsenal manager, won't be in the job by Christmas. Maurice thinks it's unlikely that they will sack Rioch. He feels the board is in turmoil and there is more likelihood that we shall see a change there, unless Arsenal have stayed out of the transfer market because they know something other more spend-thrift clubs do not; or it is their intention to float the company and take them public. It is therefore an excited Maurice who at four o'clock starts bleeping his car horn to attract my attention to inform me that the BBC news has just announced that Arsenal have dismissed Bruce Rioch. There is no news of his intended replacement, only that he is leaving the club in their best interests this afternoon.

Well, I'm shocked, I have to admit it! I believed they would probably allow him to leave after a bad first half to the season, but the Arsenal board obviously feel now is the time, that the man is not performing the Arsenal way – or is there something more devious involved? We shall never know, we are only the fans. Maurice and I go to our fitness training class this afternoon spec-ulating on who will be the next Arsenal manager. The three names that I come up with are Terry Venables, George Graham (that is if Arsenal would take him back) and Alan Ball, although perhaps he hasn't a strong enough track record. I'm not sure that Venables hasn't already joined Portsmouth, but everyone knows that Manchester United and Arsenal are the plum English managerial positions and many managers, I should imagine, would jump at the opportunity to bring glory to Arsenal and themselves.

On the BBC's Six O'Clock News, those being spoken of as Rioch's replacement are George Graham, Johan Cruyff and Tony Adams. Surely Adams still has many years of playing ahead of him? And would Arsenal really put their reputation on the line by re-employing George Graham after the disgrace he brought to the club, even though his vast ability as a manager is not in doubt? And where does Cruyff, former manager of Barcelona, fit into the picture? It is highly exciting for any Arsenal supporter, but those interviewed by the news outside the Highbury ground this afternoon seem not to think it's exciting at all. They think Rioch was all right. He took Arsenal into Europe in his first season, we finished fifth, reached the semi-final of the Coca-Cola Cup, what was so bad about that? These supporters believe there is something wrong with the board and it is they who should be under the spotlight. Something tells me the fans are right.

Maurice and I are writing a four-part drama series on Oswald Mosley and we had hoped to complete the first draft of the final episode today. However, before we can do so, I find we need to know very much more about Mosley's tribunal hearing in 1940. Therefore this evening I read the relevant chapters in A.W. Brian Simpson's *In The Highest Degree Odious*, a book about detention without trial in wartime Britain. Even when I've finished this text, I'm little the wiser about what made Mosley's stay in prison quite so lengthy, particularly as there was no evidence against him for treason.

On the Nine O'Clock News, the names of George Graham and Johan Cruyff are mentioned again; also a man named Wenger who has suddenly stepped into the favourite's position to become the next Arsenal manager. I go to bed and listen to an interview with Tony Adams about the Arsenal situation, but he doesn't know anything. He does say quite categorically that he will not become the next Arsenal manager, his only aim is to get fit and return to the first team. The Arsenal v. West Ham fixture on Saturday will be fascinating for many reasons. Bruce Rioch will not remember today as 'the glorious twelfth' – he spent less than a year at Arsenal, took them into Europe and then got the sack.

Tuesday, 13 August

This afternoon at four o'clock Maurice and I finish 'Mosley'. It is only a first draft but at least we have finished that tumultuous effort of reading, translating and creating what I sincerely hope will become the best serial on British television in the year 1997. I don't know just how long it has taken us to complete this quartet – I shall count the days in my diary – but I believe we are talking in excess of four or five months. Spending that long on a project takes me back to the old Highworth Road days of 'Shine On Harvey Moon'. I have thoroughly enjoyed it. Now four episodes are ready for editing. It is going to be an unusual feeling to come into the Cattle Shed – my work space happens to be an outhouse, the name seems appropriate – each morning and not spend my day surrounded by books relating to Oswald Mosley, and not have to try to keep in my head all the information I've ever read about British politics between the two World Wars. The script is sent by modem to Elaine at ALOMO, our television production company. She will in turn send a copy to Nicholas Mosley, Oswald's son, and one to Guy Slater, ALOMO's managing director, so hopefully by the middle of next week we shall have received notes from them both and we can get on with improving the piece ready for pre-production.

Now Maurice and I have 'Birds of a Feather' to look forward to. We must write two excellent episodes before moving on to two excellent episodes of 'Goodnight Sweetheart'. Then we must concentrate our minds upon 'Unfinished Business' to which I have continually been giving serious thought, especially in the areas of marital breakdown and rediscovery. This last project might prove to be the most exciting of all. Pauline Quirke was married to Stephen Sheen last week. I know this for it was fairly splashed about the tabloid newspapers. Neither Maurice nor I received an invitation. Maurice put Pauline up, indeed he handed her his house, when she was in the slough of despond. All right, she needn't have invited me, but in those days of the early 1990s, Pauline was at her lowest ebb, found a friend and took the friendship offered, and I would have thought that she would have remembered this sanctuary.

After dispatching 'Mosley', it is the subject of Arsenal that dominates our thoughts. This morning, before I even began writing my diary, I sent a fax to Yvette at Highbury asking if she can sell me a ticket for the Arsenal v. West Ham match on Saturday, the first game of the season. She telephones me back to say I'm in luck; really it's my old friend Alan Ager, a West Ham supporter, who is in luck. We then, inevitably, discuss the sacking of Bruce Rioch and who will become the next Arsenal manager. I suggest George Graham which Yvette dismisses out of hand (Yvette is a mainstay of Arsenal's commercial department, in the midst of where events are happening, and has her ear to the ground). She almost positively knows that the Frenchman Arsene Wenger will be announced as the new Arsenal manager come Thursday morning. I ask her how she can be so positive, and she replies, 'We have all put two and two together and got one hundred and ninety.' So it won't be Johan Cruyff? It appears not.

Maurice suggests I telephone Harry Harris, our good friend the football journalist on the *Daily Mirror*. Harry and I used to work together on the *Weekly Herald* and have maintained our friendship since those far-off Tottenham days. Harry tells me that he conducted the last ever interview with Bruce Rioch as the Arsenal manager, he knew his time had come, and the Arsenal are right, of course, Wenger will become the next Arsenal manager, if for no other reason than he is a good friend of vice-chairman David Dein's, which appears to be a pre-requisite for the new man. I discuss with Harry why Rioch was sacked, why the man didn't buy more than one player in this close season, and Harry suggests I buy this morning's *Daily Mirror*. He doesn't really want to talk in his office, the competition for stories is fierce, but why don't we meet this evening for dinner? This sounds like a good idea and over drinks and a fine Italian meal Harry tells me about the Inland Revenue investigation into the Arsenal and the complete story behind the sacking of George Graham, the appointment and sacking of Bruce Rioch, and why David Dein is intent on appointing Wenger. I tell Harry why I believe George Graham would be the fans' choice, despite his flagrant breach of the law, and Harry immediately seizes the opportunity to ask me if I would write it for the *Daily Mirror*'s back page.

I explain to Harry that this is a craft in which I am unskilled, to be able to sit and write a feature for Thursday morning's newspaper on the spur of the moment. I have to give what I write deep thought and consideration, so perhaps I am not the best person to do this. Harry wholeheartedly disagrees, takes out his notebook, finds some pages that do not have shorthand notes scribbled across them and begins taking down my thoughts about the re-appointment of George Graham. It takes about ten minutes to explain why we must forgive and forget if the best man for the job has paid his debt to society and is ready to resume his post. It is rather abstract and certainly not a usual point of view, but it pleases Harry who sells the idea to his sports editor over the tele-phone.

I wonder what George Graham will think when he reads the feature on Thursday morning. I wonder what David Dein will feel as he sits down to his breakfast come Thursday and reads the opinion of one of the tens of thousands of Arsenal fans. I shall be interested to note the reaction to me when I go to the Arsenal v. West Ham game on Saturday.

It appears the *Daily Mirror* are pleased with my 'ghosted' column and ask Harry to ask me to be a monthly guest columnist. They would like me to write one match report a month, involving Arsenal. I tell Harry I should very much enjoy doing this. I'm saving all tonight's adventure to tell Maurice when I see him on Thursday morning.

And all this on the day 'Mosley' has been completed. Quite a day.

WEDNESDAY, 14 AUGUST

Coffee at Renzo's Café this morning. I stayed over at my flat in Clarges Street after dinner with Harry rather than returning home to Spring Hill, and Renzo's is nearby. Renzo is a fervent Arsenal fan and he, like all of us, is keen to exchange opinions about who is to be the next boss of the club we support. I told him what I learned last night – it seems that Arsene Wenger will take over the leadership some time this week, that Arsenal really wanted Frank Clark of Nottingham Forest, and that Johan Cruyff has never been anything more than speculation.

I have to tear myself away from this interesting discussion to go and meet Simon Nye, the author of 'Men Behaving Badly', in a smart basement in Charlotte Street where he works with other writers of mirth. Smart it may be, dark it certainly is and Simon and I adjourn to the brasserie across the road for coffee (more coffee!) and lounge in the comfy chair section for over an hour, until Simon feels it is time for him to return and make the British television viewing public laugh. I am there ostensibly to talk about the 'Lost Over Denver' session at the Edinburgh Television Festival, but I'm fascinated to learn more of his life as a writer before he came by the huge success of 'Men Behaving Badly'.

It seems Simon worked as a translator at a book publisher but always wanted to write. Therefore, as with most of us authors *manqués*, he wrote during the evenings, novels mostly, or rather exclusively. After he had had two books published, one of which was *Men Behaving Badly*, he decided to try to rewrite it as a television comedy. He managed it most successfully, although after just one series it was taken off the air at ITV. He tried to sell it to Channel Four but was given a brusque rejection. Alan Yentob at BBC1 bought it – the rest is history. Simon, a born writer, then came up with 'Frank Stubbs' and 'Is It Legal?', but all the time it was 'Men Behaving Badly' that was his first love and he will continue to write this series for as long as the actors wish to perform it. It is now being shot in the USA, which I am particularly interested to hear about.

I really like Simon. He is essentially a shy man, as are most comedy writers I have met across the years. He says that he would much rather back down from a confrontation than stand his ground, which is why he is becoming a little frayed at the edges with Martin Clunes, who seems forever to want to change or expand his character. Perhaps this is an occupational hazard with actors. I tell Simon about how we are currently having to recast both the women in 'Goodnight Sweetheart' and the two husbands in 'Birds of a Feather'. I have now come to accept that the secondary roles of a comedy will change during a long-running series, but that doesn't mean you have to stop making the series. Perhaps it's better to cast unknowns – they might be more appreciative of the work.

THURSDAY, 15 AUGUST

Back at the Cattle Shed, I am expecting to dive straight into 'Birds' this morning, but Maurice feels we can afford to take the day off, meaning doing nothing too strenuous, so I tell him the A to Z of my evening with Harry Harris, as well as all the other news. Maurice is fascinated to learn why, according to Harry, David Dein and Bruce Rioch had to go their separate ways – the vice-chairman was no longer prepared to tolerate the whimsical behaviour of the manager he had appointed. A cruel joke doing the rounds at Highbury is that Rioch was known as 'Dagenham'.

'Why?' asks Maurice.

'Because he was two stops past Barking.'

I mention, too, how Harry believes we ought to try to buy shares in the football club, or at least voting rights from those who own the limited number of shares. Maurice thinks this might be a good idea, although it has to be said that neither of us have any interest whatsoever in having a say in the running of Arsenal football club. We should like to attend shareholders' meetings and say our piece if necessary, that's all. We ring up the stockbroker we used when selling SelecTV and speak to Richard Slape. He quotes the Arsenal shares at between £1,550 and £1,650 a share, that is if he is able to find any, such is the difficulty in obtaining them. He will call us back when he has located some. How many do we want? Maurice thinks ten shares each would be a good investment.

Friday, 16 August

There is a row currently in progress, a political row despite the politicians being in recess, but this is an interesting row for it has little to do with politics and policies and everything to do with advertising. The Tories, in their usual sleazy way that they imagine is humorous, have released an advertisement picturing Tony Blair as the devil, a demon who will when elected make demons of the entire nation. The Church of England is really angry that anyone should be portrayed in this fashion – they've done it by replacing his eyes in the picture – for it shows a signal lack of respect for Christianity, but the Conservatives say it's nothing more than a joke, which tells us all what they consider funny. I wonder how they would have reacted had the photograph with the devil's eyes been of John Major. Leading this campaign is none other than Michael Howard, the Home Secretary. It saddens me to think of the depth to which political parties will sink in order to get a point across. Surely the chamber of the House of Commons, and intelligent oration, is the place and manner in which political point scoring should be made? No, not any more. Now we use advertising agencies who are led by the poor-quality ideas from members of the Conservative Party.

Maurice and I have nearly as leisurely a day as we had yesterday, only today we do work a little. We open a new directory entitled 'Birds '96' on the computer, and begin working out and putting down the storyline for the third episode of this new series. As ever, we argue about certain factors, largely to do with how quickly to introduce Dorien, and what her function is in the piece.

Adam Faith is coming to see us today and we plan to go for a pub lunch. It's the first time he has been to Spring Hill and he loves it and its surroundings. If my wife Brigitte (Briggy) and I had not visited his Westerham home back in 1992, I doubt we should have seriously entertained the idea of living in the country, but Adam says that this is the *real* country and I do believe he's right.

At the Mason's Arms, a pub where you will never hear it said 'I'm terribly sorry but we stop serving food at one o'clock', the conversation turns to Cuba. Adam became interested in Cuba while he was in St Petersburg filming 'Love Hurts', so that must have been in 1992. He realised much business was to be done both in the new Russia and in Cuba, so he took himself off to the largest of all the Caribbean islands (apparently Cuba is the same size as England) and spent some months there, something an Englishman never does. When he returned, the government department of the Foreign Office and the Department of Trade and Industry invited him to sit on a committee that was interested in not only knowing more about Cuba, but also learning of the trading possibilities.

Adam's as busy as ever. He has an autobiography *Acts of Faith*, coming out soon, a new chat show, 'Faith', and a money programme entitled 'Dosh' he is making and fronting, both for Channel Four. He's contented, but he isn't at all sure that he's happy. As he mentions to Maurice and me when we return to the Cattle Shed, 'Happiness comes for me in the shape of a woman.' Adam and Michael Winner – and how many other men of a certain age whose heyday was in the 1960s? Adam just adores Oxfordshire and starts browsing through the *Oxford Times* at the property section, so I invite him to come for Sunday lunch in the next few weeks and I will show him the surrounding areas. If he doesn't fall completely head over heels in love with the area, he will love nowhere again in his life.

This afternoon a fax arrives from Nick Mosley with his notes on the fourth script in the 'Mosley' quartet. It's as encouraging a letter as were his previous three, although the list of notes is considerably longer, but as he points out, 'This is the episode where my own memory comes in.' I'm taken, although I'm not sure whether I'm pleased he is able to write this comment or not, with his line, 'I think you've been amazingly fair to my father. I'm quite wide-eyed about it all.'

SATURDAY, 17 AUGUST

A beautiful summer's day, fitting weather for the first day of the football season. I'm sitting here thinking how much I'm failing to be excited about it, the one annual event that I have looked forward to over the past goodness knows how many years. Perhaps Euro '96 has lessened my appetite for the forthcoming season, or perhaps I'm simply jaundiced by the fact that football these days is based upon what a player can get from the game rather than what he's prepared to put into it. Perhaps I'm slowly losing the appetite I once had.

However, I don't intend to miss the first game of the season. It's likely to be as much a social event as a visit to a football stadium. Alan Ager and I leave Spring Hill and travel by way of my garage to the Boot Inn where we meet up with Maurice, and the three of us travel in the sublime comfort of the Bentley to Highbury. On the journey, Alan explains why he chose to stop watching West Ham United in 1975. He had been attending their matches from 1955 to 1975, missing few games, but on a very wet Friday night, standing on the same slab of stone he had stood on for twenty years, he decided it wasn't worth it any more. In 1975 West Ham reached the FA Cup final and Alan, who had applied, failed to get a ticket, yet Margaret Thatcher was there and the king and queen of some remote nation and other dignitaries none of whom had the slightest interest in soccer; certainly they had never stood on a rain-drenched terrace on a winter's night. Today he will be watching West Ham United live for the first time in twenty-one years and, in all honesty, he's looking forward to it.

We arrive at Highbury at twelve-thirty and drive into the players' entrance, passing my old school chum the great Charlie George and his friend whom we always see at Highbury. We park in the privileged parking spaces – where else are they to put a Bentley? – and collect the four tickets that await us in the reception area. Maurice seeks out Tony Willis, the editor of *One Nil Down, Two One Up*, one of Arsenal's alternative magazines, at the north end of the ground to see if he knows what precisely has been going on at Highbury over the past six weeks.

Arsenal manager, or should I say acting manager, Stewart Houston, fields the most peculiarly balanced team this afternoon: Seaman, Dixon, Linighan, Bould, Keown, Winterburn, Morrow, Parlour, Merson, Bergkamp and Hartson. It seems as if Houston wishes to play six at the back, three in midfield going forward, and poor old John Hartson upfront alone. I wonder whether Houston, knowing he will be out of his job in a month or so, has fielded a team that will not lose, if he's lucky, rather than an entertaining turn-out that might thrill the capacity crowds Arsenal will get this season. Why, we all wonder, is there no David Platt, neither on the field nor on the substitutes' bench? Platt is in my opinion a great waste of money; the sooner Arsenal recoup some of it the better. He has never appeared to me to be 100 per cent committed to playing for Arsenal. Perhaps I'm doing the man immense injustice, or maybe I'm not.

And so to the match. It's pretty equal; West Ham may have the better of the midfield battle, but Arsenal look fitter and sharper and Hartson could easily have given Arsenal the lead after five minutes but failed to connect with a Paul Merson cross. Arsenal do take the lead in about the twenty-fifth minute when Lee Dixon, of all players, turns up on the left wing, beats a man, crosses the ball, Hartson gets a toe to it and the ball rolls against the West Ham post; then Hartson gets up and blasts the ball in from all of one yard.

Merson and Ray Parlour play reasonably well, but Dennis Bergkamp stands head and shoulders above every other player on the pitch, and it is the Dutchman who scores when Marc Reiper unnecessarily handballs a cross and gives Arsenal a surprise penalty. Arsenal therefore go in at half-time 2–0 to the good and are unlikely to sacrifice such a lead. The second half is dull, dull, dull. There isn't a solitary highlight that I shall be able to recall in half an hour, let alone half a year. I do remember that Stewart Houston brings Bergkamp off (is he saving him for Monday evening's battle at Anfield?) and introduces Ian Wright, much to the applause and cheers of the Arsenal faithful.

This Arsenal victory does nothing to raise my enthusiasm for their chances of winning a domestic trophy this season, nor for the quality of football I shall experience over the next nine months. English football has become stale, and despite the influx of ageing foreign stars I can't see me becoming excited by the fare on offer; perhaps this should be reflected in my *Gunners* column each month.

So today has been well and truly dominated by football, as has the start of every season since my dad started taking me to Highbury back in 1953. The world seemed rosy and real back then, now it's corrupt and nothing is as it seems, or as I would like it to be – child-like. I want the world in which I live not to be real, but rather as I would have liked my childhood to have been – naive, mysterious, fabulous and beautiful. I suppose having settled down here in the country is a step in that direction. Perhaps my life should really start now, today, and perhaps I should wipe away the memories of the past that never quite lived up to my expectations. What brings all this on? I suppose it's the fall-out of having written 'Mosley', and being in contact with Nicholas Mosley, whose childhood seems to me to have been the idyllic one I never had and wish I had. I wonder if Nick's childhood was everything I imagine it to have been.

MONDAY, 19 AUGUST

Rabbi Hugo Gryn died today. I am saddened and moved in a fashion that I would be had he been a dear friend, maybe even related. I never met Hugo Gryn, but I did receive the kindest letter from him just before the premiere of 'Wall of Silence', and that letter will remain with me for the rest of my working life. It was written by a dear and compassionate man, a thinker, a religious man who was brave enough to put his head on the block when it was necessary. The radio report of Rabbi Gryn's death mentions he was sixty-six but not how he died. Sad though I am at his death, I suppose he would say that he received fifty years' bonus of life, for having managed to survive Auschwitz, anything thereafter has to be looked upon as good fortune.

Born in the Carpathian mountains, he emerged from Auschwitz, aged fifteen, with his father who died almost immediately after they were liberated. After working as a rabbi in New York and Bombay, he became rabbi of the West London synagogue in Mayfair, the largest and most fashionable reform Jewish synagogue in England. Through his work on Radio Four's 'The Moral Maze', he became one of the most respected religious broadcasters in the country, and the leading voice in the field of interfaith where Jews and Christians (and now Muslims) come together in an effort to understand other religions through meetings, lectures and personal encounters.

The news leads me to spend today wondering how many other men as great, if not greater than Hugo Gryn, were murdered in the Nazi death camps. Briggy, who is German, appears to have taken the rabbi's death more deeply even than I.

Sky Sport One's live match this evening is Liverpool v. Arsenal. I can't see Arsenal winning for the reason that they don't have any strike power. A lone John Hartson isn't going to put the fear of God into the Liverpool back four. Whatever Hartson might be, he isn't Ravanelli! I therefore think Liverpool will have a field day, even against the highly organised Arsenal defence. My prediction is 4–0 to Liverpool. Maurice feels if Arsenal gain a point from this evening it will have been a remarkable result, but he believes Arsenal will lose 2–0.

Arsenal play some extremely tidy and organised football, and with the exceptions of Ray Parlour and Andy Linighan continually giving the ball to the opposition, I believe Arsenal's performance this evening to be far better than on Saturday. Against a tidal flow of attacks, Arsenal hold out in the first half and in all truth had the opportunity to take the lead, but Hartson's first touch is poor and he wastes a possible goalscoring opportunity. Arsenal simply don't have the strike force and this is going to be the problem with their season. Maurice is right. Arsenal lose 2–0 and have three points from six. They play Leicester City up there on Saturday and should take three points, but I can't help feeling everything at Highbury is in limbo, including their style of play, until Arsene Wenger arrives at the club. An announcement is expected tomorrow.

WEDNESDAY, 21 AUGUST

Now 'tis the time to seek a new Darryl Stubbs for 'Birds of a Feather'. This has been necessitated by Alun Lewis not being freed from 'Emmerdale Farm' to rejoin us for this new series we are about to make, and this after us having bent over backwards to accommodate them when they wanted to use him. We have five actors to see. The list of applicants was never going to be very long because many actors don't want to step into a role that has been up and running for six years; also there aren't many Darryl Stubbs types of the right age, accent, build and with a sense of dramatic comedy.

All morning long, in twenty-minute bursts, we listen to the five actors read three pieces from 'Porridge', then an old piece from 'Not In My Back Yard'. The first reading by Douglas McFerran is so on the button, with so much understanding of both the confidence and confusion of the character, that he sets the standard which the others must surpass. We all feel in our hearts, including Linda Robson (Tracey), that Douglas McFerran is our man and, short of knowing how he will behave in front of a live audience, I think we should offer him the job. This thespian left the audition to go to the social security office to collect his weekly unemployment benefit. When he arrives home this afternoon, he will learn that he might have no need to draw benefit for the next two years. It will be a very rewarding experience and I should guess that this quiet (or so he appears) young man will be celebrating with his nearest and dearest this evening, having found himself walking into one of the most popular comedy shows on British television.

FRIDAY, 23 AUGUST

Briggy and I fly to Edinburgh for the International Television Festival. This year, it's going to be a working holiday. Although I'm taking part in several events, mostly I shall be doing what everyone else is here to do – meet people and talk shop.

This evening we are attending what is thought to be the highlight of the festival, the McTaggart lecture at the McEwan Hall. The honoured speaker is the Director General of the BBC, John Birt. He arrives on stage wearing a greenish coloured suit, sober shirt and grim tie – certainly not Georgio Armani – to a subdued round of applause. The lecture begins at 7.33, I looked at my watch, and for fifty minutes John Birt speaks about why we can never allow the BBC to disintegrate and die. The longer the speech goes on, the more of an automaton Birt sounds, spouting statistics endlessly. There is little about the artistic merits of the BBC, its programmes, its creative personnel, although he did touch upon this topic for about thirty seconds. He drones on and on about the licence fee and how the visual world is going digital and woe betide all the terrestrial stations. And though John Birt may well be right in the glory of all his statistics, these figures do not a riveting lecture make. The speech was about three times longer than it need have been, with too much repetition, and not once in all the minutes he was at the podium did Birt use the word 'I' or 'me'. I was, I am sorry to say, disappointed.

SATURDAY, 24 AUGUST

Phew, what a day! Just looking at my diary I can see that this will be one of the most emotionally draining days of the year. I am about to perform before my peers, once on a panel and then chairing what I want to be the best session at this year's festival – not that I'm competitive, you understand.

I'm on a panel at the Church of St Andrew and St George. I get there early, although I'm the third of the four panellists to arrive, and am miked up and introduced to the extraordinary Peter York, and my fellow panellists. The session, entitled 'Knowing Me, Knowing You', looks at the rise of the focus group, which for the less than knowledgeable is a market research tool used to test television programmes. The market research company send their report back to the company who commissioned it, and the writer or editor of the programme is told the changes he/she must make based on what the focus group says. It is, in essence, interference with an artistic process and I am wholeheartedly against it. On my side of the sofa is Donna Franceschild, the American-Scottish writer of 'Taking Over the Asylum', the BAFTA award-winning drama of last year. Her 'baby' was sent out to a focus group and the results will be partially what this morning's session will reveal. I'm going to talk about 'Birds of a Feather' and how a market research company did a test on the first episode of this series, but by the time the results came in the programme was gaining a weekly viewing figure of over 12 million so any testing was really irrelevant.

Peter York handles the session beautifully, with exquisite taste as one would expect, and he makes it humorous instead of deadly serious. All credit to him for that. The audience seem to enjoy themselves, although Peter York doesn't allow enough questions from the floor and his summing-up is too long, but besides that I have managed to get the day off to a good start and all, I suppose, bodes well for my own session this afternoon.

'My Character Wouldn't Say This', which has been billed as a comedy script masterclass, is the first session I have produced at Edinburgh. Inside the Royal College of Physicians, the steep-banked auditorium that holds 500 people is packed. The session is a sell-out. After a short concise introduction to explain what we hope to achieve this afternoon, I introduce the actors and they read 'Revived 45' by Damon Rochefort. The panel is made up of Caryn Manderbach, the most successful comedy producer in the world, Humphrey Barclay and Maurice, and I introduce them with clips of their work. The surgery begins, and what precision surgery it turns out to be. Humphrey, Caryn and Maurice do not hold back, are never rude or insulting, or even discouraging, and all three get straight to the heart of what is wrong with this funny script. It is painful for the writer, it must be – in the first half of the session he heard his script read beautifully and receive many laughs, now he is hearing from the top people in the industry why it isn't at all a very good piece, which, being cruel about it, is why this session is working like a dream. I invite questions from the audience and receive a few. Quite honestly, this session could have gone on for another hour, many wanted it to, and could quite easily be staged in London at, as somebody suggested, BAFTA.

Damon receives the heartfelt sympathy and applause of the packed house. He has been subjected to a brutal battering by three experts who have done nothing more than try to make his script better. He has the chance to speak and defend what he has written, the whole session is warm, friendly and light-hearted, my panel-lists are excellent, as are my actors, and after the show is over Tom Harvey, who ran the Edinburgh Festival until this year, says to me, 'That is without doubt the best session we have had in five years.'

SUNDAY, 25 AUGUST

By eleven o'clock, at the Royal College of Physicians the auditorium is filling up for 'Lost Over Denver'. By half past, maybe just a little later, I think every seat is taken and my guests are nervously awaiting their shout. Caryn Manderbach is performing yoga, lying down on the hard floor; John Sullivan (the brilliant creator of 'Only Fools and Horses') is nervously wandering up and down; Rick Mitz (US comedy historian) looks fairly calm; Beryl Vertue (doyenne of comedy) has disappeared; and Simon Nye? Well, his plane is delayed so I suppose we could say he is lost over Denver, or is it Edinburgh? The name of the session comes from what happens to British comedy shows that are bought by the Americans, and when they arrive in the USA the main features of their original success have gone missing.

I'm in the chair again and, with the help of marvellous clips, introduce my guests one by one. The session, as with yesterday's, goes superbly well and far from not having enough material we have more than enough. The audience is laughing from the word go, my panellists are vigorous in debate, Beryl is absolutely fabulous, telling many anecdotes from her earliest experiences in the United States, and Caryn is, as always, exceptional value. The audience I sense are with us all the way, and when Simon Nye finally makes an entrance the applause is thunderous. Simon joins the debate as I'm approaching the 'Men Behaving Badly' clips, so he really couldn't have timed his entrance better.

To leave them wanting more is better than to have them slowly walking from the auditorium, as I have seen audiences do during this festival, and I end with a summary of why the Americans believe we British make comedy the right way, and why we British believe it is from the Americans we can learn. The truth is we each do it the way we do it, neither is better, it's just different.

WEDNESDAY, 4 SEPTEMBER

To Highbury for Arsenal v. Chelsea – a match that whets the appetite, or does until I see the side that Stewart Houston is putting on the pitch: Lukic, Dixon, Bould, Linighan, Winterburn, Keown, Morrow, Parlour, Merson, Bergkamp and Hartson. Not a great deal of creativity and balance there, would you say? Against us is a side full of flair. Chelsea surround their new signings – Di Matteo, Vialli, Leboeuf – with players of great skill and wisdom – Hughes, Wise, Clark, Myers. On paper at least, Chelsea have a side that could, if consistency reigns, become Premier League title contenders. Indeed, in the first half of this match they completely outplay a disorganised Arsenal, Chelsea displaying silky skills, keeping the ball on the floor, playing in the style Ruud Gullit, their manager, once played.

Chelsea take the lead with a penalty by Frank Leboeuf in the fifth minute, awarded when Steve Bould brings down Dennis Wise. Then John Lukic, playing his first game for Arsenal in six years (he has been playing for Leeds United in the interim), and a goalkeeper I described in *The Gunners* magazine as the worst I have seen between the Arsenal posts, makes a typical error when he allows a Vialli shot to squirm between his hands, his body and the Arsenal near post. The ball finishes in the Arsenal goal and Chelsea are cruising with a 2–0 lead – and we all suspect there are more goals to come. This is going to be a trouncing. Arsenal never look as if they know how to score and their first shot, not on target, comes in the fortieth minute from Paul Merson. However, against the run of the half, Paul Merson scores a goal in injury time and a 1–2 half-time score looks more respectable than Arsenal deserve.

The second half is one of the biggest turnabouts I have seen at Highbury in years. Arsenal play as if they are a new team. David Platt, making one of his rare appearances, starts the half for Steve Morrow (certainly not a midfield player of note, and that is being kind to the man), and suddenly Arsenal's balance appears better. They take the game by the scruff of the neck and attack Chelsea incessantly. They have their first shot of the half after forty seconds, and thereafter throw wave upon wave of attacks at the Chelsea defence, who look as though they cannot cope with this pressure. It is no surprise therefore when Arsenal equalise. A short corner by Platt to Merson is followed by a beautifully weighted cross to Keown who heads the equaliser.

When Arsenal bring on Ian Wright for Steve Bould, one senses we are going to win this thriller, probably the most exciting match I have seen at Highbury in years. Wright does the trick. He has only been on the field for ten minutes when he puts Arsenal into a lead they should keep or add to – but they do have Lukic between the sticks so anything might happen. Arsenal 3, Chelsea 2. In the seventh minute of injury time, just as Maurice and I are walking up the gangway to celebrate the win, Dennis Wise fires an equaliser past a stranded John Lukic, although those who saw the goal say it was the fault of Lee Dixon. So the match ends Arsenal 3, Chelsea 3, and the West Londoners concede their first goals of the season.

I think a draw is a more than fair result, although had Arsenal held out they would have been lying second in the Premier League tonight. The season is, however, new and really these lost two points will not, I'm certain, prove significant. What is significant is that tonight a dull Arsenal side (at least on paper) turned in a gutsy, not skilful, performance and helped produce one of the best matches I have seen down at Highbury this decade.

THURSDAY, 5 SEPTEMBER

This evening I have to travel to London – I'm staying at Clarges Street tonight – and on the way I listen to Kenneth Wolstenholme reading his book, *They Think It's All Over*, about the 1966 World Cup victory. It is a wonderful story and he makes the events of the summer of '66 sound so romantic and historic. He describes the night we won the World Cup as being similar to VE night, but I don't remember too much about it. I was definitely in the West End of London and I do remember hooters sounding off and Eros at Piccadilly Circus being awash with people, but more than that seems to have escaped my memory. I wonder where I went and with whom on this historic night.

Sir Alf Ramsey knew he would win the World Cup but I didn't think so, any more than I believed we would win the Euro '96 final, although we came very close. England in 1966 had three world-class players forming the backbone of its team – Gordon Banks, Bobby Moore and Bobby Charlton – whereas in Euro '96 we had one; David Seaman proving to everyone that he is without question world class. Yes, Kenneth Wolstenholme's reading is a delight and it takes me from Oxfordshire to London past the imaginary scenery of 1966. By the time I arrive at my flat, I feel that I have made a journey back almost to where I was thirty years ago – Piccadilly – only tonight there are no honking horns, no cheers of

'England, England', just far more traffic and a life that I could not have begun dreaming about then.

FRIDAY, 6 SEPTEMBER

Maurice and I are guests of Michael Jackson, the newly appointed Controller of BBC1. We have known Michael since about 1984, when he worked for Colin Callender and Maurice and I were to write a drama series entitled 'Spotty & Hill', about the two foremost gangsters in London during the 1950s. The project never came to pass and we each went our own ways. This triumvirate are to sit down to lunch at Alastair Little's other restaurant. It is white and its exterior reminds me of an estate agent's shop. The conversation quickly moves on to the subject of programmes and it becomes apparent that what Michael will need is long-running comedy shows like 'Birds', that he calls a work of genius. I wouldn't say that! We tell Michael that as well as twenty more episodes of 'Birds' to write, we have another eleven episodes of 'Goodnight Sweetheart' and a new series entitled 'Unfinished Business' to prepare. Nevertheless, we discuss some other ideas – Maurice and I are positively brimming with them – which Michael likes. I am warming to Michael as I have never done before; I have always found him to be a cold fish, but he is really a fun-loving person who shares a desire with Maurice and me to make television very much better than it is. I think we three are children of television and we look back on the good old days with a fondness and a desire to know why they got it so right and we do not.

SUNDAY, 8 SEPTEMBER

Today's the day of our promised lunch for Adam Faith. He is to bring his latest flame, Emma, and we are looking forward to meeting her. One thing is for certain, she will be at least half Adam's age for it seems that he likes women young enough to be his daughter; I suppose it makes him feel very young.

Briggy prepares a fine lunch, one that Adam can relate to – roast beef, Yorkshire pud, roast potatoes (the best in the world), and two veg, followed by sticky puddings and custard – and Emma is charming! Her mother is German, her father oh so terribly English. She was working as a production assistant for Esther Rantzen when she was chatted up by Adam, and since February they have been going around together. Emma is the sort of girl I can imagine Adam would be attracted to, any man would be – tall, long tanned legs, full mouth, long blonde hair, charming personality.

The conversation is largely about the joy and fun and surprise of being a pop star. As Adam says, 'Kids like me, Cliff and Tommy had never earned money before,' and Adam is talking of much money. When my dad was making £12 a week in the late 1950s, Adam was making about £1000 a week. It must have been enormously exciting and terrifying in the same measure. For all his fame, talent and charm, I sense we have here a lonely man, always seeking young company for some unconscious reason that takes him back to his happiest times – the late 1950s. I think his recent separation from his wife, Jackie, has affected him greatly, and even with a 24-year-old blonde media-studies student on his arm, and him crawling all over her, Adam seems to be lost in a search for something to replace Jackie, which I suspect he'll never find. You can't replace history and memories, although you can create new ones. Nevertheless, Emma is delightful and I hope their relationship continues to grow, although I am slightly cynical about the age gap. I am aware of Emma's age when we start to talk about the Beatles.

'Who were they?' she asks.

MONDAY, 9 SEPTEMBER

Howard Wilkinson has been sacked as manager of Leeds United. Does this mean that George Graham will take on the job of restoring Leeds to the glory days of the 1970s? I should imagine he will be top of Leeds United's list.

TUESDAY, 10 SEPTEMBER

It is late morning when the front gate bell rings and Daniel Wiles and Leo Burley, his researcher from the 'South Bank Show', arrive from London. Leo is an Arsenal supporter and is going to this evening's UEFA Cup match against Borussia Moenchengladbach, as am I. However, they are here to discuss a programme they are going to make about Maurice and me.

We spend hours discussing why we wanted things in television to change, how we changed them, what resistance we came up against, and why comedy is so much more difficult than drama, yet nobody seems ever to acknowledge this is the case. Also the 'South Bank Show' is very interested in how we set up an independent company and why we wanted to, and how we became extremely interested in business as an adjunct to being creative writers. Should the combination of both encourage all other writers? I don't know the answer to this last question, but it will make for an interesting segment of the programme.

Kick-off is at seven-fifteen tonight for the benefit of German TV, and Maurice drives us to Highbury. We wonder whether it will be worth making a day trip to Germany for the second leg. Our friend, Mark Burdis, believes that Arsenal will win 2–0 tonight, but he obviously doesn't know that Borussia have a world-class player in Stefan Effenberg. Any team that contains even one world-class player is usually extremely difficult to beat. I therefore predict, and put my money where my mouth is, that Borussia will gain a 3–2 victory tonight, a prediction that is mocked by all around me. Well, I reckon Arsenal are capable of scoring, but lately their defence has been leaking goals and Borussia with their quick and skilful forwards will capitalise on this.

Arsenal have chances enough to settle the tie in the first half an hour, even though they lose Dennis Bergkamp with a thigh injury – he is replaced by Glenn Helder, not an adequate replacement – but Hartson hits the post, Wright draws a superb save from the Borussia goalkeeper and other chances come Arsenal's way. To Borussia's credit, they have several good chances and it is only the agility of David Seaman, returning to the first team, thank goodness, that prevents Borussia taking the lead sooner. Juskowiak scores before half-time and a very sharp and typically clinical European finish it is too.

In the second half, the masterly Stefan Effenberg (why, oh why, can't Arsenal buy this genius? We need someone of this class to control our midfield) scores a second for Borussia, following in his shot that bounces off Seaman's chest and putting it coolly wide of the goalkeeper and into the net. Arsenal 0 Borussia 2 doesn't bode well for the second leg in Cologne, does it? And yet the match isn't nearly finished. Paul Merson hits a delightful goal (Merson has for the past three weeks been playing some of the finest football of his unstable career) and we are back in with a chance, or at least so we believe until Borussia score a third goal through Passlack and then it is all over for Arsenal. I, however, am on a 40–1 bet and now all I need to happen is for Arsenal to score one more goal – and they do. With a minute left to play, and with the German supporters celebrating wildly, Ian Wright hits a shot at goal from close range, it rebounds out to him and at the second attempt he rifles the ball into the roof of the net. Paul Merson nearly equalises with a screaming twenty-five yard drive that the Borussia goalkeeper manages to tip over his bar. From the ensuing corner Arsenal nearly equalise, but they don't and I have won £40 and Arsenal look certain to exit the UEFA Cup at the first time of asking.

After the match, I bump into Charlie George. He believes Arsenal must go out to Germany and attack, leaving behind them any fears of conceding another goal. Charlie felt Borussia Moenchengladbach are not an accomplished side, although he does concede that Effenberg is one hell of a midfield player. Charlie also points out that Helder is useless, and to be truthful he might well be right. I have seen not a shred of evidence to suggest that Glenn Helder is a player designed for the English Premier League. It has been a pretty dreadful evening and what is even more worrying is that Arsenal have now let in eight goals in three matches, a deficit one would never ever associate with the Gunners – this on a day when we hear that George Graham, who took the club to heights not reached since Herbert Chapman's day in the 1930s, has been appointed as the new Leeds United manager. I wish him well and I am certain he will give new life to the Yorkshire club in the same manner that he did when he arrived at Highbury in 1986. It will take Graham some time, maybe a season or two, but he is competent and confident and one thing Leeds can be sure of is that GG will work from the back and give Leeds United a solid foundation on which to build their game. I wonder what he made of Arsenal's performance this evening and how he might have done it differently had he still been Arsenal's manager? But perhaps managers have a given time in which to make certain players play for them. After that time, as Howard Wilkinson may have found to his cost, one cannot get any more out of players who once performed, therefore they buy new and sometimes the wrong players to fit the pattern they have created.

George Graham will change Leeds's fortunes while watching his old club players grow old together and turn from a very competent and sometimes exciting club team into a group of has-beens.

WEDNESDAY, 11 SEPTEMBER

The Cattle Shed is the venue for this evening's European Champions League game between Juventus and Manchester United. The entire match is broadcast live. Manchester United have more than met their match. They concede what seems to be a perfectly good and fair goal that the referee disallows, but then two minutes later Juventus score a legitimate goal and take the lead, which they are never really likely to relinquish. Juventus are a class above the best team in England, which further endorses my feeling that English soccer is eight years behind what is being played in Europe.

Here we have Manchester United, double Double winners, hard to live with on a weekly basis in the Premier League, made to look less than mediocre against an Italian team, excellent though they are, that is rebuilding and have lost some of their greatest players. Yet for all this, the likes of Cantona, Giggs, Beckham, Butt and others do not get a look at the ball, let alone do anything constructive with it. The same was the case when Arsenal were defeated by Borussia last night. Ian Wright, usually like lightning, always finding space, time and goals, was obliterated from the game by defenders who made sure he never received the ball. The Europeans are very good at doing this as Manchester United learn this evening. The final score is 1–0 to Juventus, but it could so easily have been 4–0, and nil is the operative figure, for United never once looked as though they knew how to penetrate Juventus's defence.

THURSDAY, 12 SEPTEMBER

'Birds of a Feather' day. Tonight we shall record the first episode since December 1994. It is an exciting prospect. This show, perhaps more than any other Maurice and I have written, is one of the nation's favourites and it will be very interesting to see just how the studio audience react to meeting Sharon, Dorien and Tracey again after all this time.

The audience is full to bursting, and bursting with anticipation to see the Birds again. Sue Teddern has written as good a script as she has ever written for this show. Everyone is ready. I make my way to the old room; we call it 'The World of Leather'. I've watched more of our shows from here than from anywhere else.

The girls are even better than they were in the dress run. The audience react as if they know Sharon, Dorien and Tracey intimately, Baz Taylor directs the show with the ease of a conductor in front of the finest orchestra in the world, and the show is over and in the can by quarter-past nine. If all the shows are made with the fluency and ease of this first one, we are in for a marvellous time and a wonderful series.

What makes this episode such a great kick-off is the way in which all the laughter, and there is a lot of it, comes from naturalism; the humour that Sue has injected into her script is based on truth. The girls' timing is an example of how situation comedy should be played – for when it is played with this confidence there is never a need to add canned laughter afterwards. The audience just wishes to be friends with these girls. It must be a proud moment for Sue when we finish for I contend that this is by far her best ever 'Birds' episode, although she doesn't agree.

At the drinks party afterwards the girls are all in good spirits, although perhaps an alien might not know this were they to see Lesley Joseph sitting alone looking depressed. Pauline and Linda are, though, glad to be back with the show that made their names and faces known throughout Britain, and in many other parts of the world, too. They both tell me how much they have enjoyed tonight. Pauline says that she was far less nervous than she usually is – I wonder whether this could be because she had so much confidence in the script.

Friday, 13 September

Before going to Renzo's for breakfast this morning, I listen to the 'Today' programme and on the sports news I hear, much to my astonishment, that Stewart Houston, Arsenal's caretaker manager, has left the club to pursue a career elsewhere. Of course, speculation is rife – will he become manager of Queens Park Rangers, or will he join George Graham at Leeds United? I haven't the foggiest idea, but what I do know is that the Arsenal management have well and truly made a pig's ear of this event. For a start, they sacked Bruce Rioch before they had acquired another manager. Arsene Wenger's appointment still hasn't been announced. It is believed he is coming to Highbury but contractual difficulties with his Japanese club prevent him from so doing yet. Then Houston who, to his credit, has taken Arsenal a lot higher in the Premier League than anyone could have hoped for, decides he doesn't wish to stay on as caretaker manager, not even knowing that he will become Wenger's assistant, and now the club, always in the past associated with consistency, is having to turn to its youth team manager, Pat Rice, to lead the first team through some difficult months. It could be that by the time Wenger joins the Gunners, and there is still no guarantee that he will, they will be in a dangerously low position, with club morale even lower.

Renzo and I commiserate with each other. Despite writing for *The Gunners* magazine, I know no more than he. Arsenal are not in the habit of telling their fans anything, and those even loosely associated with the club are kept equally in the dark. No doubt we shall be informed in due course whether Wenger is or isn't coming – I'm sure Arsenal must believe he is or why else would they have dismissed Rioch? – and if so, when.

SATURDAY, 14 SEPTEMBER

'Match of the Day' is worth staying up for – David Beckham's
wonder goal from the halfway line wins the goal of the month
prize. Arsenal are not playing this weekend, instead they meet
Sheffield Wednesday in a Premier League game on Monday
night, led into battle by the non-battle-hardened Pat Rice. There
was a big feature on 'Football Focus' this afternoon about the
shambles Arsenal now find themselves in. This morning, Tony
Adams, their captain and captain of England, called a press conference to announce that he is an alcoholic. Oh dear, how much
worse can things become at Highbury before somebody starts
pointing the finger where it deserves to be pointed, at the board of
directors?

MONDAY, 16 SEPTEMBER

It was announced this morning that Arsene Wenger will be
Arsenal's new manager (probably the worst kept secret in world
football) and he will take up his post in time for the Blackburn
Rovers v. Arsenal match in two or three weeks' time. Everyone is
excited, although Wenger, in an interview for Sky Television, says
that it is nigh on impossible to put his plans into operation now
the season has started, and what he must do is work with the
players he has at his disposal, while looking for new players to
improve the team. That is what the fans want, too. There are too
many makeweights at Highbury, players who will not move on
because they are earning more playing in the reserves than they
would playing for the first team in a lower division. Wenger will
sort the wheat from the chaff, and I believe when he has developed
a solid defensive strategy and filled his midfield with talent,
Arsenal will become a force to be reckoned with.

This evening I hurry to Highbury for the Sheffield Wednesday
game. I'm meeting old schoolfriend Bob Hartley outside the ground
at a quarter to seven. Much has happened since we last met. Bob is
excited about a film he is currently putting together. It's about a
Geordie spiritualist who transfigures herself into the dead person
who is communicating through her. He has, apparently, captured
the transfigurations on film. Astonishing! Bob explains how when

the medium contacted his long-deceased father, her face transformed into his. I'm a little sceptical. I'm not sure I can believe in it all, so Bob invites me to see for myself. She is coming to London soon. Bob would like me to bring Briggy and Maurice along to allay any doubts they might have. Why, I wonder, does Bob want to convince us all that spiritualism is real and wonderful?

The match. Oh yes, the match! Well, it's delayed for half an hour as the stadium suffers a power cut and the turnstiles, which work electronically, cannot operate. Supporters can't get into the stadium and there seems to be chaos in the street outside. The kick-off will now be at half past eight.

Forty-five minutes after it should have begun, I settle down to watch Arsenal v. Sheffield Wednesday. A victory for Wednesday will send them back to the top of the Premier League table. They don't win though, they lose by the remarkable score of 4–1. Sheffield Wednesday could and should have gone in at half-time 4–0 to the good. They miss chance after chance after chance, although they do score a goal. Arsenal never really look like scoring. Although they play some neat one-touch football, it seems to get them nowhere at all. Ray Parlour is brought off after fifteen minutes, and Patrick Vieira, one of the two new French purchases, takes his place in midfield. He is black, he is tall, he is more skilful than any other midfield player on the field, and his presence simply turns the match. I start to imagine what he might be like alongside another midfield player as good as him. David Platt equalises early in the second half, following some outstanding holding-up work by John Hartson, who this evening plays his finest game in an Arsenal shirt, and over the course of the second half Ian Wright bags a hat-trick. His second is from the penalty spot after Des Walker trips Paul Merson. For this Walker is dismissed and Wednesday are down to ten men. From then on, Vieira stamps his class all across the Highbury pitch and it is the first time in years that I have seen a midfield player of great quality wearing the red shirt of Arsenal. Vieira's talent highlights Parlour's deficiencies. I should imagine young Ray will not figure in the plans of Arsene Wenger when he arrives in a fortnight's time.

THURSDAY, 19 SEPTEMBER

Maurice and I leave Clarges Street as early as we need to get to
Foubert's Place for today's recasting of the part of Phoebe in
'Goodnight Sweetheart'. Dervla Kirwan, who created the part and
made it her own, decided to leave the show because after three
series she felt she couldn't take the character any further. Dervla
will appear in only 'Ballykissangel' from now on and so we have
the invidious task of replacing her with an actress who will have
the same charisma that came through the television screen when
watching young Dervla. It is not an easy assignment. It was difficult enough to cast the part originally – although back then we
hadn't a template on which to base our feelings of how the character should be.

We are seeing two Yvonnes today, too. Hers was an even more
difficult part to cast originally and a strong gut feeling on my part
gave Michelle Holmes the role. She played it beautifully as far as
I was concerned, and I think others shared my opinion.

The star of this morning's auditions is, funnily enough, the
girl whom Maurice and I saw in an episode of 'Men Behaving
Badly' and commented on her likeness to Dervla. Her name is
Elizabeth Carling, a young vivacious woman from Teesside,
whose reading of the piece is about as good as we could have
ever expected.

SATURDAY, 21 SEPTEMBER

Much to my astonishment, I learn Arsenal have won 2–0 at
Middlesbrough. I think to myself there is something of an irony in
the fact that Pat Rice, currently acting manager of Arsenal, has
started with two wins from two matches, while the far more experienced and honoured ex-Arsenal manager, George Graham, has
begun his managerial career at Leeds with two defeats. Arsene
Wenger arrives at Highbury next week, the team are currently
third in the league table, and suddenly they have become rather
interesting.

SUNDAY, 22 SEPTEMBER

I speak to Sue, my ex, this evening. She brings me up to date with all her and her family's news, tells me it's the beginning of the party conference season so she is off to Brighton tomorrow morning, and that the inside word is that the general election will be on 1 May 1997. If that's the case it would allow Maurice and me adequate time to write and produce a 'New Statesman' election night special, which is what everyone at ALOMO would like us to do.

WEDNESDAY, 25 SEPTEMBER

After a wonderfully positive meeting about 'Mosley' at Channel Four, I discover that Arsenal have lost 3–2 in Cologne this afternoon, thus going out of the UEFA Cup at the first hurdle by an aggregate score of 4–6. Oh well, to be perfectly pragmatic, it will be one less set of fixtures to worry about and perhaps they might turn their attention to winning the Premier League title. Maurice and I, as excited in my case as I was when we left London Weekend Television in 1979 after Humphrey Barclay had commissioned us to write a pilot episode of 'Holding The Fort', take a taxi to BBC Television Centre where this evening we are to record the final episode of Paul Makin's 'Grown Ups'.

SATURDAY, 28 SEPTEMBER

Arsenal are playing Sunderland today and a win of 4–0 or more will take the Gunners to the top of the Premier League, perhaps only for twenty-four hours, but at the top we shall sit. Sunderland will be no pushover; they have been playing some attractive and stubborn football of recent weeks. The game starts promisingly for Sunderland, who are much the better side. They come close to scoring twice before Arsenal settle down and Ian Wright puts the ball into the back of the Sunderland net, only to be pulled up for offside. Then two incredible twists of fate go against Sunderland, pushing the game beyond their reach and spoiling the remainder of the afternoon. Inside thirty minutes, two Sunderland players are dismissed from the field of play: Martin Scott, the full-back, for two mistimed fouls on Lee Dixon, and Paul Stewart for two of the most innocuous handballs one could ever see in a football match.

Peter Reid, protesting vehemently to the referee about the dismissal of the second Sunderland player, is himself sent off, so to
speak, and banished from the dug-out to a seat in the grandstand
from where he can be of no influence upon his players. With only
nine men, Sunderland line them up across the back and the game
is killed. At half-time Arsenal 0 Sunderland 0 is the score, with
Arsenal unable to break through the wall protecting the goalkeeper.

I'm surprised by Arsenal's refusal to vary their tactics against
this eight-man wall in front of the goalkeeper. I mean, why would
Pat Rice want four men at the back of Arsenal's defence when all
Sunderland are doing when they break down yet another Arsenal
attack is kicking the ball as far into Arsenal's half as possible?
Surely the sensible tactic to employ would be to play two players
at the back and bring on some more forwards, preferably wingers.
The problem for Pat Rice is he doesn't have any forwards to bring
on, and so Arsenal continue to batter away at Sunderland's eight-
man defence without a modicum of success.

At last Rice brings off Winterburn, now excess to requirements,
and replaces the one-footed full-back with Paul Shaw an attacking
midfield player. Rose is twenty something but because of his bald
head he looks ten years older. He makes the difference, and within
ten minutes he plants the cross that John Hartson heads home.
Well, 1–0 isn't 4–0, but it is three points. Sunderland make some
substitutions and start searching for the equaliser and cause many
little flutters in the hearts of Arsenal supporters. Patrick Vieira
comes off to be replaced by Parlour and startlingly with his first
touch of the ball Ray Parlour scores an immaculate goal from a difficult angle. It is Parlour's first goal for Arsenal in something like
three seasons. He is, I ought to remind myself, an attacking midfield player! Arsenal 2 Sunderland 0. That is the final result,
Arsenal move into second place, which is where they will probably be when Arsene Wenger takes over as club manager on
Monday morning.

Arsenal have not performed well this afternoon and maybe
would not have taken three points had Sunderland been allowed
to keep their full complement of players on the pitch. There again,
the match would have been better and more exciting had we seen
eleven men against eleven, and my prediction of 4–2 in Arsenal's
favour might have been the right result. Never mind. It may have

been an extremely boring match, but Arsenal gain another three points so I have little grounds for complaint.

WEDNESDAY, 2 OCTOBER

Apparently, a feature written by Bernard Levin entitled 'Oswald and Nicholas' appeared in *The Times* of 27 September. In vehement and aggressive terms, Bernard Levin put forward his argument why the four-part serial Maurice and I have written shouldn't ever be shown. He attacked Oswald Mosley for marching through the East End of London and using the Jews as the scapegoats for his movement, and derided Nicholas as something of the naive son for saying his father wasn't an anti-Semite. Levin remembers the Blackshirts coming through the East End while he and his mother sat petrified at their kitchen window looking out into the street. I imagine any Jew who was there feels the same, but surely Levin cannot condemn the series without reading or seeing it, or even knowing its content? Nick replies to *The Times* thus:

> Sir,
> Bernard Levin is generous to myself in his article about my father and me ('Oswald and Nicholas', 27 September) and has every right to stress the evils of my father's alliance with anti-Semitism. But he mentions the left-wing radicalism of my father's early years and the way in which his economic ideas are said to be being taken up by 'Tory grandees' now, and he also says that he himself believes that Oswald Mosley was not a 'rooted Jew baiter' – so he might surely see there is an interesting story here somewhere.
>
> I have read an early draft of the scripts of the proposed TV drama-series about my father commissioned by Channel Four, and in no way is the anti-Semitism of my father's middle years glossed over: in fact there are scenes in the East End of London precisely like those which Bernard Levin so painfully remembers. But if anti-Semitism is to be understood, and thus combated successfully, it has to be reacted to with more subtlety than a simple turning away in horror.

Channel Four aims at presenting the story as a
dramatisation, which is the most telling way of
illuminating complex issues. Any remark I might have
made about my father 'not being a racist' referred to his
private, not his public behaviour.

Bernard Levin, who makes much of my stammer, has an
effortless way with words; so had my father; perhaps if one
struggles with complexity, it is sometimes appropriate to
have a stammer.

Yours faithfully,
NICHOLAS MOSLEY
2 Gloucester Crescent, NW1.

THURSDAY, 3 OCTOBER

What else is there to talk about but Bernard Levin's article and
Nick's response? Maurice and I largely agree with Levin's analysis of Mosley's career, but what right, we ask, has he to shout from
the rooftops that the programme should not be made? We agree
that a reply is necessary and for the first time in our lives we sit
down and do something we thought we should never do – begin
a letter to the Editor of *The Times*, Sir.

Sir,
As the writers of the proposed Channel Four serial on the
life of Sir Oswald Mosley, we hope it is not too late for us to
comment on Bernard Levin's column of 27 September

We do not find very much to disagree with in Mr Levin's
analysis of Mosley's career. However, we are rather irked
that he has assumed that we two Jews are about to
perpetrate the whitewash he so condemns. After all, our
parents were Jewish East Enders too, though family fable
has it that they were manning the barricades rather than
sitting at windows.

On what does Mr Levin base his denunciation of our
unseen work? Simply on the outrage expressed by 'leaders
of the Jewish community' when they heard that Michael
Grade had commissioned a 'sympathetic reassessment' of
Oswald Mosley. In fact, neither Mr Grade nor Channel

Four has ever used the word 'sympathetic', it simply cropped up in another newspaper article. It rather looks as if Mr Levin is supplying us with a fine example of prejudice, dictionary definition: 'a judgement formed beforehand or without due examination'.

We have, as they say, been here before. When we ventured to write a television film set in the ultra orthodox Chassidic community, we were told synagogues would burn and it would be our fault – this well before the film was transmitted, of course. At that time we were delighted to receive a letter from a real Jewish leader, the late Rabbi Hugo Gryn. He assured us of 'his great empathy for all those responsible for the film, [undergoing] the kangaroo trial in the media', and affirmed 'my total confidence in your integrity, based on actual track record'.

Finally, we should like to place on record that one of the undersigned, Maurice Gran, was a committed Levinophile as a schoolboy. Indeed Mr Levin and Mr Coren and Mrs Gran [Maurice's mother] were his three main literary influences. However, that was back in the days when Mr Levin wrote for the *Daily Mail*, only had a single column to fill each day, and so was not compelled to catch and mount such tiddlers for his readers' delectation.

Yours faithfully,
LAURENCE MARKS & MAURICE GRAN

I wonder if it will appear in tomorrow's *Times*, and whether we will receive any reply from Bernard Levin? I doubt it.

MONDAY, 7 OCTOBER

Udi Eichler is my psychotherapist friend. Today we discuss the subjects of love, emotion and loss; it's the last of these that really captivates me. I learn that not being able to mourn for a father and mother both lost to me before the age of twenty-six was because I had nothing to lose. They were neither of them the parents whom I imagined them to be, not behaving as I was told parents should behave, and in the last ten years with them my life was made a misery and happiness was elusive. I learn today that you can only mourn those you truly love, where the loss is great, and I suppose that is why I was more upset by the death of Harvey, our driver, than I was when my mother died. To explain this to any other member of our family would be to invite accusations of callousness, but they cannot understand my feelings, my truth.

Still there is no sign of Nixon, our Maine Coon. It's three weeks since he disappeared and I have to presume something untoward has happened to the cat. Today Briggy went to the Blue Cross animal shelter in Burford but the cat she thought might be Nixon wasn't. Perhaps he will come home one day.

WEDNESDAY, 9 OCTOBER

This afternoon an extraordinary event occurred. Scotland were due to play in Estonia in a World Cup qualifying match. The kick-off was moved back from 4.30 to 1.30 because the Scottish FA had made a protest that the floodlighting was not of sufficient strength to illuminate the entire pitch. FIFA had ordered the match to be played at lunchtime and when the Scottish national team took the field of play there wasn't an Estonian footballer to be seen. The Scots kicked off, the referee blew the whistle, the game was finished after two seconds, and the tie awarded to Scotland with a healthy scoreline of 3–0. What will happen to Estonia as a result of their bizarre behaviour we shall have to wait and see.

This evening – Glenn Hoddle's first game at Wembley in charge of the England team – a capacity crowd sees the English side completely outplayed by an exciting Polish team. The Poles score inside six minutes and could have had two more before half-time. A dreadful error by the Polish goalkeeper, who failed to come out quickly enough for a David Beckham cross from the right (Joe Royle described the goalkeeper's action as 'coming for the ball in instalments'), gives Alan Shearer, England's captain, the opportunity to head the ball into an unguarded Polish net. England 1 Poland 1 and England are, it has to be said, fortunate in the extreme.

About five minutes before half-time Alan Shearer receives a lay-off from his fellow Newcastle striker, Les Ferdinand, and hits a fierce shot that brings back memories of Bobby Charlton. The ball fizzes into the Polish net before the goalkeeper can move and England are, quite remarkably, 2–1 in the lead and heading towards three more points. It is undeserved and every pundit (I listen to six in total over two different programmes) agrees that without Shearer this evening England would have never looked like scoring a goal. In the second half, both teams have many scoring chances, in fact I don't remember seeing quite such an open and exciting competitive match at Wembley, but none are taken and the score finishes England 2 Poland 1. England have six out of six points and are heading towards the World Cup finals in a fashion that can be criticised, but the points speak for themselves. It's Georgia next, over there, and then the vital match against Italy, which should England play as they did this evening, will not only see them beaten, but probably badly beaten.

It's early days for Glenn Hoddle, and I'm sure he will get the team's balance correct before too long. The trouble is he hasn't got too long if England are to qualify for the 1998 World Cup finals. Whereas Terry Venables didn't have a competitive match until Euro '96 came along, Hoddle has been thrown in at the deep end; for him, every match is a cup tie. Still, perhaps this is easier than facing non-competitive matches.

From my vantage point in the producers' box at Teddington Studios, I spot my guests arriving for this recording of 'Birds'. There is Bob Hartley, plus two elderly women – I wonder who they might be – and Harry Carson Parker and his latest flame. There's a huge round of applause before the girls are introduced to the audience and I wonder what has happened. I look down into the audience and see that the England and Arsenal goalkeeper, David Seaman, has arrived with Pauline Quirke's guests, and the audience rise as one to welcome him. Perhaps there lies next month's *Gunners* magazine feature: David Seaman at 'Birds of a Feather'.

Tonight's show is probably the best of the five, certainly for the girls' performances. The enjoyment that was missing from last week's show is evident tonight. While they are performing and making another capacity audience laugh their socks off, in the producer's box we try to think of shows which have scored a century of episodes. We can only come up with 'Last of the Summer Wine', but one of their main characters has changed several times. Nevertheless, they have made over 150 programmes in twenty or more years, while we have made over eighty in six years. Clare has worked out that at the end of the next series we shall have notched up ninety-nine shows (counting one hour or longer Christmas specials as one show), so if we were to make a Christmas special in 1997 that would be the century. If the atmosphere among us all remains as it has been this afternoon and this evening, there really isn't any reason why this magic figure and a piece of television comedy history should not be achieved.

After the show, I manage to speak briefly to David Seaman, reminding him (as if he could ever remember) how Maurice and I had our photograph taken with him at London Colney, and how we are regular contributors to *The Gunners* magazine. The England goalkeeper says he has had a wonderful evening and really enjoyed seeing 'Birds' being made. I'm glad I have managed to help give him pleasure, for he has given me plenty, not least in Europe when goalkeeping for Arsenal.

One of Bob Hartley's two guests turns out to be the Geordie medium who takes on the appearance of the spirit coming through her. I ask her how she started as a medium and the story she tells is incredible to the point of being unbelievable. I can't wait until Wednesday evening, when Briggy and I are going to visit her, to see who passes through this woman and whether it is anyone I know. I wouldn't mind having a small wager that Briggy will see Ronnie, her late husband, and he will be sending her messages about her future as an actress – or am I just entering the realms of fantasy? Perhaps I might come face to face, quite literally, with my mother or father and they will express their feelings about how my career has panned out. Perhaps, perhaps, perhaps.

SATURDAY, 12 OCTOBER

Barry Took is chairing 'Make 'em Laugh', one of this evening's events at the Cheltenham Festival of Literature, in which Maurice and I are involved. We are to meet at Maurice's Cheltenham home and walk to the Town Hall.

Briggy and I, with my sister Shirley and her husband Alex, arrive in Maurice's drive at ten minutes to eight, to find the house empty. Maurice, Carol, their two children Jessica and Tom, and Barry have gone for a Chinese meal, having decided that they will not accept the sponsor's invitation to dinner after the session. We wait. Just as I am unloading Maurice's two huge framed posters, from the Reel Poster Gallery, back they all come. It's good to see Barry, our guru, again (were it not for him, would Maurice be living in such grand style?). Once inside the house – a place I have visited no more than ten times in three and a half years – the children are eager to show us their pets. Cats we think, dogs maybe. They come into the sitting room with large rats on their shoulders. As the children display their pets proudly, Barry becomes more and more tense. It becomes painfully obvious to me that he isn't in the least bit comfortable and he tells me he can't stand rats of any description. The moment comes when he can bear it no longer and he collects his overnight bag, telling Maurice that there isn't any way he will be able to stay the night, not with the thought of rats running around. Maurice is so apologetic. Perhaps he should have mentioned the rats before, but he didn't. Carol scrambles around trying to put Barry in another room away from the rats, not realising a phobia knows no logic. Not only will Barry not be able to stay the night in any room in the house, he probably won't be able to go inside at all, knowing the rats may make an appearance at any moment. Barry and I stand outside, somewhat forlornly waiting for the others to walk the ten minutes walk to the Town Hall.

By the time we arrive, Barry is even more agitated. Not only has there been the rat incident, but it has been a rather lengthy walk for somebody with arthritis, something Maurice had not known about before. Not an auspicious start to making 'em laugh, but Barry is the consummate professional.

The auditorium is a vast room with very high ceilings, where I imagine the sound could easily get lost, and seating laid out for about two hundred. When we eventually take the stage, to a welter of applause, I notice the room is only three-quarters full. My immediate gaze around the room stops at Briggy; it always does. For one hour Maurice, Barry, Jan Etherington and I discuss comedy and our philosophy about this art form, something each of us has done so many times before, and then Barry opens the session up to questions from the floor, of which there is no shortage.

Afterwards, Maurice and I go into a marquee to sign copies of *Shine On Harvey Moon*, *The New Statesman* and *Dorien's Diary*, and believe it or not a few people actually buy copies of 'The New

Statesman' scripts. We sign books, posters, programmes and any
other pieces of paper put before us, before our sponsors, Bang and
Olufsen, come to meet us and take us all to dinner in Matcham's,
the restaurant atop the Everyman Theatre.

SUNDAY, 13 OCTOBER

Over breakfast, Briggy, Shirley, Alex and I discuss Maurice and
Carol, and I have to admit to all around the table that I know little
of Maurice's inner feelings for he so rarely discusses them with
me. Maurice remains my closest friend and there isn't a bad word
I can say against him for he is a caring and considerate person. He
is eminently sensible, he has annoying habits, but then who
hasn't? But as for ever knowing what he feels emotionally about
anything at all, well, there I should have to pass. I know little of his
likes and dislikes, socially that is. What he does when he leaves the
Cattle Shed remains largely a mystery to me as he chooses not to
tell me. I believe he derives more enjoyment from the social world
around his work than around Cheltenham. That is, though, no
more than an impression, for, as I say, Maurice never talks about it
and he is something of a closed book emotionally – yet not so
when working on explaining characters' lives.

This afternoon, we watch the one-hour-long 'Panorama' made
about Oswald Mosley in 1968. Like Hitler and Thatcher, Mosley
was driven, with mad staring eyes and a determination to be a
leader. Where it worked for Thatcher and Hitler (both from the
lower orders), it signally failed for Mosley, perhaps because of his
class. I can't see the comparison between Mosley and Blair though,
and I should like to ask the political commentators why they imagine there are similarities.

For the remainder of this afternoon, and well into the evening, I
watch 'Match of the Day'. The second featured game is Blackburn
Rovers v. Arsenal, a game my team won by 2–0, with Ian Wright
scoring two marvellous opportunist goals and moving ever nearer
to becoming Arsenal's top goalscorer of all time. This is a record
held by Cliff Bastin since 1946, but Wright has only about another
twenty something goals to score before he passes Bastin's tally
and goes into the Arsenal record books. What an achievement!
Wright can only have been with Arsenal for six or seven seasons.

This also happens to be the first match with Arsene Wenger, our brand-new manager, in charge of the team. I watch all the other day's matches and see Mark Bosnich, Aston Villa's goalkeeper, give a Nazi salute to the Tottenham supporters, which causes ructions on the terraces, and after the final whistle Bosnich is interviewed by the police who might press charges. Certainly the FA should charge Bosnich with bringing the game into disrepute. The Villa goalkeeper claims it was a joke that backfired.

WEDNESDAY, 16 OCTOBER

The day of the seance! Briggy was in such pain with her back first thing this morning she could hardly move. The injury occurred during an exercise session. This afternoon, she took herself off to Cheddington to be treated by Michael van Straten's assistant, and I collect her, having spent the afternoon on a dry-run to find the evening's destination.

At seven o'clock, we enter this chi-chi detached house in a private road. Briggy and I are the first to arrive and while we are waiting for the others to turn up, sitting in the kitchen drinking mugs of tea, Bob attempts to heal Briggy's back. Whatever he does, and never once does he touch her, it seems to alleviate the pain, much to Briggy's surprise. Perhaps tonight will deliver many surprises. At seven-thirty other people start to arrive, and by eight o'clock I am involved in a conversation with a young Jewish divorcee about the reasons for being Jewish, and whether it is a religion or not, and if it is, why she does not believe in it. When everyone has arrived – about twelve of us – we file into the sitting room to await the arrival of the transfiguration medium. I have already been into the room where we shall experience whatever it is we shall experience this evening; Bob showed me where whatever it is takes place as he was setting up his camera and sound equipment.

Bob is wholly taken with spiritualism and believes there is life on 'the other side'. I am equivocal, not sure I even want to be convinced.

Anyway, the evening begins. The spiritualist sits on a chair in front of a black curtain. The lights are dim and she covers her hair with a black scarf so all you can see is her face. She explains what might possibly happen this evening; Bob says some prayers. In order to entice the spirits into the room, we are encouraged to sing and laugh, thereby making the room a desirable place to be. Well, that seems reasonable enough. To hear us all obediently singing 'It's a Long Way to Tipperary' and 'She'll Be Coming Round The Mountain When She Comes' over and over again is enough to make anyone laugh, and then it happens. The woman from the north-east of England, with the broad Geordie accent, suddenly transfigures herself into a Chinaman, the spirit guide through whom everything will happen this evening. I am fascinated, almost hypnotised, by this occurrence and watch with eyes open wide. If we recognise the person coming into the room through the Chinaman, we are to be brave and acknowledge them, and talk to them as if they were actually there. Then there is silence and the medium's face starts to change.

She focuses upon me. I am anxious, I do admit, but I watch intently to see if I recognise the spirit covering the medium's face. I don't. It isn't anyone I know. I am asked if I know someone who used to knit? Of course, my mother was a zealous knitter, and a very good one, too. Does the name Mary mean anything to me? No. Do I know somebody who was deaf but what they missed with their ears they more than made up for with their eyes? Well, yes, my grandmother was a little like that. The months of April and August are going to be significant for me. Was there something I was doing that I wanted to keep from the world? I suppose I could imagine 'Unfinished Business' was under wraps, but for no good reason. Was I expecting somebody at Christmas whom I hadn't seen in a long while? No. Well, I am told, somebody will turn up and surprise me. Who could that be?

Two aspects of the evening made me rather jaundiced. The spiritualist seemed to take each person in turn, as if we were waiting in line to be called by the spirit. Surely if a spirit was coming through it would not have been as selective as to have chosen each of us, one at a time, without returning to one already chosen? And when one chap, George, thought he saw his grandmother (it was mostly grandmothers) and spoke to her in his native tongue, Greek, the spiritualist did not reply at all, let alone in Greek! Briggy later comments that the spiritualist is only the receptacle through which the spirits pass, and if she cannot speak the language, it is impossible to pass on the message in Greek,

German or French, each language being represented here tonight.

The evening has given me much food for thought. It went on about an hour and a half longer than Bob said it would, yet it wasn't as if there was much happening. It was vague, of that there can be little doubt, and perhaps some of the dozen people there tonight did benefit from the experience. There was a moment when I think I saw the face of my mother, although only in part. It must have been convincing for Briggy seemed to recognise her too, and she has only seen photographs of my mum. But I would have had nothing to say to my mother and I wouldn't really welcome seeing her again, no matter what side she came from.

SUNDAY, 20 OCTOBER

Newcastle United v. Manchester United, regarded by many as the match of the season. Whoever wins will overtake Arsenal who have been sitting at the summit of the Premier League since yesterday afternoon, following their goalless draw with Coventry City, a match they should surely have won.

A very able Manchester United side is taken apart by the skill, flair and raw enthusiasm of this Newcastle United side. With 40,000 plus Geordies roaring them on, it takes Newcastle only fourteen minutes to score their first, and a most controversial goal it is. Darren Peacock, the centre-half, heads the ball goalwards; Denis Irwin attempts to kick the ball clear after it has beaten Peter Schmeichel but the linesman, not the referee, sees something the advanced technology that is modern-day camera equipment only just sees, and that is that the whole of the ball had crossed the line. Newcastle 1 Manchester United 0. But Manchester United play attacking, forward-moving football and the feeling is they will equalise soon. They well might have done after Karel Poborsky seems to be brought down after taking the ball around the Newcastle goalkeeper, but the referee believes the Czech made a meal of it and play continues. Then David Ginola scores a goal made in heaven – a shot from twenty yards or further, and wide on the left, that is so fierce Schmeichel seems not to move. The game should be won, but having seen the Geordies give games away when 2–0 up, nothing is certain. In the second half they score three, yes three, further goals. Scorers are Les Ferdinand, Alan Shearer and, the best of them all, Philippe Albert, a delicate chip from twenty-five yards over the well-off-his-line Peter Schmeichel. Newcastle United 5 Manchester United 0. This is the final score, and it could easily have been six or seven. It is Manchester United's heaviest defeat since Alex Ferguson took over as club manager in 1986, and United's heaviest defeat since 1984 when Everton beat them by the same score.

Newcastle prove this afternoon that they are going to be the team to beat to win the championship, but for all their five goals and superb display, it's only three points. This evening they sit atop the Premier League, but they could easily find they have been knocked off the top by next weekend. Football is a transitory game, one week the best in the land, the next week rubbish.

WEDNESDAY, 23 OCTOBER

I have been invited to take part in a programme, broadcast out of Aberdeen, entitled 'The Slice'. A peculiar excuse for a programme this: the principle is to take any word out of the *Oxford English Dictionary* and make a programme around it. This week's word is pipe, so it's obvious why they have invited me on. I was the Pipesmoker of the Year 1990, and am currently the chairman of the Pipesmokers' Council – a natural choice.

The programme makers at BBC Scotland asked me to get to the BBC Thames Valley studios with fifteen minutes to spare (the programme starts at eleven o'clock) and this I do, just. I am then kept waiting in Thames Valley reception area until about a minute before eleven – somebody else is in the one link-up studio they have. Moreover, the line to Aberdeen is mighty difficult to link up with. I'm eventually taken up to the studio and, after some difficulty, connected to Aberdeen. Eventually, I'm told I shall be on in thirty seconds. The programme's presenter, a woman with a broad Scottish accent that thankfully I am able to understand, begins by asking me what is my interest in this week's word. I reply that I smoke a pipe, and go on to explain when and why I started, how I was a definite non-smoker when I was given my first pipe. We speak for a short while – the interview is to last only eight minutes – about pipes and pipe smoking, then it inevitably moves on to my work, and even more inevitably to 'Birds of a Feather'. Would Dorien smoke a pipe? I reply that Dorien has far more erotic things to put in her mouth than a pipe, which seems to break whatever ice there is, and we continue the interview about how the pipe plays a part in my work. I'm most surprised that the presenter doesn't ask me how Maurice, with whom I share an office (and we talk about the Cattle Shed), copes with the aroma of pipe smoke floating around his head.

TUESDAY, 5 NOVEMBER

Possible Oswald Mosleys occupy us today. I think we have to see Jonathan Cake before we move on to any others. Cake has been in our minds since we saw him do his first television in 'Goodnight Sweetheart', and we were both impressed hugely by the man's ability to fill the screen. He is now an extremely busy actor, starring in many prestigious productions, one for Channel Four, and we rather think that we would really be thought of as clever clogs were we to book him just before he became a big star. 'Mosley' might even make him that big star. Other casting at this moment is all rather superfluous and so it is best we avoid it. There is little more for us to do than appoint a director and designer, and get the pre-pre-production into operation by 10 December.

FRIDAY, 8 NOVEMBER

This morning Maurice and I have to go to the Carlton Towers Hotel, off Sloane Street, where we are to meet with Guy Slater and Irving Teitelbaum, the producer. This is the second time this week Maurice and I have interviewed a potential producer for 'Mosley'.

Maurice tells me that last night's 'Birds of a Feather' was a long trawl. The audience were less than on the ball, the kind of audience who roared with laughter when Sharon said 'fart', but when subtle lines passed her lips didn't find it at all amusing. They wanted seaside postcard humour and anything else went completely over their heads.

The four of us sit and talk for an hour and a half, discussing not so much the first three episodes – although Guy believes the first is running seven minutes short – but rather the last. This leads to the most pertinent question: what happened to Oswald Mosley between the time he formed the New Party in 1931 and the moment he decided that anti-Semitism was to be the primary policy of the British Union of Fascists, which he led? It is a question to which I have no immediate answer, but it is the key that will help us unlock one of the components, perhaps the most important one, of Mosley's character. Irving also talks about Fascism and anti-Semitism in a broader sense and it is this that really occupies us. Irving believes we should try to allow the audience in on why Mosley knew what he was doing when he attacked the Jews, and what sort of England he wanted were he to succeed and become the leader of the country. Irving would also like us to look at Mosley's kind of Fascism and compare it with that which existed at the time in Germany and Italy, and even maybe in Spain.

I don't know whether it is because I am tired, or yesterday's drive from Leeds to London took more out of me than I imagined, or that the talk was really wearing, but I seem not to exude the same interest in this week's 'Birds of a Feather' read-through that I do usually. I find everything jaded and unimportant, even though I'm quite aware that comedy series don't take care of themselves. Have I suddenly become jaundiced about half-hour comedy, in the light of this morning's intriguing and educative conversation about British Fascism in the 1930s? Claire Hinson talks to us about the many other shows we have in pre- or ordinary production, and tells us that Barbara Flynn has accepted a part in a Shakespeare play at the National Theatre, which means if we wish to use her in 'Unfinished Business' we shall have to record the show on a Sunday night. This doesn't present any difficulties for Maurice and me; what does is that she is not prepared to sign an option to appear in further series. We do not want to work with anyone who won't give us that commitment and so I think we might well be working with a different actress in the leading role of our new comedy. Who, I have no idea just at this moment, but it will have to be someone with weight for I want it to be seen as an adult comedy that deals with areas of life normally not discussed at home nor on television. If we have Henry Goodman, we should have an equally brilliant female lead.

SATURDAY, 9 NOVEMBER

An interesting selection of players wearing England shirts takes the field for the World Cup qualifying match against Georgia. The national anthems seem to go on forever. The average annual wage in Georgia is, apparently, £150, yet today's tickets cost about £6. No wonder the stadium is only half full.

England win this match by 2–0, and find themselves leading their group with the maximum number of points available to them. They have beaten Moldova, Poland and Georgia, and will meet the group favourites, Italy, at Wembley in February. I think this afternoon's match is a personal triumph for the tactical planning of Glenn Hoddle and his team, and it might just be that he will be as skilful a manager as he was a player. He may lead England to the World Cup finals in France in two years' time, and who knows, perhaps take the trophy. He seems the most confident and single-minded of men and I can't imagine Hoddle taking any truck from the press, all of whom seem to like him.

WEDNESDAY, 13 NOVEMBER

Tonight is the Coca-Cola Cup replay between Arsenal and Stoke City. Arsenal managed to scrape an equaliser at Stoke in the last minute; tonight they play controlled, tidy, though not flair football, and their casualness leads to Stoke scoring the first goal of the game ten minutes before half-time. The commentators, Martin Tyler and Andy Gray, keep saying that if Stoke can hold out until half-time, they are really in with a marvellous chance of creating a major upset. Three minutes before half-time, with Stoke still holding a 1–0 lead, Dennis Bergkamp is brought down in Stoke's penalty area and Ian Wright scores from the penalty spot. In the second half, Arsenal go on the rampage. Within ninety seconds of the start, the most wonderful cross from Ian Wright finds David Platt almost standing on the Stoke goalline and he chests the ball into an empty net. Then Wright scores his second, Bergkamp scores the goal of the night with a fierce drive that the goalkeeper barely sees, let alone stops, and finally Paul Merson adds a fifth. Stoke, to their credit, continue to go forward and Mike Sheron scores his second goal of the night, but it can't prevent the final scoreline reading Arsenal 5 Stoke City 2. It is Arsenal who will travel to Liverpool, surely the match of the next round.

Arsenal look good this evening, but they were playing only competent first-division opposition. The real tests will come later this month at Old Trafford (this coming Saturday) and St James's Park, and when Spurs come to Highbury. If Arsenal can take six points from these three matches, they can consider themselves to have done well, although perhaps Arsene Wenger believes nine points are possible. If I were asked to put my shirt on the results of these three games, I would plump for a draw at Old Trafford, a defeat at Newcastle and a victory over Spurs. That's only four from a possible nine points – not good enough for serious championship contenders.

THURSDAY, 14 NOVEMBER

In the pub, Maurice and I talk about last night's Arsenal v. Stoke City game, analyse it, discuss how well Arsenal are beginning to play and the influence of Arsene Wenger. Maurice turns the subject to the controversy that has so angered Mr Wenger. I don't know what it might be, other than the fact his girlfriend is having Wenger's child and, Wenger being a married man, this has excited the racier Sunday tabloid newspapers. Maurice believes it has to be much more than that for it has brought Peter Hill-Wood, Arsenal's chairman, and David Dein, the vice chairman, into the frame, commenting on the outrageous behaviour of the *People* newspaper. Harry Harris would know, perhaps we should ask him. What might Arsene Wenger have done that is so terrible that he talks of resigning from his post at Highbury? Surely Arsenal won't find themselves having to seek a fifth new manager this season?

MONDAY, 18 NOVEMBER

The entrance to BAFTA is surrounded by press photographers, here to spot famous faces and especially Bob Monkhouse, who is in the news because he has recaptured his missing volumes of jokes and comedy research. The books, containing Monkhouse's life works, were on their way back to him after his agent Peter Pritchard was handed the books by a man asking for £10,000. Bob tells Maurice this evening, 'Every idea I have, I write down in the books – dialogue, thoughts for plays, books and shows, all in long-hand, and I always kept them in my possession.' Also present at tonight's bash is Salman Rushdie, another good reason for the press to start whirring the remote controls on their Nikons. The high and mighty, as well as some of the more lowly, of British television are assembled.

So why are we all here? It's the inaugural BAFTA lecture and it's being given by Alan Yentob, Director of Programmes at the BBC. His subject is 'A Journey In Television'. I make my way to the Princess Anne Theatre with Salman Rushdie. He's a Spurs supporter, so what else should we talk about? Rushdie has lived under constant police protection since the Ayatollah Khomeini put a fatwa on him, and somewhere in the room this evening I wouldn't be at all surprised to find armed policemen. I wonder if he ever manages to get over to White Hart Lane?

SUNDAY, 24 NOVEMBER

We are going to attend what, for Arsenal supporters, is the biggest league game of the season, the visit of Tottenham Hotspur. I'm wearing my furry coat, hat and gloves and I don't much care if I do overheat. I'm also going to wear my furry boots; I remember sitting at an Arsenal v. Coventry City match last year, with Bob Hartley, when we were both inadequately dressed and spent the match in a frozen heap at the front of the West Stand.

The journey is enlivened by the castaway on 'Desert Island Discs', Tony Blair. We play a little game among the three of us, guessing how many records were Blair's own choice and how many were politically acceptable to Peter Mandelson, Blair's political guru. Of the eight records chosen by Blair – although I have to say that his life story was far more captivating that his choice of music – I think the Beatles' 'In My Life' and Free's 'Wishing Well' were among the more imaginative. In many ways 'Desert Island Discs' paints a much clearer picture of somebody than any number of television documentaries.

We take our seats and await the arrival of the north London rivals.

Arsenal will play the next four or five vital matches without their number one goalkeeper, David Seaman, through injury. Many would classify him as the world's number one goalkeeper, so it is a great loss to our team not to have him between the sticks. What makes matters even worse is that his replacement is John Lukic. Are we being unfair? Lukic lost us two points against Chelsea earlier this season. What might he do this afternoon?

In wet, slippery conditions the teams battle out a first half in which the best two chances fall to Sheringham and Armstrong, and they both miss them. Arsenal play this new smooth, along-the-ground, Wenger football that is a delight to watch, although still too many passes are going astray. However, we take the lead when Ian Wright converts a penalty kick after Dennis Bergkamp has been roughly handled in the Spurs penalty box. A chance falls to Wright following a marvellously fluent build-up, one that he would have converted ninety-nine times out of a hundred. Instead he hurries his shot and the ball flashes wide of the post. Never mind, I can forgive Ian Wright anything, and after all no one should expect the man to score with every shot he takes. Arsenal lead 1–0 at half-time.

The second half is interesting. Spurs have many chances, most fall to Chris Armstrong and he misses them all. Lukic to his credit pulls off two fine saves, but when he is called on again to stop what seems a fairly tame shot from Andy Sinton, Lukic seems to dive late, the ball hits the post, rebounds on to Lukic's head and finishes up in the back of the Arsenal net. It's all too predictably sad – 1–1, and this is the way it looks as though it is going to stay. Arsenal mount attack after attack but they are found to be impotent and shots from Keown and Merson flash well wide. Well, flash implies speed. These shots bobble. Then Arsene Wenger makes a typical continental tactical change. He takes off the ineffectual David Platt and brings on John Hartson.

Sol Campbell, Spurs' big central defender who has until now managed to keep a tight rein on Ian Wright, becomes confused. Who should he be marking, Hartson or Wright? He opts for Hartson, leaving Wright to create all sorts of openings upfront, and with four minutes of play left Hartson flicks a mid-air ball into the path of, of all people, Tony Adams (unquestionably the man of the match) who delivers an over-the-shoulder volley that crashes past Ian Walker into the Spurs net – 2–1. With one minute of play left, Ian Wright tricks and teases the Spurs defence on the far side of the pitch, wasting precious seconds, and then having sold several dummies to two Spurs players, he crosses an accurate ball that Bergkamp picks up. With a slight sway of his hips, Bergkamp sends his marker somewhere just west of Highbury New Park and slams in a shot that gives Walker not a chance. Arsenal 3 Tottenham Hotspur 1 is the score I predicted on my Ladbrokes betting slip, and it means I have won £16. It also gives Arsenal three more points and places them second in the premier division.

Next Saturday we have Newcastle United at St James's Park, and maybe it's possible to gain a point if Seaman is in goal. With Lukic between the posts just one of his mistakes can cost Arsenal the match. Let's keep our fingers crossed that Arsenal can avoid injuries at Liverpool on Wednesday evening, and take on Newcastle with a full-strength team. Meanwhile, every Arsenal fan is jubilant at beating Spurs. We walk back to the hospitality lounge and there Mark Burdis just can't believe it when I tell him I have again predicted the correct result. He stares at me and exclaims, 'You never lose! Want to join a lottery syndicate? Have you ever thought of going to Las Vegas?!'

WEDNESDAY, 27 NOVEMBER

I watched a brand new episode of 'Morse'. It's billed as a detective thriller, although it isn't at all thrilling, just mysterious, but at two hours it occupied the best part of the evening. By the end of it, once I think I know whodunit, I also know courtesy of Ceefax that Liverpool have beaten Arsenal 4–2 in the Coca-Cola Cup, Bolton have thrashed Tottenham 6–1, Leicester have beaten Manchester United 2–0 and Middlesbrough have knocked out Newcastle 3–1. So four of the best teams in the Premier League are out of the Coca-Cola Cup. I suppose Liverpool must be odds-on favourites to win the trophy, but I wouldn't rule out Wimbledon or Middlesbrough.

THURSDAY, 28 NOVEMBER

I am fifteen minutes late for my meeting. Maurice is already sitting in Guy Slater's office talking to Irving Teitelbaum. Weather conditions did not allow me to be here any sooner. We are there to watch the videos of two pieces of work by the director Stephen Whittaker. The first is entitled 'A Portrait of a Marriage' and is the story of Vita Sackville-West's love for Harold Nicolson and Violet Trefusis. I believe we watch the third of a four-part serial and next we watch an episode of 'Hearts and Minds'. There could not be more of a contrast between the pieces, one being a period piece of stunning locations and great beauty, although painfully slow in the sense one would find a beautifully written piece of literature slow, the other a fast-paced, inner city riotous piece of violent drama, from the pen of Jimmy McGovern. However, both are exquisitely directed and I am particularly impressed by how Stephen Whittaker directs crowd scenes. He works with the extras as if they are very important members of the cast; consequently they do not resemble extras, rather players who have a meaningful part in the story. This will be consequential in 'Mosley', where many of the scenes contain more than the leading characters. 'Hearts and Minds' particularly shows this quality. It is set in an inner-Liverpool comprehensive school, so there are always plenty of children and adults in the same scene. Stephen Whittaker handles this well. He is able to get through the story with pace, although he chooses not to do this in 'Portrait of a Marriage', where long lingering shots stay on the principals just long enough for you to beg for the next shot. For all my nit-picking, Stephen Whittaker knows how to make pictures, tell a story, direct actors, and I believe give us what we want in 'Mosley', and that is somewhere between the two pieces we have watched this morning.

Stephen is younger than I imagined he would be. He is shyer and less formal, and he discusses just how excited he is by the four 'Mosley' scripts and how he really wants to direct this film. He puts a lot of questions to us and after about fifty minutes of chatting I feel we shall be able to work with this totally 'un-lovey', non-precious man, and between us we might be able to make a film of outstanding quality. After Stephen has gone, Guy reiterates how Stephen is his favourite, Irving too thinks he is our man, and although Maurice and I have seen not one other director, we really should take the advice of the two experienced film makers around us and go with our gut feeling. It usually serves us well.

After tonight's show, 'Goodnight Sweetheart', our casting

director Susie Parris greets me warmly. She thinks 'Mosley' will be a dream to cast and we discuss should we go with Jonathan Cake or Ralph Fiennes? Who will play Cimmie? Who will play Diana Mitford and where might we ever find the most beautiful, elegant and confident twenty-one-year-old on the planet? What about Boothby and Strachey and Lloyd George? I think 'Mosley' will be as interesting for Susie as it has been for Maurice and me.

'Unfinished Business' is not yet cast. Who might play Amy should Barbara Flynn pull out, as seems probable? The favourite emerges as Maureen Lipman, with Alison Steadman chasing up the rear. Time is slightly on our side with this one and I think we can wait until I return from holiday before we discuss it further, but Susie just wants to talk and talk and learn more about Mosley, a character she wanted to dislike but finished up being attracted to.

SATURDAY, 30 NOVEMBER

Briggy is doing the packing for our holiday in the Maldives. Don't suppose we'll need much. I'm occupied with the biography of Alec Douglas Home, or Alec Dunglass as he is in the early part of his life story, but Schumann in the background slowly takes me over. I seem to take in his piano music more than I have ever done. For some reason it is meaning much more to me – the emotions, the sadness. Perhaps in a way it is a reflection of my own life as I see it at this time. What is happening to me? Why am I getting these terrible headaches? Can it be my glasses? I have now reverted to my old ones, which seem to be better.

The second-half commentary from St James's Park may cheer me up. As I turn on the radio, the half-time score is 1–1. Arsenal took the lead, quite amazingly, through a Lee Dixon header, but Alan Shearer equalised from the penalty spot after he was brought down by Tony Adams. The foul brought Adams a red card and Arsenal have been battling on with ten men for the second time this week. As I listen to the second half, I am amazed to hear how much more dominant Arsenal are than Newcastle. I am also amazed when Ian Wright puts Arsenal in front. I am flabbergasted when the final whistle blows and the ten men of Arsenal have won 2–1 up at St James's Park. They now go to the top of the Premier League. Quite remarkable!

SUNDAY, 8 DECEMBER

Neil Simon's autobiography, *Rewrites*, strikes a chord. Some passages are reminiscent of my own life and I can understand the answer to the question I am so often asked – 'Why do you write comedy?' He is such a shrewd observer of behaviour. In one lengthy passage he describes the two people within him – the boy and the man. It is certainly a passage I shall return to in the future when I am trying to make sense of my life and why I seem unable to enjoy it in the manner I suppose I think it ought to be enjoyed.

SATURDAY, 21 DECEMBER

The weather seems to be getting colder, the light is fading fast, as one would expect, this being the shortest day of the year, and so after about an hour in Burford, looking in and out of all the shops, I headed for Jackie's Tea Rooms only to find them empty, closed, no longer in existence. I can't work out quite why. I mean, who would give up a shop in a prime site in Burford High Street? Perhaps Jackie's lease had expired, or someone retired, but then Burford is the most sensible place to work when one is already retired. So I go home, listening to the second-half commentary from one of this afternoon's games. It happens to come from the City Ground, Nottingham, and features Nottingham Forest and Arsenal. The score as I switch on is 1–1, Ian Wright having put Arsenal into the lead, but moments later Ian Wright is involved in an unnecessary affray and sent off. Arsenal are down to ten men, Forest equalise, and it seems to be heading for a 1–1 draw, which isn't too bad for the Arsenal. However, with a minute or two of play to go, and Arsenal's defence, without Seaman and Adams, under the cosh, they allow Forest to score the winning goal, thus giving away three valuable points. It is Arsenal's third defeat of the season so far and to me seems completely against the run of play. I wonder how much Lukic's positioning had to do with the two Forest goals. I shall watch the highlights on 'Match of the Day' tonight and decide for myself. It is good news for Forest, today under Stuart Pearce's management for the first time. The win, though, doesn't lift Nottingham Forest off the bottom of the Premier League. The defeat still leaves Arsenal in second place, as Liverpool and Wimbledon don't play today, but on Sunday and Monday.

Thursday, 26 December

If Arsenal were to win tonight's game at Sheffield Wednesday, they would close the gap on Liverpool, who only managed a 1–1 home draw with Leicester City this afternoon. Ninety minutes of uninspired, and at times downright dull, football later, the game finishes goalless. The one point will do Arsenal's championship hopes no damage at all, but it is a missed opportunity, and none was missed more than a chance that fell to the well-below-par, some would say overpaid, David Platt in the first half of the game. After that Dennis Bergkamp had the only other chance, and from a Paul Shaw cross the Dutchman hit the post with a header. I suppose 0–0 is a fair result, but not the finest match to take me out of 1996. I shan't see another live match before the middle of January.

Sunday, 12 January 1997

An Arsenal supporter from Hackney has written to ask if I will draw up a Mastermind-style quiz about the Arsenal. His pub have reached the final of a north London pub quiz competition, and want to practise with some really difficult questions. This sounds like fun. Yes, why not? I think I'll use them in my *Gunners* magazine feature, too. Scouring all my Arsenal books, I manage to come up with twenty suitably difficult questions:

1. What was the name of the public house in which Arsenal were formed in October 1886?
2. Arsenal took part in the very first football match ever transmitted by ITV. Who were their opponents?
3. Against whom, and in which year was the last match to be abandoned at Highbury?
4. Who was the first Arsenal player to win a full international England cap?
5. Against whom did Arsenal play for George Armstrong's Testimonial?

6. What is Arsenal's heaviest ever defeat, and by whom?
7. Arsenal helped create an English first-class match record on 21 April 1930. What was it?
8. Who, in 1980, scored the only goal in Arsenal's outstanding Cup-Winners' Cup semi-final victory over Juventus in Turin?
9. How much did Highbury cost in 1913, and for how long was the lease?
10. Which two conditions did the leaseholders specify before Arsenal could buy Highbury?
11. Arsenal took part in the longest semi-final in FA Cup history. On which ground did the tie finish?
12. Which team knocked Arsenal out of their first ever FA Cup?
13. What was remarkable about Arsenal's 1942–43 season?
14. In which year and against whom did Tony Adams make his league debut?
15. Who was Arsenal's first professional manager?
16. For which newspaper was George Allison (Arsenal's manager from 1934–47) London Correspondent for over thirty-five years?
17. Who were Arsenal's first opponents in a European competition?
18. Which club was responsible for Arsenal wearing red shirts, and why?
19. Which Arsenal player cost the club £1,250,000 and never played a league game for the Gunners?
20. What is Arsenal's lowest league position since returning to division one in 1919?

A good morning's work – time to adjourn to the pub for a pint.

TUESDAY, 14 JANUARY

No sign of Maurice. We have a black-tie dinner at the Plaisterers' Hall tonight and I have the news on as I get ready. Within the past half an hour, Newcastle United have announced that their new manager is Kenny Dalglish. Why he took the job is something of a mystery to me, having professed on many occasions that he didn't much care for the pressures of football management. I can only imagine it is down to money and ego. He has already won the title with Liverpool and Blackburn Rovers. Should Dalglish manage to win the Premier League title for Newcastle, he will become the first football manager in English League history to manage three championship teams. Kevin Keegan has left a very solid foundation on which to build and it will be interesting to see how Dalglish goes about his task. When the item is shown on this evening's news, vox-pops are taken in the streets of Newcastle, and while many of the club's supporters believe Dalglish's appointment to be a magnificent one, others feel that Bobby Robson was their man, him being a Geordie and former England manager. I am sure Dalglish won't let the team down and once he has won for them the Premier League title he will disappear into the wilderness knowing he is the most successful manager ever in British football.

The guest speaker at tonight's annual bash is Michael Winner. On the offchance that he can give me a lift, I give him a call. As he picks up the receiver, he is giving somebody a savage bollocking, as is his wont. He tells me he will call me back. I hang up, then realise he doesn't know where I am and even if he did he doesn't have the telephone number. So I call him once more. He is coming to the conclusion of the bollocking to Mercedes-Benz, and the following conversation ensues.

'Michael, it's Laurence . . .'

'Yes Laurence?'

'Michael, are you coming by way of Mayfair this evening?'

'Why should I be coming by way of Mayfair?'

'On your way to the City.'

'I'm not going to the City. I'm having people to dinner.'

'I think you'll find you are the guest speaker at the Plaisterers' Hall in about an hour and a half.'

'What are you talking about? There's nothing in my diary. It's not tonight it's . . . it's . . . it's . . . Oh fuck, it is tonight. You're right! Why isn't it in my diary? FRASER. Yes, it is here. City speech. Oh shit! No, take a taxi. I'll see you there! FRASER.'

Fraser is Michael's main man and Mercedes will not be the only ones to receive a tongue-lashing from Winner this evening. I wouldn't like to be in Fraser's shoes . . . although I suppose the man has grown used to it by now.

What a piece of good fortune for the Livery Company! Had I not telephoned Michael Winner to ask him for a lift to the City, he wouldn't have turned up and all of my tales about Winner being the most reliable man, a man good to his word, a man to be trusted, would have gone by the board and would have definitely cast doubt on whether I am a good judge of character. I suppose had he simply not turned up, the onus would have been upon me to deliver an unprepared speech. I wouldn't have enjoyed that.

WEDNESDAY, 15 JANUARY

Today is the thirty-third Pipesmoker of the Year luncheon at the Savoy Hotel. It never ceases to amaze me just how quickly a year passes and the smokers' showpiece comes round again. I am ready. I'm quite sure it will be every bit as good a lunch and event as it was last year when Sir Colin Davis took the award. This year it falls to Malcolm Bradbury, novelist, critic, television dramatist, and until recently Professor of English and American Studies at the University of East Anglia.

The award is a magnificent special pipe – a briar base, a pipe with a mortar board on its head, and a silver scroll that doubles as a tamper. When the pipe is turned upside down, so it is resting on its mortar board, you can fill it with tobacco and enjoy its sensations. Another masterpiece from Dunhill.

On the way out of London, we get as far as the Marylebone Road before we turn back. The fog seems to be getting thicker and LBC news and weather say that visibility in places will be down to five yards. There isn't any way I intend to take the Bentley on to the M40 if all I am able to see is five yards ahead of me. So it's back to the flat.

The problem for Maurice and me is how we are going to watch the Sunderland v. Arsenal FA Cup tie on Sky tonight? The Samuel Pepys comes to our rescue. Just across the road from the flat, the pub has a huge screen but no commentary. Instead, there's driving and deafening disco music, so loud that I can barely hear myself think. The pub is packed with office types, girls on the look-out for attractive men to screw. I overhear enlightening conversations and realise how out of touch I am with street culture.

Through the cigarette smoke, I watch Dennis Bergkamp score what must surely be one of the goals of the season in the second minute of the second half, giving Arsenal a 1–0 lead. Young

Stephen Hughes adds a second, Arsenal win 2–0 at Roker Park, and progress into round four to meet Crystal Palace or Leeds United (they drew 2–2 last night and replay next week). Either team should find a win at Highbury intensely difficult. Well done Arsenal. I don't want to start counting chickens, but a place in the fifth round is a real possibility.

SUNDAY, 19 JANUARY

I switch on Arsenal v. Everton with ten minutes remaining of the first half. The score is 0–0, although Everton have had a perfectly legitimate goal disallowed for offside. When the incident is repeatedly played back to the viewer, it is apparent that the goal was as good and fair as any Nick Barmby will score this season. Arsenal have had a let off and are lucky to find themselves on level terms at half-time. In the second half it is a different story. Ian Wright, back for the first time in three matches following suspension, does not take the field for the second half, having picked up a slight hamstring strain. Arsene Wenger is playing it safe, knowing that Dennis Bergkamp begins his three-match suspension after this game.

Arsenal score two dazzling goals in two minutes soon after half-time, and effectively kill off the game. Bergkamp's first goal is another masterpiece, and Patrick Vieira (surely the buy of the season) smashes a shot from twenty yards past a static Neville Southall for goal number two. Paul Merson adds a third after Bergkamp tears the Everton defence apart with his forceful running and high level of skill, assuring Arsenal of three valuable points. Duncan Ferguson scores a consolation goal for Everton and the match ends 3–1. Arsenal stay in third place behind Liverpool and Manchester United, both of whom have soon to come to Highbury. This season's run-in may so easily have died following the dismissal of Bruce Rioch; in fact, it is as exciting as any we have seen since 1991. In the space of three months, Arsene Wenger seems to have thrown off the boring tag that has dogged Arsenal for sixty years. Their football is as attractive as any team's in the Premier League.

SUNDAY, 26 JANUARY

The BBC still have the concession to show one live Cup match per round, and this afternoon they have the cream: Chelsea v. Liverpool at Stamford Bridge. The ground is full to bursting – that means 28,000. John Motson tells us that with the demand for tickets for this match they could have filled Wembley. Before the game begins the shock news comes through from St James's Park that Newcastle have been knocked out of the Cup, losing 1–2 to Nottingham Forest. I believe Forest are a good bet to win this year's trophy. If Wimbledon win their replay against Manchester United, as they should, and Liverpool lose today at Chelsea, Arsenal should have a clear run towards Wembley, and might even win the FA Cup. I should love that, but there are many battles to be fought first.

Chelsea v. Liverpool turns out to be the most exciting televised match I have seen since Newcastle v. Liverpool in the League last season, and I cannot remember a more scintillating FA Cup match. All the professional pundits were predicting a really close match, yet Liverpool were 2–0 up inside twenty minutes. Robbie Fowler, inevitably, scored the first from inside the six-yard box, and Stan Collymore picked up on a dreadful Chelsea defensive mistake and slid the ball underneath the advancing Kevin Hitchcock, Chelsea's goalkeeper, to make it 2–0 and a safe passage into round five for Liverpool. Indeed, Liverpool could easily have scored two more, both through Fowler. On the first of these two chances, Steve McManaman failed to square an obvious cross to an unmarked Fowler, standing just six yards from an open goal. Instead, McManaman took a half-hearted shot. On the second occasion, Fowler, again unmarked, headed a cross just inches over the Chelsea crossbar. Gianluca Vialli had a golden opportunity to pull a goal back for the Londoners but he shot high and wide from ten yards, a disgraceful miss from a player of Vialli's pedigree. So at half-time Liverpool lead 2–0 and must surely be heading for the next round, and as favourites. A two-goal cushion is going to be enough . . . or so I, and everyone else, believed.

At the start of the second half, Chelsea manager Ruud Gullit alters his tactics, playing just three at the back, removing Scott Minto and bringing on Mark Hughes to boost the attack. This tactical change will rank among one of the greatest in modern FA

Cup history, for within twenty-six minutes the scoreline is Chelsea 4 Liverpool 2. Chelsea score through Mark Hughes, Gianfranco Zola and Vialli (twice), and Chelsea are running Liverpool ragged. When Vialli scores his second (Chelsea's fourth), the camera finds a close-up of Mark Wright, Liverpool's mainstay in defence, looking bewildered, lost, and thoroughly confused . . . as well he might, for who could have imagined Chelsea would turn on a display such as this after such a dismal first half?

Chelsea go through to round five where they are drawn to play at Leicester City. Arsenal, if they beat Leeds United, will play at Highbury against Portsmouth, which on paper looks like an entry to the quarter-finals. However, strange things happen in the FA Cup as we have seen this afternoon. For the fifth-round draw, televised live by the BBC, there is no Newcastle, Liverpool, Everton or Spurs in the hat. Could this be Arsenal's year?

THURSDAY, 30 JANUARY

The BBC Toyota comes for Maurice and me and takes us the short distance to Hallam Place at the back end of Broadcasting House, and there we await someone to take us down to the studio where we shall sit from ten o'clock to ten-thirty speaking about 'What makes a good Member of Parliament?' We are on this programme, 'The Magazine', with Edwina Currie MP and Andrew Roth, a leading parliamentary writer and profiler, and a man we met a decade ago when we were writing the 'Profumo' movie. It was Roth who first broke the story in a Westminster in-house magazine about the relationship between Profumo and Christine Keeler. We meet Currie and Roth as we are taken to a waiting area just outside the studio.

Edwina Currie introduces herself to us and asks us what we do. When we tell her, it transports us into a controversy about both Alan B'Stard and Oswald Mosley. This in turn brings me into conflict with her about Adolf Hitler and his place in the list of people who have most influenced the twentieth century, for here we beg to differ. She picks up her *Times* and gets on with catching up with the news. Maurice by this time has got into conversation with Andrew Roth about the forthcoming general election. Talk is of how Labour could have won the 1992 election but they lost their nerve when it mattered most, and Andrew was not talking about the infamous Sheffield Rally.

We file into the large studio and Diana Madill, the presenter of this programme, leads us through what is one of the most enjoyable debates I have ever had on the radio. It is a witty, enthralling twenty minutes in which Maurice and I talk about how difficult it is to trust Members of Parliament, and why ego and blind ambition start to impair their judgement. Edwina Currie is very fluent and professional, although intensely guarded. Andrew Roth is vastly knowledgeable and humorous at the same time, and between the four of us sitting around the table (and I note that all are Jewish) we contribute to a hugely entertaining and enjoyable item – well, for the participants anyway. As we leave the studio, I discuss her soon-to-be-published novel with Edwina Currie, also her chances of holding on to her seat in the soon-to-be-called general election. She thinks her seat is too marginal to be sure of her being returned to Westminster; indeed, she feels she will lose her seat and be ousted from parliament. I think she might be right, and she tells me that she really can't see the Tories being returned for another five years. I suppose here I am standing with an honest politician, someone, I have just said on network radio, one rarely meets, a dying breed.

At our offices, we are accosted by Guy Slater who wishes to bring us up to date on 'Mosley'. It seems we have to find a further £200,000 to pay to Channel Four for an indemnity bond which means we will have to make further cuts and adjustments to the script and I am beginning to feel pessimistic about the end product. Guy assures Maurice and me that Channel Four is still gung-ho about making the drama serial, but there are the financial considerations and we must cut our cloth according to their coat. It really focuses my mind on the way television is changing, for now it seems nobody cares about the artist, it is the accountant who rules the roost and they care not one jot about the finished product.

FRIDAY, 31 JANUARY

Harriet Walter has been offered the job as Amy in 'Unfinished Business'. All the loose ends are being tied together, such as

Harriet must dedicate her talents to us and us alone. She won't be able to perform in 'Hedda Gabler' unless the dates are all right. She must also sign options and it is here that the problem lies, not at Harriet's agent's end, but at ours. We need to discuss when we would write and make a second series before we can offer a contract for Harriet to sign. Maurice and I are unsure, for so much depends upon our input into 'Birds' and 'Goodnight Sweetheart'. It is a subject we must discuss when we all have more time and clearer minds – last thing on a Friday afternoon isn't the time for clarity of thought.

SATURDAY, 1 FEBRUARY

Manchester United beat Southampton by 2–1, having been a goal down for much of the first half. Liverpool take all three points from Derby County at the Baseball Ground, and this means that Arsenal really must try to capture all three points at Leeds. They do not. The match ends 0–0, although Leeds put the ball into Arsenal's net on three occasions, all of them ruled void by a linesman waving his flag for offside. I'll have to watch 'Match of the Day' this evening to see how accurate was the linesman. I mean, I can imagine being offside once, perhaps twice, but surely not three times! Manchester United lead the Premiership, Liverpool are hot on United's heels, then come Arsenal. I have yet to rule them out, they have United and Liverpool to play at Highbury, and six points will fix them at the pinnacle of the table.

SUNDAY, 2 FEBRUARY

Yesterday's *Independent* serves me a shock – Iris Bentley has died of cancer in her middle sixties. Who is Iris Bentley? She is the sister of Derek Bentley. Derek was nineteen years old at the time of his death, hanged for the murder of PC Sidney Miles. Bentley never fired the gun that killed the policeman, had been under arrest for at least fifteen minutes, never uttered the words 'Let him have it, Chris!' (Christopher Craig was Bentley's accomplice in a bungled robbery), claimed not to have known Craig was even armed, yet because Craig was too young to be hanged, Bentley was found guilty, sentenced to death (with a strong recommendation for mercy) and executed. The whole case stunk of Bentley being the scapegoat for the British judicial system. A policeman had been murdered and someone was going to have to pay the price for that killing. It was poor, dim-witted Bentley. Ever since the morning of Derek Bentley's execution in January 1953, Iris Bentley campaigned tirelessly to prove her brother's innocence.

I met the Bentleys in 1973, at least around that time, when I joined the Derek Bentley Committee, headed by David Yallop, who had just written the book *To Encourage The Others*. Bentley's parents, Will and Lil, did everything they could to make the Home Secretary reopen their son's case, but they died without officialdom acknowledging anything might have gone wrong with the machinery of justice. Iris took over her parents' banner and I believe, through her never-ending hard work, managed to get Derek's remains removed from a prison courtyard and buried in consecrated ground. She is now buried next to her brother. She was close to getting him a posthumous free pardon, but now she has died just months before the Home Office is sending the case of Derek Bentley back to the Court of Appeal to be reopened. Iris Bentley's daughter is to continue carrying the baton on behalf of her mother and the Bentley family, and perhaps in Bentley junior's lifetime she will manage to obtain the free pardon for the uncle she never knew. She must feel as if she has lived with his ghost for as long as she can remember.

TUESDAY, 4 FEBRUARY

The usual routine comes before tonight's fourth-round FA Cup match, Arsenal against Leeds United, led by ex-Arsenal manager, George Graham. If Arsenal win this match, as they should, they have a fifth-round home tie against Portsmouth, which they surely should win and then find themselves in the quarter-finals. Should . . . should! It isn't the same as have . . . have! And they don't. I can't believe it. Arsenal, fielding a relatively strong side, at home, playing very well, lose to a Leeds team whose defence has certainly improved over the past months, but whose attack is impotent. Leeds score the only goal of the game after eleven minutes when, in my opinion, David Seaman makes the vital mistake by not coming to collect a ball that is his (a touch of the John Lukic). Rod Wallace fumbles the ball against the foot of the post, as it rebounds Martin Keown fails to clear the ball for a corner, it returns to Rod Wallace who fires the ball high into an empty Arsenal net.

One-nil it stays, despite all Arsenal's efforts to equalise, and what this means, after the most frustrating night of Cup football, and not a very attractive match at that, is Arsenal are out of the competition I wanted them most to win. Leeds United play Portsmouth in round five and I wish them well, for this evening they played like the Arsenal of 1986/87/88, defensively impenetrable, but without looking as if they would ever score unless an opportunity of such ease was presented to them, which it was and they took it.

Manchester United lose at Wimbledon 1–0. This means United, Liverpool, Arsenal, Newcastle, Aston Villa, Spurs and Everton have all been knocked out of the FA Cup by the fifth round. It's the first time since 1975 such an event has occurred. It is anyone's Cup this season and if I had to put a small wager on a winner I would plump for Nottingham Forest, with Derby County, Chelsea and, of course, Wimbledon, following close behind. But I am so irked that my team have fallen at what seemed to me to be a relatively easy hurdle, with a performance that really belonged to another era, not what one has come to expect under the early guidance of Arsene Wenger. Arsenal do need more players of high quality, for the likes of Parlour and Morrow belong to another era here at Highbury.

Maurice and I sit right behind Frank McLintock, the captain of Arsenal's League and Cup double-winning side of 1971, and he feels Arsenal's tactics are completely ill-suited for tonight's match. It is interesting listening to this Arsenal legend talking us through the game, failure by failure.

FRIDAY, 7 FEBRUARY

Poo, the floor manager, tells me to telephone Guy Slater. When I do, Guy's tone of voice informs me that all is not well. He has just spoken to Channel Four's accountant – there is no more money in the kitty beyond £3.6 million for 'Mosley'. Guy does not believe we can make the four episodes on this budget, neither does Irving Teitelbaum, neither does Stephen Whittaker, who might well leave us should we not be able to acquire any more money and time. Guy is arranging a meeting with Peter Ansorge, Channel Four's head of drama and the man who commissioned the scripts in the first instance. My first question will be, 'What were you expecting when you commissioned an historical drama of this scale? A chat show?' Somebody somewhere inside Horseferry Road must have known that 'Mosley' was going to cost Channel Four somewhere in the region of Guy Slater's predicted budget of £850,000 per episode. Indeed, they confirmed they could afford it after delivery of the first two scripts. It encouraged us to write the next two episodes. Now we find ourselves in the horrible situation whereby Channel Four wants this project badly but the accountants are telling the artistic side of the house that they cannot afford it as it stands.

WEDNESDAY, 12 FEBRUARY

At ten o'clock, as arranged, Maurice and I turn up at Channel Four's space-age building to meet Guy Slater, Irving Teitelbaum and Stephen Whittaker, in other words the creative force behind 'Mosley'. We have a meeting here this morning with the chief production accountant at Channel Four, Peter Ansorge, and Jessica Pope, the script supervisor.

Forty-five minutes later the upshot is that if Channel Four wish to make this most important drama serial, they are somewhere going to have to find the money. We can make no further cuts to an already anorexic script. We shall have to wait and see, although my gut feeling at this moment is that they will not find any such money, neither will they want to pay for the insurance bond, so the project will fall by the wayside, at least at Channel Four. Maurice cleverly throws in an inducement to Peter Ansorge – if he makes this four-parter, we will write another four-parter next year that will be only £750,000 per episode, well within his budget. The most annoying aspect of this meeting is that all at Channel Four so desperately want to make 'Mosley', but of course if they want to make it that desperately somehow they will draw upon their vast resources.

Fortunately, there's this evening's World Cup qualifying match between England and Italy at Wembley to look forward to.

Shouldn't have looked forward to it – more frustration. Italy take the match 1–0 and seriously hamper England's chances of qualifying for France 1998. Glenn Hoddle, England's coach, makes what many a commentator sees as a serious error of judgement by playing Matthew Le Tissier. The Southampton man's impression on this evening's game is so negligible as to be hardly noticeable, although I think he has a good opening twenty-five minutes. The fact nobody gives him the ball doesn't help his cause, but he manages to find much space.

Gianfranco Zola, Chelsea's midfield ace, scores in the nineteenth minute and seals the game for the Italians. It isn't a game I shall remember, and Wembley is not a stadium I ever wish to visit again.

WEDNESDAY, 19 FEBRUARY

Deng Xiaoping, whose two decades as a paramount leader of China brought the country both great economic reforms and the horrors of Tiananmen Square, died this evening at the age of ninety-two. Maurice and I learned this as we were driving home from Highbury after seeing what should have been the most important Premier League match of the season, and might well prove to be so – Arsenal 1 Manchester United 2. This means that Manchester United stride further ahead at the top of the Premier League table, and Arsenal remain third. More dropped points but surely Arsenal are not out of a championship race that they could never have expected to win at the start of the season under the managership of Stewart Houston. The match itself was exciting, with United taking a two-goal half-time lead (Andy Cole and Ole Gunnar Solskjaer the scorers, and both goals coming from the breakdown of an Arsenal attack well into the United penalty area). Arsenal had their chances. Wright could so easily have put Arsenal ahead inside ten minutes, and again ten minutes after that, but these two misses rather blew the wind out of Arsenal's sails and it has to be said that they were facing a much better, much faster, much better-organised team. Arsene Wenger will have seen tonight what he must do to bring this Arsenal team up to scratch.

Arsenal pulled a goal back with twenty minutes of the game left to play. A ferocious shot from Dennis Bergkamp from within the penalty box gave Arsenal some hope, and indeed they might have equalised when Ian Wright headed down and as the ball bounced upwards, Schmeichel managed to tip it over the bar. A right how's your father went on between Schmeichel and Wright, which culminated with the police having to restrain Ian Wright to prevent him from attacking the Manchester United goalkeeper when the final whistle blew.

THURSDAY, 20 FEBRUARY

The day begins for Maurice and me today in Renzo's cafe, discussing with the man himself last night's match at Highbury. We each of us agree that Manchester United was far the better side, although Arsenal could so easily have nicked the game had Ian Wright been a little more on song. Now, far from improving his strike rate, he will face a disciplinary committee on the most serious of charges: bringing the game into disrepute. He might receive a seriously heavy fine, he might be banned for many games, the latter being far worse for the club. I wonder just how Arsene Wenger feels about Wright's disciplinary record. It's too difficult to dismiss a man with a goalscoring record such as Wright's, so what do you do? Send him to a behavioural therapist? Well, it's an option.

After breakfast, Maurice and I walk through Mayfair to Foubert's Place where we have a meeting with Claire Hinson and Jacob Micheàl prior to seeing Pauline Quirke and Lesley Joseph to discuss the next series of 'Birds of a Feather'. Linda Robson should have been with us too but Lauren, her daughter, is not at all well and Linda wisely places her family above her career. The BBC have informed Clare the series of 'Birds' we have recently made will go out in May. Clare tells us that the Beeb are desperately keen to have a Christmas Special for 1997, which doesn't present too many difficulties. Pauline arrives, looking as jovial as ever, and she sits down and begins talking about social stuff that doesn't really matter and certainly doesn't interest me. Lesley arrives soon afterwards and we begin discussing where we believe the series should be picked up. Lesley is a spring of good ideas, most of which we take on board and develop. What is unusual is the harmony between Pauline and Lesley, but these days Pauline appears to be more contented with herself and with life. Who knows, it might be the calming influence of Steve Sheen. What transpires from this meeting is that there is still a rich seam to be mined, and mine it we shall.

Guy should have heard from Peter Ansorge this morning. Peter was supposed to let Guy know Channel Four's decision about whether the money we require for 'Mosley' is forthcoming or not. Unfortunately, Peter is in the north of England filming one of his other drama projects. Guy is annoyed for he was promised a call and here we all are waiting for a decision and to know what we should do next. A week after our meeting with the Channel Four folk, we are no closer to knowing whether 'Mosley' will hit the screen after the Channel Four logo, or perhaps an original BBC2 logo.

Isn't life interesting? If only Channel Four had been straightforward with us from the beginning, we should have all known where we stood. Well, we can't dwell on this forever. It's out of our hands. We can only sit and wait, and that's what we must do. It's Guy I feel sorry for – if this project falls by the wayside I fear Guy's job will be on the line and I shall feel it is our responsibility.

Peter Schmeichel could become the first footballer to face criminal charges for alleged racial abuse as his feud with Ian Wright bursts back into life. Everyone expected the Arsenal striker to be charged with misconduct by the Football Association for his behaviour last night at Highbury, but it is the Manchester United goalkeeper who finds himself in deeper trouble. Wright's complaint that he subjected him to racial abuse during last November's Premiership game at Old Trafford has not, as everyone believed, been quietly shelved. Instead, the police have been carrying out an extensive investigation and papers have now been lodged with the Crown Prosecution Service. There were no close witnesses to the alleged incident, Radio Four's midnight news tells me, but several lip-readers claim that television pictures show the Danish international swearing at Wright. If the CPS decides the evidence is strong enough, Schmeichel will find himself in a test case.

Sunday, 23 February

At four o'clock, I'm in the Cattle Shed for this afternoon's live match on Sky – Arsenal v. Wimbledon at Highbury. In the event, it's a match that puts an end to Arsenal's title challenge. Wimbledon score in the first half through Vinnie Jones, shortly after Arsenal could have found themselves 1–0 up – Ian Wright burst through the Wimbledon defence and smashed his shot against the post. Once Wimbledon are ahead, it is going to take an almighty effort by Arsenal to equalise, let alone find their way through for a winner. Steve Bould, today's captain, goes off the field with an injury and the side on the pitch at the start of the second half is drawn by stretching Arsenal's resources to the maximum: Lukic, Dixon, Marshall, Morrow, Winterburn, Hughes, Vieira, Merson, Garde, Bergkamp and Wright. Arsenal lose the match 0–1. It means we have gained just one point from our last three league matches, losing twice in four days, both games at home. No, I think Arsene Wenger is realistic enough to know that any dreams he may have had about leading Arsenal to the championship in his first half-season are well and truly dashed.

Back in the house, I sink into my armchair and light my pipe, even though I have a blocked up nose, and read the remainder of the *Observer*. I can't help but notice that on the front of the Business section is a large colour photograph of the Birds. 'What do you suppose Sharon, Dorien and Tracey are doing on the front of this section?' I muse aloud. According to the long story beneath the photograph, television producers and writers at Pearson (and this does not include Maurice and me) are threatening to walk out of their productions if Greg Dyke, chairman of Pearson TV, leaves the company this week. Apparently, Greg has been trying for the past seven months to buy Pearson TV from Pearson PLC without success. He has now served an ultimatum that if they do not allow him to buy the division of the organisation, he will walk away from Pearson altogether. I wonder to myself, all too selfishly, where that would leave Maurice and me, currently thoroughly disgruntled by the lack of support from our masters. Will Pearson TV be its own master, or can we expect a new leader? I hope Greg stays for I do find him down-to-earth and engaging company, even if I find Pearson to be less than interested in the quality of programmes they make.

WEDNESDAY, 26 FEBRUARY

What is becoming unfathomable is the relationship between Pearson TV and ALOMO, which is part of it. It is now a year since SelecTV sold its shares out to Pearson TV, and before we did we were told by Greg Dyke that the reason we should all work together is to have fun, and Pearson knew we were capable of providing them with a library of programmes, new as well as old, which would add greatly to their status as independent producers. However, since last year they have steadily shed most of the 'family' that were SelecTV, leaving our business affairs department almost naked so that nobody quite knew what was going on inside ALOMO – certainly few at Pearson.

From where I'm sitting, it seems to me that they will not make a television programme if it is not financially worth their while. Now this flies in the face of everything Maurice and I, and chief executive Allan McKeown for the matter, believed in. We set up ALOMO to make as many good programmes as we possibly could and now three of Maurice's and mine ('Mosley', 'Unfinished Business', and 'Patient A') are being well and truly stymied by the management of Pearson not, in my opinion, working hard enough to help ALOMO. Of course, it might not be Pearson's fault that there is a major hold up on each of these projects; it might be all the doing of Channel Four, the BBC, and Stoll Moss Group, but somehow I think not.

FRIDAY, 28 FEBRUARY

It is at fifteen minutes to seven this evening, as I am preparing to depart from Chrissie Skinns' and John Hambley's leaving party here at Foubert's Place, that Guy stops me. We are summoned into John Hambley's office, and while struggling to put in the new cufflinks bought for him as a leaving present, he announces to us: 'I'm pleased to tell you that the deal with Channel Four is done. "Mosley" will be made.' I'm so thrilled I would like to throw my arms around him, but I restrain myself saying nothing more than, 'That's marvellous.' If there were a bottle of champagne to hand I would open it, but there isn't so all I can do is express my earnest thanks to John Hambley, wish him good health (something he hasn't had of late), and success wherever he may choose to work next. This is fantastic news and the perfect message to end the week.

SATURDAY, 1 MARCH

Arsenal win at Everton 2–0, but Manchester United have an easy 3–1 home victory over Coventry City. Newcastle United lose 0–1 at home to Southampton, and this means Arsenal pull away from Newcastle, but no closer to Manchester United, who must now be odds-on favourites to retain the Premiership title, although Liverpool are right on United's tail, play Aston Villa tomorrow, and if they win I think there will be no more than a single point in it. And Liverpool have a home game against United that could decide this year's title.

TUESDAY, 4 MARCH

This afternoon, just as Maurice and I are getting to grips with a scene from 'Unfinished Business', two interesting letters arrive from rival television arts programmes. One is from London Weekend Television's the 'South Bank Show'. They have found out when 'Mosley' is to start filming and would like to talk to us about the best way of covering it. The other letter is from the BBC asking us if we would agree to be interviewed for an 'Omnibus' that is looking at the career and work of Dick Clement and Ian La Frenais. It would give us enormous pleasure to do so, and Maurice gets straight on the telephone to Samantha Peters, the 'Omnibus' producer, to arrange a suitable date for us to face the camera and speak highly of the two men whose work made us want to become comedy writers.

WEDNESDAY, 5 MARCH

The big news today is how the four defendants in the football-rigging case face a likely re-trial after a jury at Winchester Crown Court failed to agree a verdict after a thirty-four day trial. The judge, Mr Justice Tuckey, discharged the nine men and three women after nearly eleven hours of deliberation when it became clear they were unable to reach a verdict. None of the three footballers – former Liverpool goalkeeper Bruce Grobbelaar, former Wimbledon striker John Fashanu and former Wimbledon goalkeeper Hans Segers – commented as they left the court room. The fourth defendant, the Malaysian businessman Heng Suan Lim, said, 'I have always maintained my innocence and I will continue to do so.' The prosecution counsel David Calvert Smith said they would be seeking a re-trial; a decision – with advice from the Attorney General Sir Nicholas Lyall – is likely within a few days. Players' representatives said they were concerned about the increased strain put upon the footballers and their families.

THURSDAY, 6 MARCH

With reluctance, Stephen Whittaker pulled out of 'Mosley' yesterday for a variety of reasons, most of them to do with worrying about the budget rather than getting on with making the film work. According to Guy, Stephen was almost in tears on the telephone as he told him how he would have loved to have directed the quartet but feels he just couldn't do himself or the film justice on the money he has to work with.

So Rob Knights is now in the frame. I know nothing of his work, save that he directed 'Porterhouse Blue' and 'Sweet Bird of Youth'. This afternoon Maurice and I are introduced to him by Guy and Irving. We go to a nearby Bloomsbury hotel for tea and spend an hour talking about Oswald Mosley. In retrospect I wonder why we are talking about the man and his life when we surely should be talking about Rob Knights' vision of the film and whether he is passionate about making it.

SATURDAY, 8 MARCH

En route from Euston Station to Spring Hill I listen to David Mellor's 'Six–O–Six', the Saturday afternoon football phone-in.

Most of the calls are to do with a large mêlée that occurred at the Goldstone Ground, Brighton, this afternoon, when after being provoked by a Leyton Orient forward who had just scored a goal, Brighton supporters lost their heads, ran on to the pitch and attacked the player, other players and the referee. They may now be deducted league points. It could see them to the foot of the third division, and automatic relegation from the Football League. That would be a tragedy for such a popular club, in so much turmoil and trouble off the pitch. Business has overtaken the reason for the Goldstone Ground's existence – football.

MONDAY, 10 MARCH

Tonight Liverpool play Newcastle United in one of this season's most critical Premier League matches. Last season when these two teams met, and Newcastle had to win to maintain their championship chase, it produced one of the great matches of the decade, with Liverpool winning 4–3, their winner coming from Stan Collymore eighty seconds into injury time. Nobody expects a repeat performance tonight, least of all me. So when I watch the first half and it is a tight, very well ordered game, my money has to be on Liverpool by 1–0. When, after half an hour, Liverpool score through Steve McManaman, and quite rightly too for they have so dominated the half that Newcastle have yet to have a single shot on Liverpool's goal, I believe this is the goal that will give Liverpool all three points. However, within seventy seconds Liverpool score another – Robbie Fowler hits the post, the ball bounces straight to the feet of Patrik Berger who fires the ball into an unguarded Newcastle net. Then before half-time, and still Newcastle have yet to mount their first attack, a marvellous pass from Jamie Redknapp puts Fowler through and he doesn't miss opportunities such as these. At half-time the score reads Liverpool 3 Newcastle 0. Liverpool have wrapped up all three points, now it's a matter of whether they really wish to boost their goal difference, or whether they sit back on their lead and make sure the three points are theirs, closing the gap on Manchester United to one point, with United to come to Anfield for the crunch match.

For the second half, Newcastle put on Les Ferdinand (who isn't quite fit and comes off fifteen minutes after he is brought on) and David Ginola in order to try to salvage something, probably their pride. But Liverpool continue to attack in waves, and it seems apparent that they wish to score many more goals this evening. They could have scored seven with a little more luck when Newcastle pull one out of nothing. Well, not strictly nothing, more from a mistake by David James the goalkeeper. He allows Keith Gillespie's shot to trickle through his hands and into the back of the net. So Newcastle have a consolation goal and retain a little bit of respectability. With eight minutes to go the score remains Liverpool 3 Newcastle United 1, and then madness ensues. In the space of two minutes, and in two rare attacks, Newcastle score twice and equalise. If Newcastle take a point tonight it will be the greatest travesty I have experienced in forty-three years of watching football.

In injury time, and with Liverpool's bench incandescent with rage, the ball reaches Stig Inge Bjornebye on the left wing, he crosses and, as last season, Liverpool score an extra-time winner, tonight from the head of Robbie Fowler. This season the winner comes with the last action of the game, eighty-two seconds into injury time, and Liverpool are let off the hook. Newcastle must be feeling that a great opportunity has again been denied them, although in all fairness they really have no cause for complaint – anything Kenny Dalglish and his men took tonight would have been floodlit robbery. It does mean that Newcastle's chances of winning this season's Premier League title are more than remote, and that Liverpool's have been given a massive injection. They still have to come to Highbury, though, and this will be a test of their nerves, for whoever wins this league match has a gorgeous opportunity to win the title, or at least finish second and go into the European Cup, as two teams from the English Premier League may qualify next season. More teams, more games, more money. Money, money, money. It dictates everything that was once pure and honourable.

Friday, 14 March

This evening Maurice and I deliver a tape of Rob Knights' work to Verity and Nick Mosley. They welcome us as old friends. Marius, their son, is also there, and I feel, more than ever before, I get to know much more about Nick's life, and his life with Verity, his second wife, although, like me, there was what I term a 'midwife'

between the two. We sit drinking wine and whisky, talking about
Oswald Mosley's life, but perhaps talking more about Diana, his
second wife. The most marvellous aspect of spending any time at
all with Nicholas is that you are talking to twentieth century political history – someone who was there, someone who knew the
great figures of the inter-war years. Every remembrance is filled
with fascination for me, and a discussion about Hitler or
Mussolini, Halifax or Lloyd George, with someone whose parents
sat with these people, is perhaps more exciting to me than any
number of films I shall sit down and write. It might sound absurd,
but I am intrigued beyond words to hear that Diana Mosley,
Nick's step-mother, could refer to Adolf Hitler's wonderful sense
of humour, and call him a 'truly jolly man'. This tyrant who was
responsible for the deaths of over 50 million human beings!

MONDAY, 17 MARCH

At about ten-past three the telephone rings and a voice with which
I am not familiar asks me if I am Laurence Marks?
    'Yes, I am'.
    'I have Peter Ansorge for you.'
    What could Peter want from me? It is unusual for him to call us
here at the Cattle Shed. Peter comes on the line to say that about an
hour ago Pearson notified Channel Four that they were not happy
about the rights for 'Mosley' being offered to them. To the best of
my knowledge, all terms were agreed last week and everything
but shaking hands on the deal was done . This *volte face* by Pearson
has made Channel Four Controller, John Willis, so angry that he
has said he would like to cancel the production of 'Mosley'.
    I am aghast. And why telephone me? (Although it transpires
that the call to me, calculated or otherwise, was perhaps the best
thing that could have happened.) Peter wants to save 'Mosley'
and the only way, it seems, is for Maurice and me to go back to
Pearson and tell them to stick by the terms agreed last week. Peter
gives me chapter and verse, I make notes, read them back to Peter,
who agrees I have at least taken then down correctly, then . . .
what? What shall I do now?
    Well, first I call Maurice at home in Cheltenham, thankfully find
he's back from the visit to the VAT office, and explain to him what

has just happened. He's furious. I tell him I'm going to call the Pearson people and ask why, once agreed, anyone felt the need to jeopardise the deal? Anyone senior is in a board meeting at Teddington – isn't it always the way?! I call Maurice about five times to keep him fully up to date with progress, although there is none. I cancel my training session; I can't leave the telephones – Maurice and my futures are at stake right now. We decide that if 'Mosley' goes, so do we. I therefore telephone Greg Dyke's secretary and explain to her the situation and that Maurice and I have had enough and should like to resign.

Later this evening, I am rather surprised to receive a telephone call from Maurice who tells me that Greg Dyke has just called him, and apologised for not having called sooner only he has been 'kicking arse'. Greg explained to Maurice that this afternoon in the Pearson board meeting he lost his temper as he has never before lost it. Those around him really got not only a full earful, but also their jobs were suddenly on the line.

TUESDAY, 18 MARCH

The repercussions from yesterday's débâcle become more positive this morning. I telephone Peter Ansorge and his secretary Georgie to explain to them that Maurice and I had to resign in order to get Pearson to see sense, and that sense was simply that it is better to make a film for a small profit than not to make the film at all.

Greg Dyke telephones Maurice to inform him that everything is settled and that 'Mosley' will be made. Now could somebody answer a question asked of me yesterday – why was it possible for me to break a three-month deadlock in the space of an hour or more?

MONDAY, 24 MARCH

Briggy has taken herself off to London today, to work on a voiceover in Soho. Maurice and I leave ourselves plenty of travelling time to reach Highbury by six o'clock. We have no intention of getting stuck in traffic and being late for this evening's match against

Liverpool, as happened when we came up for the Arsenal v. Manchester United game. So we're at Highbury by five o'clock, an hour sooner than we intended to be. You can never judge the traffic. Tonight we are just lucky, but better early than late.

To kill some time, we browse around the Gunners shop, and Maurice buys for himself a yellow 1950 Cup final shirt, complete with large Arsenal badge. I bought a 1930s Arsenal shirt some while ago but I can't recall what precisely I have done with it. Maurice wants a copy of *One Nil Down, Two One Up*, but there's no sign of either the magazine or its editor, Tony Willis. The old boy who mans the old programmes stand is interested to hear that I recently found some 1931 programmes. He tells me to bring them along to him and he will offer me a good price. I don't know that I want to sell them. We wander back, sensing the atmosphere beginning to build.

Eventually, having placed our bets, we head towards our usual seats in the upper West Stand, and as we make that ever-so familiar walk, I wonder to myself whether by the year 2000 Arsenal Football Club will still be resident here at Highbury? There is talk of them being forced to move to somewhere that can accommodate a larger stadium – King's Cross was mentioned last week – because Islington Council won't give the club permission to build upwards, sideways or backwards, and David Dein realises that Arsenal have the potential to attract more than the current 38,000-capacity crowd for each home game. I think Dein is thinking more along the lines of 50,000, which will bring in much more revenue, and now football is all about money and little else I suppose a larger stadium is imperative. I wonder what my dad would say if he thought Arsenal were no longer playing at the stadium he used to visit from about 1920 to his death in 1975? Were he to come back to this life and pay a visit to Highbury today, as I'm sure he would, he simply wouldn't recognise the stadium at which I believe he had some of the happiest moments of his life.

Arsenal are lying in third place in the Premier League, Liverpool are second. Whoever loses tonight will, I believe, effectively be out of the title race, and a draw will mean Manchester United will become even redder-hot favourites than they are already. In front of a capacity crowd, Arsenal are able to field their strongest team for the first time in weeks. Ray Burdis, one of our Highbury gang, has been put in the Herbert Chapman Suite tonight – with the

Spice Girls, so it's not all bad news. In the first half, Liverpool create five clear-cut chances, most of which fall to Stan Collymore, and they and Stan miss them all. Arsenal have one excellent opportunity to score but after a dashing right-wing run by Ian Wright, back after yet another suspension, he crosses to the feet of Bergkamp who uncharacteristically blasts the ball high over the Liverpool bar. Nil-nil at half-time.

Arsenal dominate the second half for ten minutes without ever looking as if they will score. Then Liverpool strike, and who does the first goal fall to but the man who has missed every chance so far, Stan Collymore! A shot from Jamie Redknapp is fumbled by Seaman, the world's number one goalkeeper, and as the ball slips from his hands Collymore slides it into the back of the net from five yards. What a gift! About ten minutes later, Liverpool are awarded such a controversial penalty decision that even the sporting Robbie Fowler tells the referee he wasn't brought down by Seaman. The referee ignores Fowler's pleas, as well as those of all the Arsenal players, who are furious, and Fowler steps up to take the kick. I wonder whether Fowler is sporting enough to kick the ball out for a throw-in. He doesn't go that far but I do believe he takes a half-hearted penalty kick. Seaman saves but cannot hold it and the ball falls to Jason McAteer who drives it home. All hell breaks out at how the referee ignored a man who was alleged to have been fouled by Seaman yet who claimed he wasn't touched by the goalkeeper.

Arsenal score a goal through Ian Wright, now only nine goals off Cliff Bastin's all-time goalscoring record for Arsenal, but the goal is not enough to salvage one point, let alone three. So Arsenal go down 1–2 and are effectively out of the championship race, if not the hunt. It's down to Liverpool or Manchester United, who meet at Anfield in April. I'm plumping for Liverpool, they are a more honest team, who take defeat with dignity, not like Manchester United who always seem to have an excuse about the referee, the ball, the pitch, even the colour of their own shirts.

TUESDAY, 25 MARCH

On what for me is an early morning drive along the country lanes, I can understand why Maurice so enjoys doing this each morning – alone in the car, listening to the radio, contemplating the day or perhaps the day before, and passing some of the most beautiful countryside one could ever wish to see. I'm going to Burford, to the Golden Pheasant, to collect Irving Teitelbaum and Rob Knights and bring them back to Spring Hill to begin the first of our two days of work on the 'Mosley' scripts. Rob, whom I know so little, notices a Gunners logo on my sweatshirt and asks me if there is an association. I tell him there most certainly is and that Maurice and I are avid supporters and travel from here to Highbury for every home game. Rob asks me if we were at Highbury last night and I tell him that we were, that it was a very exciting first half, a less exciting second half, and that the better team won.

As we drive through the rolling hills around the back of Burford towards Swinbrook, I point out some of the landmarks as well as Mosley's association with the area during the last half of the Second World War. Of course, the real association is with Diana Mitford. She lived here for most of her childhood at Asthall Manor and then Swinbrook House, and although Mosley visited neither I think his memory rests with some of the locals of Shipton-under-Wychwood, not least those living around the Shaven Crown. No chance of visiting this pub today – something both Irving and Rob would very much like to do. We put in a good day's work on the first two 'Mosley' scripts, with not so much as a break for lunch.

I have come to like the shy, mild-mannered Rob Knights, and his intelligence stands out like a beacon. I know this film means a great deal to him in terms of his career. Here is a director who made outstanding and critically acclaimed films for television a long while ago, then got caught in the Hollywood trap and his British television career, as with so many talented TV directors, rather got lost.

WEDNESDAY, 26 MARCH

Today's the day for the Shaven Crown. Irving and Rob are fascinated to contrast the prison surroundings of the Mosleys. At one moment they are incarcerated in the most awful environment of Holloway Prison, the next they have been sent to be held under house arrest in the Shaven Crown and are not allowed to wander any further than ten miles from the pub. Well, I can imagine, and have indeed been in, worse circumstances.

We still have episode four to look at, but nevertheless we go back by way of Swinbrook. Rob, particularly, wants to go to Swinbrook church and churchyard where he will be able to see the graves of Nancy and Unity Mitford. The grey gravestones are dull and faded, although someone seems to have tended Nancy's with far more care than they have Unity's. The front door of the wonderful church is always open, just as it should be at every church throughout the land. Rob comments, 'One couldn't paint a more typical picture of a little piece of England than this.' I ask Irving whether he could live in the country, and in countryside such as this. His reply is, 'Whenever I come to the country I always I think I'm on holiday, so I don't consider it to be permanent.' Every day is a holiday and as I look at the landscape around us as we drive through Swinbrook, I know that, for all the trouble of the past two weeks, I am unquestionably blessed.

TUESDAY, 1 APRIL

Every April Fool's Day, there's a story in the newspaper that does nothing more than play an enormous joke upon its readership. I remember when I was working at the *Weekly Herald* how the *Guardian* devoted an entire four-page travel section to the island of Sans Serif, and they made it sound so glamorous and exciting that people started going into their local travel agents asking them for a brochure on the place.

I also remember an advertisement for BMW cars that introduced a device never before seen on a motor car whereby the driver could inflate the tyres of the vehicle without leaving the seat of his car. I believed it, and was so impressed that I began to wonder how BMW did it.

Today on the front page of the *Independent* there's the headline 'THATCHER LINED UP TO BE BLAIR'S AMBASSADOR IN WASHINGTON'. The story reads:

Tony Blair will appoint Baroness Thatcher to the post of
Washington ambassador in return for her endorsing
Labour shortly before May 1, the *Independent* can reveal.

Lady Thatcher has already told friends that she admires Mr Blair's disciplined determination. She was reported in the *Daily Mail* last September saying, 'He knows exactly what he wants and how to go about achieving it.' Mr Blair, for his part, has put his respect for Lady Thatcher's leadership qualities on record. He wants to create a new politics, in which talented and experienced people of all views are welcomed into government, regardless of their views. Labour advisers emphasise that Washington is deemed the perfect post, because the former Tory Prime Minister cuts a formidable figure in American political circles.

How many people will believe that one?

This morning could be described as Stage Two in the post-writing 'Mosley' process. The first was when we appointed our director, Rob Knights. Somehow this morning will be even more exciting as Maurice and I shall, for the first time, hear our words read by professionals. Rob, Irving, Susie Parris, Guy Slater and Nick and Verity Mosley have come to Clarges Street and make up the rest of the audience for this reading. The two actors we are to hear for the part of Oswald Mosley are Joseph Fiennes and Jonathan Cake, both of whom have read for the part once before.

Joseph Fiennes arrives at nine-thirty. Maurice thought that Jonathan Cake was to be the first, doesn't recognise Joseph Fiennes and thinks he is the plumber come to inspect the damp in our kitchen. Fortunately for Maurice, he didn't say anything to that effect. I make Joseph a mug of coffee, and before too long all the small talk that is supposed to make an actor relax and feel he knows everyone expires, and Joseph begins the very first reading that Maurice, Nick and I have heard.

Jonathan Cake arrives and quite simply gives the finest audition performance I have witnessed in seventeen years in this business. Not only has Jonathan every nuance and characteristic correct, without this being an impersonation of Mosley, he has learned by heart most of what he is asked to read. Therefore when Jonathan, a brilliant actor whom I predict will become a major film star, is asked to read Mosley's House of Commons resignation speech, he asks, 'May I stand?' and presents to us a speech of such force and passion that there are moments when I am too embarrassed to stare him straight in the eye. I can't imagine that I was ever party to such potent dialogue (even though for the most part it came straight out of Hansard). There can't be any question who is going to play the lead in this movie. Jonathan finishes his storming audition with a scene against Diana Mitford, ably read by Susie, and everyone in my sitting room this morning knows, just knows, that what we have experienced is a performance of 'Mosley' that could never be bettered.

Saturday, 5 April

I'm going to watch this morning's absurdly timed football match to be transmitted on Sky Sports 1. I would prefer not to as a matter of principle. Why should a Premier League match have to kick off at eleven-fifteen, just to satisfy the whim of Sky Television? Apparently, they say the police have advised such an early morning kick-off and everyone involved in soccer has to bow to the pressure of the police. It's all too ridiculous, but as Arsenal are one of the teams taking part in this morning's match and the other is Chelsea, which means this should be one of the most attractive games of the season, I'll give in and watch what happens.

Arsenal really do have to win to maintain the pressure on Manchester United and Liverpool. It's accepted that Arsenal cannot win the title this season, but they can finish second which would entitle them to enter the European Champions Cup, whether Manchester United win the trophy or not. Even if Arsenal finish third, that will give them a high enough position to enter the UEFA Cup, and Europe must be their target. Winning at Stamford Bridge has never been easy. Arsenal haven't won there since the middle 1970s, and even the last time we won the championship, losing just one game all season long, we lost that game at Chelsea. Chelsea also have their eyes on a European place by finishing high enough to qualify, so they will be fired up for this morning's match.

Arsenal are under constant pressure for fifteen or so minutes, before Bergkamp sends through a marvellously intuitive pass, Ian Wright latches on to it and fires the ball past Frode Grodas, the Chelsea goalkeeper – Chelsea 0 Arsenal 1. That's how it stays until the half-time whistle, even though Bergkamp has the most wonderful opportunity to increase Arsenal's lead just before half-time, and David Seaman has really to be on his toes to stop three lightning shots from Vialli. The second half is less than six minutes old when, following a Chelsea attack, the ball travels from Seaman to Winterburn to Bergkamp, who once again sets Wright free wide on the left. Wright moves into the Chelsea penalty area and sends a low cross into the path of the incoming Platt – Chelsea 0 Arsenal 2. The game is now surely over; up until now Chelsea haven't really threatened. Perhaps their minds are on next weekend's FA Cup semi-final against Wimbledon

Arsenal add a third, inevitably from Bergkamp, with about ten minutes left to play, and have other opportunities to increase their lead, but a 3–0 victory at Stamford Bridge is truly magnificent and takes the very composed and ever more attractive Arsenal side into second place. They have played two more games than Manchester United, who play at home to Derby County this after-noon, and Liverpool, who meet Coventry tomorrow. I suppose technically Arsenal could win the title but nobody expects it. What the victory this morning means is that they will now surely qual-ify for Europe next season.

I take myself off to Ladbroke's to place our bets on the 150th Grand National and buy a lottery ticket. With Arsenal's compre-hensive victory this morning in mind, I feel as if this could be my lucky day. What happens this afternoon tells me perhaps it might not be.

Later, settled into my armchair in front of the television, betting slips in hand, I'm ready for the off. However, the first image I see on the screen is of flashing blue police and ambulance lights, with not a horse in sight. It's obvious that all is not well. Apparently, fif-teen minutes before the race is due to begin a bomb warning has been received saying there are two bombs somewhere on the course. The police must now evacuate Aintree. There are 60,000 people there, most of whom seem in no hurry to leave. The oper-ation is moderately quick and very organised, and it is announced before too long that there will be no racing at Aintree this after-noon and that everyone, including the BBC Outside Broadcast Unit, must get out immediately. Life could be in danger. But what of the horses? They are stabled and in the safest area of the vast course, although in an interview with Des Lynam, Jenny Pitman, the trainer, is in tears as she describes the moment that she was asked to forget about her horses and just evacuate the stadium. She believes this débâcle is all the work of Animal Rights activists, but as a coded message was given to the police it almost certainly came from the IRA.

The police seal off Aintree and 60,000 people are ushered out into the Liverpool streets. Where, I wonder, are they going to go for the remainder of this afternoon, and night, until they are allowed back into the stadium to collect their belongings, cars and coaches, and return whence they came? Surely Liverpool doesn't have the facilities to accommodate this many people, and what if they are not allowed back into Aintree until tomorrow?

A newsflash tell us that the police have made two controlled explosions inside the stadium, although no one is certain if the bags blown up were bombs or not. How would these explosions affect the horses? Will the 1997 Grand National ever be run? It seems the intention is to run the race on Monday, but this is BBC guesswork and hasn't been officially announced by the Aintree management. What a mess! I wonder to myself, if this amount of disruption can be achieved by one telephone call using a designated code word, what is to stop the IRA doing it at every major sporting event? The Cup final, a Lord's Test match, Wimbledon?

The BBC, jockeys, trainers and owners are calling this afternoon a 'disaster', another example of the English language being grossly misused. It most certainly isn't a disaster, it's an inconvenience. Hillsborough was a disaster. Rwanda was a greater disaster. Aberfan was a disaster, as was Dunblane. What has happened this afternoon ought to be put into perspective. A great horse race has been postponed due to a bomb threat. There seems not to have been a bomb. Nobody was killed. Nobody was injured. The horses are perfectly all right. Yes, an inconvenience is what this is.

I stay with the rest of the afternoon's sport and hear, much to my astonishment that Manchester United are losing 2–0 at home to Derby County. How? Why? Can it stay this way? It doesn't, but although United pull back two goals, they concede a third to Derby who win 3–2 at Old Trafford. Remarkable! What this means, beside Derby County increasing their chances of staying in the Premier League, is that United are now just three points ahead of Arsenal and Liverpool, and if the Scousers win at home to Coventry tomorrow, they will go top. It also means that Arsenal can still take the title, for if they win all of

their remaining five games, who knows where that will take us?
An extraordinary afternoon's events.

SUNDAY, 6 APRIL

The surprise of the afternoon isn't that Britain have lost to
Zimbabwe in the Davis Cup tennis tournament; it is that Liverpool
have gone down 2–1 at home to Coventry City, the team languishing at the foot of the Premier League. What this means is that
both Manchester United and Liverpool have this weekend lost to
lowly opposition, and with Arsenal winning handsomely at
Chelsea, United now head the Premier League by only three
points with Arsenal second and Liverpool third. The Gunners
can't do any more than win their remaining five games; they are
not in control of what United and Liverpool do. Those two have to
meet at Anfield and a draw would suit Arsenal down to the
ground.

FRIDAY, 11 APRIL

Maurice and I have a meeting with Stuart Cosgrove at Channel
Four. It was at Michael Grade's suggestion that we are seeing
Stuart, for it seems that he is redefining the channel's comedy.
Charlotte Ashton (chairperson of the Edinburgh International
Television Festival) joins us at one o'clock, at about the same time
as a trolley full of anaemic-looking sandwiches arrives. We are to
have a working lunch. Maurice and I go through the gamut of the
ailing of British television. We say that the two greatest misnomers
are: a) Britain has the finest football leagues in the world; and b)
Britain has the finest television in the world. We then go about
explaining why we believe this.

Now, whether this is what Charlotte and Stuart were expecting
I know not, but Stuart is taking copious notes, then questioning us
on some of the controversial elements of what we are putting forward. *Controversy*, wow! I flippantly remark that we could call the
session 'Not the MacTaggart Lecture'. At some point there must
have been some silent signal between Charlotte and Stuart, for
very soon we are being asked if we would give the 1997

Edinburgh International Television Festival's MacTaggart lecture.

The remainder of the meeting is somewhat of a blur to me, and I expect to Maurice, too. Are we really only the second writers, after Dennis Potter, to receive this accolade? What we have been asked to do come August is to stand up and explain our philosophy of television to those who might know better. It is probably the greatest honour in television. I mean, I thought winning the BAFTA Writers' Award was really something, that it didn't get much better than that, but now, as well as making the *Mosley* movie and being the subjects of the 'South Bank Show', we have delivering the MacTaggart lecture to look forward to.

SATURDAY, 12 APRIL

Can Arsenal win the championship? I suspect not, although anything can happen. Ron Tabor and I ask each other this question over lunch in the Gunners' hospitality suite, and when it is time to leave to make our way to our seats in the upper West Stand, on this beautifully sunny but chill April afternoon, I tell Ron that this really is the manner in which to watch football, not the way we were brought up to watch it – arriving at the ground, being pushed and shoved in attempting to get into the ground. Having to stand in the pouring rain on an uncovered terrace. Finding nothing at all to eat or drink. Having partial vision of the entire pitch, and then at the end of the game having to struggle through traffic, following a mile walk back to your vehicle. Ron agrees entirely, and those older folk who say that the modern game isn't as exciting are, if I may say, talking out of their pom-pom hats.

The match itself ends as I predicted it would. Indeed I have taken a bet on the result being Arsenal 2, Leicester City 0, and this is exactly what the score turns out to be. A brilliant first goal by Tony Adams, recalled to the side today after recovering from an ankle injury, follows an exquisite cross from Dennis Bergkamp (who surely cannot be ignored for the title of Footballer of the Year). Then in the second half Dennis Bergkamp delivers another exquisite pass of such accuracy it almost defies belief that sets up David Platt to ram home the second Arsenal goal.

But what is so fascinating about this afternoon's victory is not that Arsenal win the match – we expected them so to do – it is the style with which they win the match. Arsene Wenger's influence is beginning to show on the beautifully lush Highbury turf. Arsenal's one-touch football, played mostly on the deck, is a pure delight to watch, and the influence upon the team of Patrick Vieira and Dennis Bergkamp, allied with the sudden ball-carrying confidence of the three back players, Keown, Adams and Bould, makes Arsenal the team currently playing the closest to European football.

As Mark Burdis, with whom I sit each week, says: 'I just can't wait for next season. We're going to do it next season when Arsene Wenger buys even more young European maestros.' I think Mark might just be a season out in his estimation, for I think it will be season 1998–99 that will see Arsene steer Arsenal to the Premier League title, and who knows, the European Cup too. Or is this just the fanatic in me believing what I have to believe in order to continue watching this club? Perhaps that is it. Whatever, Arsenal are now starting to play the most attractive football I have seen them play since I began coming to Highbury in 1953–54.

WEDNESDAY, 16 APRIL

We are assembled this afternoon to see actresses forming a short list for the parts of Cimmie Mosley and Diana Mitford (later Mosley). Also here to see them are Guy Slater, Rob Knights, Irving Teitelbaum, Nicholas Mosley, Susie Parris, and Maurice. We also have Jonathan Cake to read the part of Mosley with the women. The first woman we see is Jemma Redgrave, who will read Cimmie. Then we see four 'Dianas'.

I think we are almost unanimous about Diana, and the best reading without doubt was from Emma Davies, who one might call a dark horse. We have a lengthy debate about whether Emma Davies can give us more than she gave this afternoon, and the answer is 'we do not know', so it is suggested that she returns on Friday to be video-recorded. If she performs on Friday as well and confidently as she did this afternoon, then I suspect the job will be hers. As for the Cimmies, well, that is a more difficult choice, but as one would expect from an actress with her pedigree Jemma Redgrave read very well indeed.

It is splendid to hear the lines from Mosley being read by professionals of the calibre of those we have seen, and I have the utmost confidence in Jonathan, who seems to improve each moment as Mosley. I am impressed and moved by all the Cimmies, but one must be better than the others, and I am not certain yet who that one is. It has, though, been a wonderful afternoon and so much more enjoyable than the afternoon spent auditioning Rachels for 'Unfinished Business'.

Before we leave, a debate ensues in which Guy asks Nick Mosley whether he thinks Diana, Nick's step-mother, will serve an injunction on the film. Guy is fearful that an injunction will be served days before transmission and the programme will be withdrawn. Nick says that he thinks it is extremely unlikely, and perhaps he ought to write a letter to Diana, who lives in Paris, and tell her the current state of play, perhaps even offering to show her the scripts, an offer Diana has already once declined.

SATURDAY, 19 APRIL

That I have to go to Arsenal this morning, at the time I have to, is something of a pity for at eleven-fifteen arguably the most important premiership match of the season kicks off. It is between Liverpool and Manchester United, at Anfield, and I am not entirely certain whom I want to win. I suppose if United win and so do Arsenal it might guarantee us second place, possibly the title, but this is unlikely. If Liverpool win, then United will have dropped a further three points and might just let us through on the rails, so to speak. I don't know what the best result would be for the Arsenal, and I suppose I should be concerning myself with Arsenal victories rather than looking at other results.

I arrive at Highbury and after a brief conversation with Mark Burdis I am invited to join the top table where sit Charlie George, Frank McLintock, and other heroes from years gone by. I am struck by how the mystique quickly disappears. I don't know what it is, perhaps I have never wanted to think of George and McLintock as anything other than gods, but they are human, they do wear worn-out shoes and I wonder where all the money they earned went? I once discussed with Maurice that when I was earning about £10 a week, these footballers were on about ten times as much as me, and whilst I managed on my tenner they must have been living somewhere north of Cloud Nine. Perhaps it all goes back to what Barry Took once said to me: 'You don't get rich quickly in the entertainment industry. You have to earn very good money for many, many years'. Perhaps this was never the case with the Arsenal Double-winning side. Then again, I think of George Best. What must he have been earning in the late 1960s and early to mid 1970s?

We take our seats. It is windy and cold. Arsenal are not going to play nearly as well as they have been over the past weeks and this becomes apparent very early on in the first half. Blackburn Rovers are a tough, fighting side, and they crowd their defence making it terribly difficult for Arsenal to break them down. However, after about twenty minutes a Dennis Bergkamp cross finds the head of Martin Keown, whose header hits the base of the Blackburn post and rebounds to David Platt who scores with a low shot. I hope Arsenal are now able to build on this breakthrough, that Blackburn will come out to play, thus leaving greater gaps at the back. But they don't, it seems as if they are content to stay one goal in arrears, and at half-time Arsenal lead 1–0.

In the second half Arsenal look well below par and never truly come close to adding to their solitary goal. Neither Bergkamp nor Ian Wright have one clear-cut opportunity this afternoon, and the longer the game goes on the more niggly it becomes, and I am convinced that before the final whistle a player will be shown the red card. Midway through the second half Blackburn have five players booked, and Arsenal have two, it is that sort of game.

A sudden break sees the ball come to Bergkamp whose cross finds Vieira striding into the box. It seems from where we are sitting that Vieira chests the ball down to his feet and rifles home a superb goal past Tim Flowers. Two-nil? No, not a bit of it. The referee deems Vieira to have handled the ball and not chested it down, thus the 'goal' is disallowed and Arsenal hang tentatively on to their one-goal cushion.

At least, they do until injury time when Stephen Hughes is kicked severely and is on the ground in agony. Patrick Vieira kicks the ball out of play to allow the trainer to come and attend to him. Once Hughes is carried off, and is replaced by Ray Parlour, Blackburn take their throw-in. It is customary in British football for the person taking the throw-in to send the ball back to the opposition's goalkeeper so play can begin from there. Chris

Sutton is having none of this sportsmanship malarkey. No, he throws the ball into an area where he is able to immediately attack Nigel Winterburn, who runs to collect the ball. To the crowd's chants of 'Cheat, cheat, cheat', Sutton forces Winterburn to put the ball out for a Blackburn corner kick. From this Garry Flitcroft scores with a spectacular volley to equalise.

Arsenal players, management and fans are incensed! This is the second time this season opposing teams have pulled this stroke and scored from it. Tottenham did it earlier in the season, and now Blackburn Rovers have equalised in injury-time leaving Arsenal no time at all to respond. So the match finishes 1–1, and I am annoyed that Arsenal chose today to play as they did. On a day they desperately required three points they finish up with one and are now in second place in the premiership table, five points behind United, having played a game more. Still, the runners-up this season will enter the Champions' Cup next season, and I suppose this must be Arsenal's mission. Questions are asked on the long walk from seat to hospitality lounge; why didn't Winterburn allow the ball to run out of play instead of playing it? Why did Blackburn feel the need to use this ungentlemanly conduct to elicit an equaliser? Will Arsenal finish runners-up, for surely they can't now win the championship?

Thursday, 1 May

General election day, 1997. I so enjoy these days that come around usually once in five years, and particularly enjoyable is a day when history might be made, change might be made, and who knows, perhaps we might see the back of a Tory administration for the first time since 1979.

While I'm watching some girls on video, those that could play the role of Diana Mitford in 'Mosley', the phone rings and it is John Sullivan who the night before last won himself a BAFTA award for his comedy masterpiece 'Only Fools and Horses'. Yesterday I telephoned him to offer him Maurice and my heartfelt congratulations, telling John how we were really rooting for him, and that his victory has given us much pleasure. We discuss his evening at the Royal Albert Hall, how the evening, as ever, was far too long, and how he and Tony Dow (the director) couldn't find a drink in the Hall so went off to a nearby pub. There they sat together discussing whether there could be any further episodes of OFAH and decided that there probably could never be. After all, John asks me, who wants to watch two old millionaires and their adventures? Whilst John may have a point, these 'two old millionaires' are called Del Boy and Rodney, and they are the two favourite characters on British television.

Maurice and I take a taxi to the Reform Club and there we settle in the morning room where we take from the library shelves the Hansard of 1924, looking for speeches by Neville Chamberlain and Oswald Mosley that will help us rewrite some of the parliamentary scenes in 'Mosley'.

After dinner Maurice and I take our seats in the television room of the club and wait for the first 1997 general election results to come through. Unlike in 1992 when the first Sunderland and Basildon results told us that it was unlikely to be Labour's night, tonight at eleven-thirty the first result comes through from Sunderland and Labour hold the seat. Then before the clock strikes midnight and Thursday becomes Friday, three more seats are declared and they all fall to Labour. It really does look to Maurice and me, and perhaps all the other members that share this huge, book-lined room, that this is going to be an historic night. I can't see us leaving much before three o'clock, so we settle back, I light my pipe, and we watch Labour victories coming through thick and fast. Although as yet there are no major surprises, my impression is there will be . . . it is just a matter of time. Tonight and tomorrow morning appear as though there is going to be much excitement in store.

FRIDAY, 2 MAY

After about half-past midnight, the results now come flooding through, with almost every result flashing across the bottom of the screen with a red background – meaning that we might just be seeing a re-run of the famous 1945 general election. Throughout the early morning, some might call it night, it becomes clear that Labour are going to win this election, and probably by a landslide, cause for Maurice to order a bottle of champagne. As Tory disaster follows Tory disaster many people leave the smoking room to take themselves home, some even look to be in a state of shock, not quite believing what is unfolding before them. Yet I do not feel surprise. I was much more surprised in 1992 when I saw before my own eyes Labour's predicted victory slipping away to a point where it could not be clawed back, and by the morning I woke up knowing that John Major and his Conservatives would be in power for yet another five years.

Now, cabinet ministers seem to be falling like ten-pins. Perhaps the greatest shock of all is when I see Michael Portillo, friend and Secretary of State for Defence, lose the Enfield-Southgate seat. How could Michael with a safe majority of what, 14,000, lose this seat? I don't think a Socialist has ever won Enfield-Southgate. I look at Michael's face as the returning officer reads the number of votes cast and see he is stunned, not beginning to imagine that a huge 17.5 swing has toppled the fifth-safest seat in Britain.

By about half-past three New Labour score the sufficient number of votes to win the 1997 general election, and this is unquestionably to be a landslide even greater than Clem Attlee's in 1945. The Labour Party have won the general election with a majority projected to reach 179. Three-quarters of the new House will be either Labour or Liberal Democrat MPs. The Conservatives have the fewest votes and the fewest seats since 1906.

SATURDAY, 3 MAY

It is Arsenal's final home league match this afternoon, and they meet Newcastle United in a vitally important match that could determine whether they will qualify for a European Champions' League place in August. If they lose this afternoon, then I think they can kiss goodbye to a place in the primary European tournament and will have to settle for a UEFA Cup place – which is no bad thing.

I watch, I won't use the word 'enjoy', a jaded Arsenal performance. They create one or two chances but fail to take them. Newcastle create many more opportunities, David Seaman is kept busy, and just a minute before half-time Newcastle score the goal that wins them the match. Robbie Elliott, surprisingly unmarked in the penalty area, heads a ball past Seaman and into the back of the Arsenal net. I know that this goal is one too many for Arsenal to recover from. In the second half Arsenal look to be forlorn and not at all positive, and the 1-0 defeat means that Newcastle still have a chance to finish runners-up in the Premier League. I have to admit that Kenny Dalglish may have taken some of the enterprising, flair football out of Newcastle United since taking over as manager, but what he has done is made them far more organised, tighter at the back, and I think they will prove to be a force to be reckoned with come next season.

But what of Arsenal? Well, I might well this afternoon have seen players playing their final match for Arsenal. Will I see David Platt don a Gunners' shirt again? Perhaps this could even be the last game at Highbury for Lee Dixon and Nigel Winterburn, the full-backs who have served us so excellently in their positions for so many years? It is interesting that both have played really well all season long, and this year is Nigel Winterburn's testimonial season, for which he will be granted a match at Highbury against Glasgow Rangers.

And then there is Ian Wright. Will Arsene Wenger think it worthwhile to keep this exquisite yet volatile striker, now he is in his thirties? If for no other reason than that he would like to break Cliff Bastin's all-time goalscoring record for an Arsenal player, I suspect Wrighty will stay on, and he should pass the record for he has only eight more goals to score.

It has been a strange season in so many ways. For a start we began with Bruce Rioch as our manager, then Stewart Houston took over, then Pat Rice (who never managed a losing Arsenal team), and then came Arsene Wenger. There were times when we all believed the Premiership title to be a possibility, yet there were times when we realised this side, put together largely by George Graham, was all getting that little bit too old and needed replacing. I think next season will be a transition stage in making Arsenal a title-winning team.

THURSDAY, 8 MAY

I am curious to see on the front page of the *Independent* this morning the headline (front page, mind) 'BIRDS OF A FEATHER KNOCK PANORAMA OFF ITS PERCH'. Underneath this headline it reads:

The BBC is courting controversy by moving its flagship current affairs programme Panorama permanently to a later time to make way for a ratings-boosting comedy. From June 2, 'Panorama' will move to 10pm on Monday nights while its current 9.30 slot is replaced by a new series of 'Birds of a Feather'. The BBC denied that move signals a downgrading in its commitment to current affairs but it does admit that it has been losing the battle for ratings on Monday nights. It claims the move should boost Panorama's ratings as well as the whole channel's evening audience.

I don't quite understand why anyone should be surprised by this, or why it should have made the front page of the broadsheets. Situation comedies have traditionally been audience-getters and documentaries have not, with the one exception of 'Panorama's' Princess Diana interview, so to move to a better time in the schedules shouldn't cause quite so much debate amongst the thinking classes. I still reel a little when I read the implication that situation comedy is the lowest form of television life, particularly when it can give the greatest pleasure.

SUNDAY, 11 MAY

This afternoon I settle myself in the Cattle Shed, for this is the final day of the Premier League season, with each of the matches kicking off at the same time so as to avoid any hint of advantage to any of the clubs fighting for their Premiership lives. Of course, the championship has been settled, going again to Manchester United. At the end of the afternoon's matches, Newcastle United remarkably finish second following their 5–0 drubbing of relegated Nottingham Forest; Arsenal finish third, beating Derby County 3–1 at the Baseball Ground's last-ever match; and as Liverpool can only draw 1–1 at Sheffield Wednesday, it means they finish fourth. So Arsenal have qualified for the UEFA Cup again, and perhaps next season they will make better progress than they did this.

So that is Premier League soccer over for another season. No

more Sunday afternoons and weekday evenings travelling to
Highbury. No more Sunday afternoons and Monday evenings sitting in the Cattle Shed thrilling to the delights of some very
exciting (and infernally boring) matches – at least, not until
August.

THURSDAY, 22 MAY

To the exclusion of almost everything else that seems to be happening in the world today, I am single focused upon the first
episode ever recorded of 'Unfinished Business', our first brand
new television comedy since 'Goodnight Sweetheart' in 1993. All
day, I'm wondering to myself where it will stand in the list of all-
time great first recordings. I remember 'Get Back' not being
wonderful, neither was 'The New Statesman' although it grew to
be so. 'Love Hurts', 'Shine On Harvey Moon', 'Roll Over
Beethoven', and 'So You Think You've Got Troubles' were none of
them recorded in front of an audience, so I suppose 'Birds of a
Feather' has to be at the top of our list.

I arrive at the studio at half past four to be shown the opening
titles and closing credits by a proud Julian Meers. They are profi-
cient and professional, but they do scream SITCOM at me. Indeed,
I'm now beginning to wonder whether it is possible ever to
achieve on screen what is in your head at the time you create and
write a series. I think it is probably not. Then when I'm taken on to
the studio floor to see the sets, designed by Roger Andrews, I
realise that for the first time ever the sets to one of my shows are
exactly as I had imagined them in my head. I stand in the set that
is to be Ruth's consulting room, the Organ Grinder Café, Amy's
magnificent kitchen/living area, and the art gallery. Roger has
excelled himself and I wonder whether all the work we put in
with him in the early stages has now paid dividends.

The dress rehearsal is quite good without being exceptional, but
there's something to be said for that. An exceptional dress run
doesn't bode well for the night. Henry Goodman is still not up to
speed, Harriet Walter is a little over speed, Briggy hasn't yet got
the irony of Ruth. The others are very good and if they perform as
well tonight we should have an engaging show.

First series are notoriously difficult to play to a studio audience, for they have no idea what it is they are coming to see. They don't know the characters or what they represent, they don't know how funny the piece is supposed to be, nor do they know who it is they are supposed to like or dislike. The entire experience for the audience can be disorientating. I think we have to make an effort to attract a theatre type audience. Ted Robbins is the warm-up act and this audience seems very willing to laugh and listen. At half-past seven each of the cast – most of whom probably mean nothing to a television-watching audience – is introduced and we are about to begin what will rank among the most nerve-racking professional nights of their lives.

I watch the nerves course through the veins of both Briggy and Harriet, playing the very first scene at too great a speed, although much to my surprise the audience seems to be with the characters from the start, and it gets its share of laughter. Then comes the art gallery scene and what seems to be a very fine first take, straight the way through without fluffs, and with Henry settled a little. However, Baz wants to take it again and this leads to a lengthy delay. Art Malik, wonderfully humorous in the role of Tam, keeps fluffing his lines, although there is no question that what we have in Art is a television comedy 'find'.

The show is completed, after a fashion, by ten minutes to ten, which isn't at all bad for a new show. So what is my overall verdict? I felt from the audience's reaction that our characters were immediately engaging and their story was one that they seemed to want to discover. There was the right mixture of comedy and pathos, and I hope it will grow and get better. I'm not certain of my own feelings right at this moment. I shall have to wait until September until a verdict is taken by the television viewers of the nation.

MONDAY, 2 JUNE

This morning Maurice and I receive a telephone call from BBC's 'Omnibus'. The sequence we did for their programme on the lives and careers of Dick Clement and Ian La Frenais has come out wonderfully well. They want to know if Maurice and I would like a documentary made on our lives and careers. I explain that this is being done by the 'South Bank Show', and it would be wrong of us to do anything that would interfere with their programme. 'Omnibus' understands entirely, thanks Maurice and me for taking part in the programme that will be aired on 20 July, and as I put down the receiver I stop and take stock. The two leading arts documentary programmes both wish to make a programme of our lives and works. It is all too astonishing when we come to think about it. I can imagine, briefly, this scenario. I visit my mum and dad, now turned ninety, in their home. They are both fit and well, albeit old. I come in and tell them, 'Hey, guess what? The "South Bank Show" and "Omnibus" wish to make documentaries about my canon of work!' Please fill in the response from both mother and father. The best entry will win a fiver.

TUESDAY, 3 JUNE

As I go to collect my milk and orange juice from the shop at the corner of Clarges and Curzon Streets, I spot next week's *Radio Times* on sale and on its front cover is a large photograph of Linda Robson, Pauline Quirke, Doug McFerran and David Cardy, alias Tracey, Sharon, Darryl and Chris. This is something of an accolade. Each of the television listings magazines have 'Birds of a Feather', on their covers.

There's a tournament going on at the moment in France that includes England, France, Italy and Brazil. Tonight's opener was between France and Brazil, the game finishing 1–1. But the game doesn't so much matter as Brazil's first goal. This masterpiece has made a mediocre game memorable. From a free kick, about thirty-five yards from the French goal, Roberto Carlos, the Brazilian player, bent such a vicious shot that when the ball was halfway between his foot and the French goal it looked certain to go ten yards wide. It bananaed in a large curve, dipped and, with the French goalkeeper standing completely still, acknowledging that the ball was going well wide, turned inwards and went in his goal. He couldn't believe it. How was this done? How do you bend and dip a free kick like this? Nobody in the stadium, nor anyone at home, has ever seen such a free kick! For goodness sake, it even makes an item on the news!

THURSDAY, 5 JUNE

During our lunch break, Maurice wants to watch the first day of the first Test match between England and Australia. When he switches on the television he sees, to his utter amazement, that Australia are about 70 for 8. He describes this as a disastrous first innings, and it will leave England clear to take a commanding first-innings lead. Not that I know diddly-squat about cricket, but I can recognise that British sport under the New Labour government is on the up and up. England beat Italy last night in this French tournament; 2–0 is an impressive result, with Ian Wright scoring one goal and laying on the other for Paul Scholes. Wright appears to be getting better and better in an England shirt, and very soon he will be challenging Alan Shearer for the place of principal striker.

FRIDAY, 6 JUNE

This afternoon, for the first time since being asked to give the McTaggart lecture, I begin to feel that I am getting on top of what it is we are to do. I plan to talk about our introduction to the industry, what we learned in Hollywood, and how we brought those ideas back to the UK in 1985 knowing that everything here had to change. We'll have to learn the technicalities of today's television as we go along. We are advised to speak to David Elstein and Michael Grade, and once we have done this we can begin writing the longest speech I am ever likely to write in my life.

Of course, the BBC won't be happy with what we have to say, as many others won't, but if we can stimulate an interesting discussion in the bars of Edinburgh and at the sessions of this festival, I think we shall have done our job.

TUESDAY, 10 JUNE

I suppose I should record that this is the day I have been waiting for since 1990; this is the day when Maurice and I hear 'Mosley' read for the first time. Sometime in 1990 we discussed the possibility of writing a quartet or quintet about Sir Oswald Mosley. At first, we felt that it was just beyond us – too much homework, too much reading, too many problems. But we really wanted to tackle a heavyweight subject, so we took the bull by the horns, and we did it. This morning we shall hear the fruits of our diligence and labour.

My immediate feeling as I pass through the gates of Ealing Studios is that I am entering a really important museum. In the forties, fifties and sixties, some of the finest film comedy was made here. Neither of us have been here before.

Each episode is read in turn with a ten-minute break between each, except after episode two when we call a lunch break and inadequate and anaemic-looking sandwiches are brought up, and there is coffee (I drink much) and water, nothing else. Actors that are required for no more than the first two episodes leave the hall; actors required for episodes three and four arrive; there is constant moving around, but it doesn't detract from the excitement of the text, nor the adventure we are about to experience in making a piece of work that will receive far more serious attention from critics, viewers and people within the television industry than any number of 'Birds of a Feather' or 'Goodnight Sweetheart'. One episode of either of these two will score a higher audience rating than the complete canon of Channel Four drama added up and totalled together, but that isn't the point. The point is that 1997 is the beginning of a new adventure for Maurice and me.

It is a growing-up year in many ways. 'Unfinished Business', one of the most intelligent and grown-up comedies we have ever written; 'Mosley', a major drama series; we are the subjects of the 'South Bank Show', the highest televisual accolade for any artist; we are giving the McTaggart lecture, which is without question the most important platform any individual can be offered in television; and we are to embark upon our first stage play, 'Patient A', which is a serious piece of work. Much frivolity is being left behind. I suppose what I am saying is that we have reached, through hard work, luck and great success, a place in the industry from which it is hard to climb higher – although later today we are told that there is a little further to climb.

It is a marvellous read-through, intensely moving in places. I watch Nicholas Mosley, as does Verity, his wife, when we come to exchanges between Nick's mum and dad. They are so sad and he recognises this sadness. If Rob and Irving are able to capture on film what we have heard today, we are in for a treat of major proportions and, who knows, perhaps theatre directors will take Maurice and me with all due seriousness. I feel just now in many ways as Neil Simon or Larry Gelbart or Woody Allen must have felt when they left the writing team of Sid Caesar and went their own ways, into films and theatre. As Woody Allen once said, 'The reason I write drama is because once you do they let you sit at the grown-ups table.'

When the reading has finished, everyone congratulates each other but it seems to me there is still work to be done. In fact, a group of us go to Rob's office on the Ealing Studio lot to discuss why episode one seems to be running under time, episode four running over time, and the two episodes in the middle seem about right. Apart from that, and Irving telling us just how very tight is the budget and everyone cursing Channel Four for squeezing us as they have, we are ready to leave, and as I walk the route through studio blocks (all most reminiscent of Paramount on a far smaller scale), I know I shall always remember this morning.

WEDNESDAY, 11 JUNE

A little interesting news from the world of politics, of which I thought I had had enough following the build-up to the general election. William Hague last night won the prize endorsement of two right-wing also-rans from yesterday's Tory leadership ballot, leaving him set to snatch the Conservative crown next week. Within three hours of the result of the first-round leadership ballot being announced in the Commons, Peter Lilley and Michael Howard announced that they would not stand for the second-round ballot, but would throw their weight behind Mr Hague.

Episode six of 'Unfinished Business' features Prozac. Udi Eichler, my psychotherapist friend, gives us some advice about it, the last he will give us for this series, now that the Business seems to be Finished. Talk, as usual these days, turns to the McTaggart lecture. Udi tells us that when we step on to the stage we have a licence for provocation. This is as good a title as any for the lecture.

Udi says we must always regard the BBC as being more than a broadcaster; it is a religion. Somewhere in the scheme of things we are middle-ranking bishops, and most of those in the audience will be little more than parish vicars. At the top of this BBC church is Archbishop John Birt, and it is his intention to make sure that the faith isn't ever broken. Udi asks, 'Where is the real source of resistance to change within the BBC?' Now there's a question!

TUESDAY, 17 JUNE

To Pyrton Manor, near Watlington, to see some of the second day's filming of 'Mosley'. I have to check where Pyrton is on the map. It isn't difficult to find and with Maurice behind me all the way, it's about five-thirty when I pull into the grounds of Pyrton Manor, much to the surprise of many of the extras and technicians. My car's number plate A1OMO, is close enough to ALOMO to make them suspect that the big boss of the movie has arrived. Who has arrived is the author, but they are not to know that.

The tennis court scene is being shot, and I sit myself down to watch the laboriously slow process of film making – take after take, different angles, different lenses, waiting for the light to fall in that special direction, waiting, waiting, waiting. For me, it's really nothing more than a social event. Here we are at a large Oxfordshire country house that is almost a double for Savehay Farm, the Mosley's main home and country seat. Nicholas tells me how spooky this all is, and how for him it feels akin to 'Back to the Future'. This afternoon he introduced himself to the little boys who are playing him as an eight-year-old. Now that has to be spooky. He completely confuses the little boys when he introduces himself as Nick Mosley. The little boys wonder how he can be so old if they are playing him.

The next scene to be shot today is the one where Oswald Mosley is putting Cimmie's sarcophagus into place at the bottom of the Savehay Farm garden. It would be the summer of 1933, Cimmie having died in May. Nick is particularly keen to see this scene shot, as well as the pink marble sarcophagus. He knows it is as close as he ever will get to paying an adult's tribute to his mother's death. He is amazed, astonished and emotional when he sees the sarcophagus, a replica of the real thing. As we stand around the pink marble (although I'm not too sure what it's actually made from – probably cardboard), Nicholas tells me stories about the day when he heard from his Nanny Hislop that his mother had died. It is a moving moment, made more so by the fact we are standing around her resting place – well, not really her actual resting place.

I'm impressed by the interest taken by the actors playing the Mosleys' servants in what life was like in the 1920s and 1930s at Savehay Farm. Nick is generosity itself with his information. The more time I spend with him, the more I learn what life was like for the upper classes in those far-off days. He tells the extras that being a servant in a grand house in pre-war England meant that they were given the same health care as their masters, and that meant more than money.

On my way home from the 1930s, I hear that Arsene Wenger has managed to capture his long-sought prize, Marc Overmars, the Dutch *wunderkind* winger, who at the age of twenty-four has won all there is to win in the game. Wenger has also bought striker Luis Boa Morte for £1.75 million from Sporting Lisbon. He has already signed French defenders Emmanuel Petit and Gilles Grimandi, and this means he has now spent more than £14 million. There's more to come, apparently, for tomorrow they expect to sign Alberto Mendez-Rodriguez, a 22-year-old German midfielder from non-league side FC Feucht. Suddenly the prospect of watching an international Arsenal next season becomes an excitement that, as far as I am concerned, is unique.

WEDNESDAY, 16 JULY

Linda Seifert (our agent) calls for me earlier than we had arranged. We are to drive to Coverwood House, Peaslake, a Surrey suburb quite near Abinger Hammer, a regular haunt of my parents come a Sunday when they would visit this small village for afternoon tea.

The directions sent to us by the 'Mosley' production staff are such that we only get lost once. We find Coverwood House with the help of arrows bearing the name ALOMO pasted on trees and noticeboards in the vicinity, and soon we're parked in a large field and being taken by minibus up to the house where the filming is taking place.

Linda and I have come today because we believe it might be an exciting day's filming, or at least as exciting as filming can ever become. Maurice, Briggy, Nicholas and Verity are all coming too. Today we are filming the wedding of Oswald Mosley to Diana Mitford in Goebbels' garden in Berlin. The actual event took place in October 1936. We have found a location that resembles the woods of Berlin (where Josef and Magda had their home, I presume courtesy of the Nazi Party) and as Linda and I walk up towards the garden we see Rob Knights and Irving Teitelbaum working a shot whereby Hitler walks across the garden, adjutant in tow. A Nazi swastika flag flies from the balcony above the back door of the house, Nazi guards and black uniformed SS officers give the place a scary atmosphere. Linda and I stand there watching Hitler walk across the garden.

The house and garden are quite magnificent in real life. I don't know who lives in Coverwood House but whoever it is is a lucky so-and-so. Linda, in typical Seifert fashion, comments how the house is a mish-mash of architectural styles and is something of a delightful folly, but to my eye is seems much more than that. Should I ever want to live in Surrey, I would be more than content to live in this house. We stand around, which is what you do at film shoots. Maurice and I are to be photographed for the press pack, also for the *Sunday Mirror* and *Radio Times*. Hilary Kingsley is interviewing us.

The wedding ceremony is conducted by a large German official with Hitler sitting there in pride of place witnessing the event. The adjutant stands to attention throughout, carrying the purple box (did Hitler have a collection of Asprey boxes?) containing Hitler's wedding present. He gave the Mosleys a silver-framed, signed photograph of himself. Maurice has commented before now that the wonderful thing about being Hitler, or indeed any megalomaniac, is that you will never have trouble choosing a wedding present for a friend or acquaintance. As Tom and Diana, in the presence of the Goebbels and Unity Mitford, are married, Wagner's 'Liebstod' strikes up and the room fills with an atmosphere of Nazidom that I could never quite imagine until this morning. I certainly could never imagine it when we were writing the scenes set in Nazi Germany.

Maurice and I are driven back up to the house to be photographed by the gentleman, lovely chap, from the *Radio Times*. We stand under the flying swastika flag (is this bad taste or what?) and for about twenty minutes the photographer, using a mechanised self-winding device so all you hear is 'click-click-click-click-click', takes pictures of Maurice and me together, with the house in the background, and then portraits of each of us separately on the verandah of the house. I also ask the photographer if he would take some pictures of Maurice, Nicholas and me with my camera – I brought it with me specially, to capture the day for posterity.

I never did get to have lunch with Hitler and Goebbels as I had intended – well, at least not sharing the same table as them. I did see Hitler on his mobile phone, probably calling his agent to see where his next job is coming from (Poland?), and throughout the day I was never too sure who was Goebbels. I did manage to talk briefly to Magda Goebbels, but it was only to observe that a swastika flying over a house in Surrey is probably how it would have been had the Germans invaded these shores in 1940.

Sunday, 20 July

This evening at 10.45, 'Whatever Happened to Clement and La Frenais' is on television. This is the 'Omnibus' programme for which Maurice and I were interviewed some months ago, in the Cattle Shed. It turns out to be an intriguing programme about our heroes, the men whose work made Maurice and me want to write comedy over twenty years ago. As I said on the documentary, although it was cut, 'To have met these guys would have been an ambition fulfilled, never mind actually working with them, sharing ideas with them, listening to their words of wisdom. Quite simply, they were our inspiration.'

Monday, 21 July

After tonight's news, 'Birds of a Feather' is on. This is the first in this series that I've watched as it is transmitted, and coincidentally it is one of the two Maurice and I wrote some long time ago. It isn't at all bad, but it doesn't set my pulse racing in excitement, content or performance. I wonder whether I have just outgrown the series as I would have outgrown anything I bought eight years ago. It would be quite understandable, although I'm sure

John Sullivan never felt this way about his eight-year-old 'Only Fools and Horses'. But then again, John hadn't created nearly a hundred episodes in its eighth year.

SUNDAY, 3 AUGUST

The *Observer* business section has some concerning news under the headline: 'GREG DYKE HEADS FOR THE EXIT AT PEARSON TV AFTER '"OPEN WARFARE".'

> Media and leisure group Pearsons is set to part company shortly with Greg Dyke, head of Pearson TV. His impending exit follows the decision of chief executive Marjorie Scardino to retain Pearson TV and what insiders call 'virtually open warfare' between the subsidiary and head office after a failed attempt at a management buy-out. Tomorrow Pearson will report interim profits of around £48 million, up from £40 million last time but held back by £10 million of losses from its stake in Channel 5.

I don't know that Maurice and I would want to work for anyone else other than Greg. It was after all Greg who lured us to sell to Pearson on the promise of much dosh and fun. Well, we've had the money but we would also like to retain the fun, which might not be possible under another chairman. I know that we can't get out of our contract with Pearson, we are there until the end of the year 2000, but it's interesting to speculate who might be our new master and what he or she will expect from us, if anything at all.

The FA Charity Shield's not very exciting. I watch the entire game, with comments at half- and full-time. The score is Chelsea 1 Manchester United 1. United take the Shield, winning 4–2 on penalties. I'm not impressed by either of these sides, although they are two of the best six in the English Premier League. I suppose one has to tip United to retain their title, although Arsenal, Liverpool and Chelsea have to be strong contenders. How strong we shall see by the turn of the year, but no matter what, I can't wait for the football season to begin. I'm looking forward to those cold winter nights when I'm cocooned in the Cattle Shed watching live soccer, or even Saturday night highlights, and hopefully seeing some thrilling stuff involving Arsenal in their fight to win the championship. Well, I can dream, can't I?

SATURDAY, 9 AUGUST

The 1997–98 football season kicked off forty-five minutes ago. I want to know what's happening at Elland Road where Arsenal are playing their first game of the season. On Radio Five Live, the commentator says we've taken the lead with a goal from Ian Wright, have since conceded a goal, and at half-time the score is 1–1. The second-half commentary match is Barnsley v. West Ham. This is Barnsley's first-ever match in the top flight, so I suppose it's not surprising. They are a goal to the good at half-time, and seem to be playing much the better football, but during the second half West Ham change their tactics and are too much for Barnsley, who concede two goals and lose 1–2 at home. Meanwhile, the other two promoted clubs, Crystal Palace and Bolton Wanderers, are both winning – just the starts they want in what is to be, for both clubs, a long and difficult season.

Arsenal draw 1–1. Well, that's a point away from home and I was about to say that they should collect all three points against Coventry on Monday night, but Coventry this afternoon came back from being two goals down to Chelsea to win 3–2, with Dion Dublin scoring the first Premier League hat-trick of the season. Perhaps Coventry won't be the push-over I imagine they might be.

This evening I do nothing more than watch the first of the new series of 'Match of the Day', now very slick and professional, although the personnel do little to inspire me. If this were a piece of fictional drama, I would comment that the casting is way off target – Gary Lineker in the chair, with Alan Hansen and Trevor Brooking as the professional analysts. I don't believe any one of them has what you might call charisma or screen presence, but I suppose you watch 'Match of the Day' for the soccer not for the analysis. Changing logos, opening titles, colour schemes and studio sets doesn't make the programme any better. 'Match of the Day' stands or falls on the quality of the football it shows, and this evening I find the three matches sub-standard.

MONDAY, 11 AUGUST

It's Arsenal's first home game of the season, against Coventry, and a stiflingly hot evening. Before taking our new seats, Maurice and I stroll down Avenell Road to buy a newspaper, some fanzines and an ice cream to cool us down on this Indian-type night. The temperature seems to be climbing, not dropping. By the time the teams take the pitch – resembling a World Snooker championship final table, so smooth and green is it – not one seat is vacant. The man who sits next to Maurice has come from Durham but he make it in time for the kick-off.

Arsenal field a team that is unfamiliar to me, and probably to everyone around me, since they have stuck with essentially the same defensive line-up since the middle to late 1980s. I have to write who is playing in my programme otherwise I'm definitely going to get confused. The team that kicks off is: Seaman, Garde, Grimandi, Marshall, Winterburn, Petit, Parlour, Vieira, Overmars, Bergkamp, and the irrepressible Ian Wright, just three goals short of securing that all-time Arsenal goalscoring record.

I don't enjoy the heat and humidity. What it must be like for those on the pitch I dread to imagine. I suppose you would lose about eight pounds in body weight playing in this sauna. Still, as I sit here sweating, I think of the winter months when we'll be shivering, stamping our feet against the chill, wrapped up in heavy coats, gloves, thermal socks and hats.

By half-time Ian Wright has added another goal to his tally, as he bangs home a rebound off Ogrizovic, the Coventry City goal-keeper. Vieira's shot from twenty yards is too hot to handle, and from the rebound Ian Wright jumps in and fires the ball into the net. One more goal, only two to go for the record! Arsenal go in shattered but a goal to the good. At the start of the second half Arsenal increase their lead when a bad defensive mistake from Richard Shaw, the Coventry defender, allows Wright in (who else?) and he slots the ball around Steve Ogrizovic with the skill of a snooker player potting a colour in off the cushion. A degree of confidence and high skill gives Arsenal the 2–0 lead that ultimately gives them the three points, their first win of this new season.

Ian Wright now needs just one goal to equal Cliff Bastin's record, and two to beat it. Beat it he undoubtedly will and I suppose all of us just hope he does it at Highbury in front of his adoring fans. I suspect it will come at Southampton in the game after next, but to save it until the next home match, against arch-rivals Spurs, would be manna from heaven to us Arsenal fanatics.

One final note about tonight's game. Coventry beat Chelsea, very highly regarded, 3–2 last Saturday. By the end of the game, the Arsenal supporters on the south bank are chanting to the tune of 'Blue Moon': 'Chelsea you must have been crap!' I think they are referring to the fact that throughout the entire ninety minutes Coventry City managed only one shot on Arsenal's goal. How ever did they put three past Chelsea? One of the mysteries of foot-ball. Still, the victory tonight gives us four points in total and puts us, for however short a time, on top of the Premier League.

WEDNESDAY, 13 AUGUST

The first midweek 'Match of the Day' of the season is on tonight, but I find I'm drifting in and out of sleep in front of it, thereby missing David Beckham score the only goal in Manchester United's 1–0 victory over Southampton. I manage to stay awake long enough to see West Ham beat Tottenham 2–1, thus making their finest start to a season for fifteen years by securing six out of six points. But then so have Manchester United, Blackburn Rovers and Leicester City, who tonight went to Anfield and beat Liverpool 2–1. A remarkable result. I wonder if Leicester can keep up their form until at least Christmas. Languishing at the bottom, although I suppose languishing isn't an appropriate word after just two games, are Tottenham and Aston Villa, but surely their fortunes will change as the season goes on. The idea of Tottenham holding up the rest of the Premier League must give Arsenal fans everywhere some type of delight.

MONDAY, 18 AUGUST

It's a trip to Teddington today for the first mass read-through of the eighth series of 'Birds of a Feather'. As I walk into the studio – last time I was here was for the final episode of 'Unfinished Business' – I recall as best as I am able the first series of 'Birds'. We had our very first read-through in Pauline Quirke's Islington council flat, and that definitive reading was given by Pauline, Linda, Maurice and me. I don't remember whether we all felt that what we were reading would be a BBC comedy classic, although we were aware that we had something very good on our hands. Then we went to Acton, the BBC's rehearsal rooms, and suddenly the series came to life and we were all extremely excited. Now we're all very much older and wealthier, and possibly less hungry for success, although of course we all want the series to be a hit.

Personnel gather in the Teddington committee room on the top floor, where we have read other series of 'Birds' and 'Goodnight Sweetheart', and where we read 'Unfinished Business'. I don't quite know how I feel about this series of 'Birds'. Maurice and I have not contributed an episode, and that's a first. We were writing 'Unfinished Business' and 'Mosley' at the time, so we do have a legitimate excuse. I didn't find last series' experience pleasurable. Still, I suppose that when a group of people who have been together for eight years, or nine, as we missed a year, certain strains and arguments are going to occur and it's how the parties concerned deal with these altercations that matters.

FRIDAY, 22 AUGUST

For Maurice and me, today is a pinnacle of our careers, for we are to deliver the MacTaggart lecture.

After a whole day of final rehearsals, and redrafting, we arrive at the McEwan Hall at six o'clock, with no apparent feeling of nervousness. Roy Addison, Pearson's press officer, reads tonight's lecture for the first time and so is pre-warned of what might occur after it has been delivered. The speech is, by Roy's admittance, controversial.

At a few minutes after seven o'clock we have to leave the comfort and safety of the hospitality room and make our way downstairs to the auditorium, where Maurice and I wait in the wings as the 1997 Edinburgh Television Festival begins.

Stuart Cosgrove takes the stage and announces to the full house what is in store during this year's festival. The autocue operator and I hear his speech perfectly well from among the electrical cables and half-filled tea and coffee mugs from earlier in the day – or possibly yesterday. Then Gus Macdonald is introduced and gives a resumé of Maurice's and my career, and all too soon I hear the words, 'Ladies and gentleman, I give you this year's MacTaggart lecturers, Laurence Marks and Maurice Gran.' Slowly, I climb the steps on to the spotlit stage and turn to face a vast sea of people, more people than I have ever faced before. My only thought is, will the autocue work? So, here goes.

For the next forty-five minutes, with cameras whirring, faces a blur, we give the 1997 MacTaggart lecture. I feel a warmth coming from the audience, and the first laugh comes very quickly when I ask the audience to switch off their mobile telephones, for the caller is bound to be Alan Yentob. The laughter relaxes me even more than I, surprisingly, feel already. We get huge laughter throughout the speech, and at one point about halfway through, we even have to stop for a massive round of applause. It gives both Maurice and me even greater confidence – not that our confidence in what we had to say was ever low.

In the front rows of the audience, some very highly placed members of the Corporation are laughing and apparently thoroughly enjoying the speech. It has taken Maurice and me eight weeks to conceive and write, and as I've said before, I think we could have written a new BBC comedy series in the time we have spent on the MacTaggart.

At the end, there is tumultuous applause and we are invited back on stage to take another bow. It's all so wonderful. I've rarely felt such exhilaration, not even during any of our programmes. Is this what winning the FA Cup is like when it's you who has scored the winning goal? Charlie George never could quite explain to me the feeling; now I believe I know for myself.

In the immediate aftermath, Maurice and I are warmly congratulated by all and sundry – even by some of those in high places – but beneath the surface I believe Maurice's and my contention that the BBC should abolish their licence fee and replace it with a pay-per-view or subscription system has ruffled feathers terribly. We wander around to the front of the building, Briggy next to me, and the BBC news cameras follow us. Roy Addison has been sticking close, advising us that we shouldn't speak to any member of the press. We should say nothing tonight and assess what is said in tomorrow's national newspapers. I think this is sound advice. So when a gentleman from BBC Radio Four's 'Medium Wave' comes over to me, microphone in hand, asking if I could say something for Sunday's show, I comment, 'What is left to say? Haven't I said it all on the stage?' The gentleman from 'Medium Wave' agrees that I have.

We are carted off to a large country house hotel for dinner. I'm not hungry and eat little, but both Briggy and I are highly amused by the waiters, who all resemble the Julie Walters character, Mrs Overall, in Acorn Antiques. They are shaky, spilling food and sauce over everything in their way. Someone's tie and jacket lapel gets it. Someone else's jacket sleeve gets it. My trousers would have got it too, had I not jumped out of the way in time. Food flies across the table, on to the floor, even on to other people's plates. It's hilarious, if one forgets that these people are supposed to be professional waiting staff.

I'm worn out. It's been a long day what with rehearsals, rewriting sessions, straining my voice, and the nervous energy that went into making sure this MacTaggart will be spoken about in five years' time. I think we succeeded, I really do.

SATURDAY, 23 AUGUST

Briggy and I lie in bed this morning listening to the 'Today' programme with far more interest than usual. In the headlines we hear how the 'Birds of a Feather' writers say that the BBC's licence fee should be abolished. Later, there's a full report with news coverage of the lecture, an excerpt and comment from Bob Phyllis, assistant Director General, who says something to the effect that while it was a brilliant MacTaggart lecture, and that we are two wonderfully funny comedy writers, we aren't such gifted economists and our figures don't quite come together. Oh, but they do! The newspapers are full of the story too: 'AXE BBC LICENCE FEE, URGE TOP TV DUO – A unique Edinburgh stand-up routine yesterday demanded the scrapping of the BBC licence fee in favour of a voluntary subscription,' says the *Guardian*. 'FUNNYMEN SAY BBC IS STIFLING CREATIVE TALENT – Two of the BBC's most respected comedy writers last night accused the corporation of starving creative talent and called for the television licence fee to be abolished,' says *The Times*.We have pushed for change, but I don't believe anything will ever get done because the writers, producers and -

directors are not a powerful force, and so I tell Udi on the phone.

'The trouble is', he says, 'you are probably ten years ahead of your time, and anyone who is that, and there have been others, becomes frustrated by the lack of immediate action. But change will come, a long way down the line, and people will remember that you were the first to mention on a public platform that the licence fee should be at last abolished.'

Sunday, 24 August

Today, I have the best one hour and twenty minute's experience I have had inside a theatre in what must be two years. The first three minutes remind me of a seance.

David Benson, author and performer of 'Think No Evil of Us', comes on the stage as himself. He sits on a chair listening to Brahms . . . just listening. Then quite suddenly he transmogrifies into Kenneth Williams and the entire audience laugh with a sense of relief and amazement. When he begins talking, the resemblance is uncanny. The actor, performer, raconteur, who died in April 1988, has this morning returned to earth and is on the stage before us. For the duration of this most wonderful one-man show I am captivated, moved, made to laugh and almost made to cry (some in the audience do). David Benson has something special. In the play, he plays not only Kenneth Williams but many other characters as well, with some splendid impersonations of Frankie Howerd, the cast of 'Dad's Army', his old headmaster, his parents, and most important of all, himself.

If ever I have been lost in a theatrical performance this has been it, and when the show finishes, I feel the need to introduce myself to David Benson. I think I should like to work with this man at ALOMO.

Wednesday, 27 August

It's the 'South Bank Show' today – not on television but at Spring Hill. A large crew plus Melvyn Bragg turn up to film the interview with Maurice and me. Melvyn believes that a great 'South Bank Show' is dependent upon a great interview, the director feels that there is the potential for a great programme. There certainly isn't a shortage of great material (topped off by the triumphal MacTaggart lecture). Next week, we go to Los Angeles to relive for the programme those far-off Hollywood days of 1985.

For an hour and a half, Melvyn asks a variety of questions that don't follow the pattern of our career. Instead, the questions are more insightful and random, about how Maurice and I first met, our association as teenagers, and how we used to socialise (although we seem not to any longer, well, not much). We go on to how I came to find Players Playwrights, and what happened to us there in the early 1970s. Melvyn also talks about the MacTaggart lecture, and what we believe will happen as a consequence of giving it, and of course, we touch on our comedy programmes, as well as our serious work. However, most of the time is taken discussing our philosophy of television and television in America. I recall with some pain our time in Los Angeles in 1985. When asked what we brought back to Britain from LA, Maurice answers, 'A very large overdraft'. I brought back the belief that the way forward in British TV was to follow the route taken by the Americans.

It's a varied interview. I know much of what we have said will not be used, but I can't help feeling that the important stuff will survive and I can't now wait to see the programme come February 1998.

In the afternoon, we have to simulate a writing session, which is very difficult to do. The director wants to film us going over a scene from 'Unfinished Business' as if for the first time. Maurice sits behind the keyboard, I pace the room, smoking my pipe, trying to get conversation going. We manage to spice up the sequence when the telephone rings. I answer it. 'Hello? Sigourney, I have told you time and again not to phone me at the office while I'm working. How many times must I tell you that it's over. Yes, I know you can't accept that but we really have nothing left between us.' Actually, it's Claire Hinson, who thinks I've gone off my head. When the telephone rings for a second time, Maurice picks it up. 'Who? Mia. Mia who? Oh, Mia. No, look I don't want to be adopted. You have eight already.' Now Claire thinks we've both had a good lunch at the pub!

Throughout the evening, while I'm reading my book on Hitler and Geli Raubel, I tune into Ceefax to see how Arsenal are performing up at Leicester. They are 1–0 up, with a goal from

Bergkamp. With ten minutes of the match left they are 2–0 up, Bergkamp having added a second, and this is how the score stays until the ninetieth minute when Leicester pull one back. Then I'm bewildered to see that Leicester have equalised, and before I know what's happened, Dennis Bergkamp has given Arsenal a 92nd-minute lead and completed his hat-trick. So another three points for the Arsenal? Well, that's what I imagine, but in the ninety-fifth minute – yes, the ninety-fifth minute – Leicester equalise yet again and the match ends 3–3, Arsenal clumsily and annoyingly dropping two points. It seems when Tony Adams isn't playing the defence is brittle, which is so damn distressing as the forwards are scoring hatfuls of goals this season. Fancy allowing a two-goal lead to disintegrate! Really! It kind of puts a damper on what has been an otherwise memorable and historic day in my life.

SATURDAY, 30 AUGUST

This is the big one. Arsenal are playing Spurs. Once there would have been a crowd of 65,000; today we shall see an all-seated crowd of 38,000, although the gate receipts will almost certainly be greater than they were when 65,000 poured into the stadium. In the good old days, I would have waited until two o'clock and walked from my flat in Finsbury Park to the ground, a walk I made more times than I now care to remember. However, now I live eighty miles from Avenell Road it means I must leave early and a visit to the Arsenal becomes a whole day out. Today this includes lunch with Melvyn Bragg and his friends, one of whom is Anthony Holden, former *Sunday Times* and *Observer* journalist, Prince Charles's biographer and professional gambler. Tony's ambition to become the world poker champion made him give up, for one year, a marvellous and distinguished career in journalism and writing. He is a softly spoken and charming man and I wonder what made him do it. How do you become a poker champion? He made the top hundred (I believe his highest ranking was ninety-two, which, he tells me with a smile, was higher than any British tennis player at the time) and he explains about the poker season. It makes for riveting listening. He lends me his book *Big Deal*, which I shall read with interest. It may even be the subject of our next film for Channel Four.

I talk for some time to Tony about his biographies of Prince Charles and whether the Prince of Wales is now happier to be apart from Diana, a woman who was a thorn not only in his side – for she would always stand in the way of him marrying or being publicly involved with Camilla Parker Bowles – but also in the side of the royal family. Tony explains to me a little of Charles and Diana's relationship, which doesn't sound at all a happy one, and I ask Tony if perhaps one day *someone* might just 'get rid' of Diana and leave the way clear for Charles to remarry. Tony smiles, draws on his cigarette, and replies: 'I think that is the stuff of fiction or high drama.'

'Probably,' I reply.

Tony Holden's grandfather played for Derby County and England. He was a left-winger, and I think I remember him playing in the same team as Nat Lofthouse. The next time we meet will be for the Bolton Wanderers game.

And so to the match. I'm expecting Arsenal to clobber Tottenham, but how much of that is wishful thinking? The match finishes 0–0. Arsenal have effectively lost four points in the last two matches and rather dented hopes of staying in the top three when the tables are published at the end of this month. However, as Arsene Wenger says after the game, Arsenal are playing delightful football and quality will shine through in the end. This is also the view of Trevor Brooking and Mark Lawrenson on 'Match of the Day'. When I see it again, I can't believe the luck that Spurs brought with them to Highbury this afternoon – neither can Gerry Francis, their manager. It's just one of those afternoons when the ball refused to go into the net. I contend, and I know these are still very early days, that Arsenal are missing a player with the qualities of Liam Brady or Paul Davis, a player who can make the ball talk and unlock tight defences. I don't know how often they will play better than they played during the first forty-five minutes of this afternoon, but I bet they manage to score many more goals playing less well than this.

SUNDAY, 31 AUGUST

The radio alarm is set and wakes up Briggy and me at about ten minutes to nine. James Naughtie, who isn't usually on the radio on a Sunday morning, is talking about 'her life', and 'how do you think she will be remembered?' Someone of importance has died during the night, but who? Soon we're wide awake, hearing that at two o'clock this morning, in a tunnel in Paris, the car carrying Diana, Princess of Wales, and Dodi Fayed crashed at high speed and Fayed was killed instantly. Diana was cut free, eventually, rushed to a nearby hospital, but at four o'clock this morning died from a massive heart attack.

I'm filled with sorrow for here was a young woman who was at long last finding happiness in what was an otherwise tragic life. She seemed to have found love. She seemed to have found a purpose in her life, involving herself in a mission to have landmines banned, as well as her chosen charity work. Now, at the age of thirty-six, she was dead.

And this week of all weeks. Early in the week, Diana had proclaimed just how 'hopeless' the Conservative government had been in the effort to get landmines banned, and how this New Labour government had performed with enthusiasm and gave hope to all that the banning of landmines was firmly upon their agenda. This comment caused furore for it crossed constitutional and political lines and that is a definite no-no.

BBC1 and 2, and Radios One, Two, Three and Four and Five Live have joined forces and are sending out just the one programme to our nation. Classic FM, the only other programme I bother to listen to this morning, is playing sombre music as a mark of respect. How long will this go on for? I was once told that a six-day mourning period could be expected for the deaths of any senior member of the royal family. Is Diana considered to be senior? I suppose not, especially when I notice that Channel Four is running to its original schedule. I also check satellite television in the Cattle Shed and find that other than the news channels, everything is running as if nothing has happened. But we stick with the BBC. A major historic event has just occurred and it sends strange feelings through my bones.

The *Observer* has nothing at all of today's tragic news; it must have gone to print before the Mercedes-Benz hit the kerb. On the television, more 'experts' and 'royal watchers', including Tony Holden, and anyone whom the BBC can drag into the studio at short notice on a Sunday afternoon, talk about their memories of Diana. The saddest scene of the entire event, other than the mangled Mercedes being towed away for examination, is seeing the Prince of Wales and Diana's two sisters arriving in France to collect Diana's coffin and flying it back to RAF Northolt. I watch with a cold shiver as the coffin is removed from the aircraft, draped in the Royal Standard and put into the back of a hearse. Leaving RAF Northolt, the hearse takes the A40, a road I use regularly, and this main arterial road is lined by sad Londoners, all waiting to get a glimpse of the hearse, or perhaps just say goodbye to a young woman they all believed they knew.

MONDAY, 1 SEPTEMBER

The *Independent* has never taken a royal line editorially, so there is no hyperbole in their obituary, just plain facts. This is perhaps why I am moved greatly by their words:

> The twentieth century will have many symbols. Few however will be as potent as Diana, Princess of Wales. In a sense she was the ultimate product of the age of celebrity, sought after as no other for celebrity's ephemeral trappings of elegance, beauty and high fashion, all lent especial allure by the life-long role that fate had thrust upon her, as mother of the future British monarch.
>
> She was a peculiarly bewitching blend: the public goddess who in private knew more misery than joy, a figure as far removed from the serious business of high politics as it is possible to imagine, yet a person who would become an extraordinary ambassadress for her country. In many respects, her life was a happening – but one which may yet exert greater impact on Britain than a clutch of the weightiest public dignitaries of our time.

What a peculiar day it was yesterday. Today, people are talking of her as they talk of Marilyn Monroe, Elvis Presley, James Dean, those who will always be remembered for the way they looked when they died, never growing into old age, just remaining the icons they were in life. Of course, every national newspaper has issued a very special edition this morning and the news is that they have all, especially the tabloids, sold out very quickly indeed.

Even in death, Diana can sell whatever publication she appears in. I don't feel quite as shocked this morning as I did all day yesterday, which rather indicates that I shall be completely over the death of this young woman by the middle of the week.

Will Buckingham Palace give her a State funeral!? She was no longer classified as Her Royal Highness. Whatever they do, the British nation will turn out or tune in in their millions. I shan't be here to watch it, but I have little doubt it will be televised live throughout America. I have never before lived through a royal death. I think Diana's may well be the first in the age of television. The BBC could never have imagined that they would have to cover the funeral of the Princess first, when the Queen and the Queen Mother were far likelier candidates to pop their clogs.

Saturday, 13 September

Arsenal are playing Bolton Wanderers. I remember this fixture more than any other. One cold evening in 1958, my father took me to the North Bank and positioned me down the front, behind the goal, to watch a truly exciting match in which Arsenal thrashed Bolton by 6–1. It was Danny Clapton's finest hour. He tore Tommy Banks, the England left-back, apart and made several goals for David Herd. These were exciting times watching Arsenal. It was all a little mysterious and the thrill I experienced as a nine-year-old when I saw the Arsenal pitch and surrounding stadium has never been equalled.

Today Arsenal field a team I don't know, at least I don't know most of them, although they are playing infinitely more enjoyable football than I used to watch in 1958. It's an international side, including Englishmen, Frenchmen and Dutchmen: Seaman, Dixon, Bould, Grimandi, Winterburn, Vieira, Parlour, Petit, Overmars, Bergkamp and Ian Wright. A potent concoction, I hope.

My guest, as he was around this time last year, is Alan Ager, a West Ham man through and through. He attended the first floodlit match at Highbury, back in the early 1950s; today he might be attending another historical event at Highbury, if Ian Wright scores that elusive record-equalling goal. If Wright scores twice, I imagine the noise would take off the stadium roof, if only there was a roof to take off.

Arsenal, fluent and elegant, dominate the play for the first twenty minutes, and then they concede a goal completely against the run of play. Alan Thompson is Bolton's scorer. He heads home a cross from the ever-dangerous Nathan Blake, who is left free on the left wing, crosses the ball to find the unmarked Thompson free inside the Arsenal penalty area. What a setback! Bolton's lead doesn't last very long. In fact, Arsenal almost equalise straight from the kick-off, but Overmars's shot, having beaten the Bolton goalkeeper, Keith Branagan, is not strong enough to cross the goalline. Never mind, playing with this fluency it can only be a matter of time before Arsenal level the score. They do it when Bergkamp, with a deft flick to the right side of the Bolton penalty area, puts in Ian Wright, and with a low cross shot from about fifteen yards the England striker equals Bastin's fifty-one-year-old record.

Within five minutes, again after Bergkamp has teased Bolton's defence and sent them all over the place, Ian Wright taps in an impossible-to-miss opportunity at the clock end to become Arsenal's all-time greatest goalscorer. Everyone in the stadium stands to applaud the magnificent striker. Never will Ian Wright score an easier or more important goal in his professional career – unless, of course, he scores the goal that wins England the World Cup, which I doubt very much. Ian Wright runs down the East Stand touchline, shirt over his head, vest reading '179 Goals', to be smothered by fellow Arsenal players. It's a wonderful sight to behold, and must feel even better to Wrighty. Now he has that weight off his shoulders, he might go on to score many more goals for Arsenal and ensure that his goalscoring record will never be broken, at least not for another fifty-one years.

Ray Parlour scores with a firm shot from some distance, right on the stroke of half-time to give Arsenal a comfortable 3–1 lead, one I'm quite sure Bolton will not overtake in the second half. I comment to those around me that surely Ray Parlour is the most improved player in this Arsenal side. What has Arsene Wenger done to Parlour's game that has made him at times quite special?

In the second half the game slows down, although Bolton have two very good chances to score a second goal, perhaps even an equaliser. But the only goal of this second half comes once Arsene Wenger replaces Ray Parlour with David Platt, and Marc Overmars with Luis Boa Morte. It is then that things start to liven up, and when Platt sends a beautifully weighted chip right behind the Bolton defence, Ian Wright is there to hit a side-footed volley into the Bolton net to make the score 4–1.

Now Wrighty has scored his hat-trick and really has nothing left to prove to anyone, Mr Wenger takes him off and replaces him with the young pretender, Nicolas Anelka. Wright leaves the pitch to a standing ovation and cheers and cries that are usually reserved for Cup Final winning goals. Ian Wright deserves it. Where would Arsenal have been without the man I believe to be England's number one striker? I think Arsene Wenger is thinking ahead to Tuesday's European adventure in Greece, when Arsenal begin their UEFA Cup campaign, without Dennis Bergkamp, who won't go on the trip as he has a fear of flying.

Arsenal continue playing as elegantly as they have this season, but they don't manage to score again, although they have at least three further chances. Arsenal 4 Bolton Wanderers 1 is a fair result, that should give Wanderers nothing to complain about. Alan has had a magical afternoon and tells me so. He has witnessed more than I have at Highbury – two historic moments, both of which he'll always remember.

TUESDAY, 16 SEPTEMBER

The hostile Greek fans definitely give a lift to the Salonika team, and although Arsenal look very sound defensively, they look less than assured in attack. The match finishes PAOK 1 Arsenal 0. Arsenal could well have done with an away goal but it wasn't to be. Now they will have to win at Highbury by two goals, just in case the Greek side score one goal. I think Arsenal will win and progress into the next round of the UEFA Cup where they will meet a team more accomplished than PAOK, and where life will be much more difficult than it proved tonight. It was good to see Tony Adams back in the heart of the Arsenal defence. He does make such a huge difference.

THURSDAY, 18 SEPTEMBER

A really interesting story appears in the newspapers and on the radio this morning, one that makes me awake quicker than usual. It seems that John Birt has again upset his employees at the BBC and further reduced their morale. He's a lad! He seems to

disregard good, solid advice, setting up the structure and policy of
the BBC as if it were a government office and not an artistic environment in which those with creativity wish to work. That might
just be, for Birt hasn't a creative bone in his body and can't understand those who have.

The big story this morning could be headlined 'BBC Staff In
Revolt'. By staff I think the newspapers and radio mean journalists.
Having upset the creative community with his poor management
skills, he is now turning his attention to upsetting the journalists. I
would have thought Birt would understand journalists. Presenters
of the BBC's most popular news programmes launched an
unprecedented attack on their employers last night over proposed
changes to the way radio and television news is run. John
Humphrys, James Naughtie and Anna Ford, all presenters of the
'Today' programme, have signed a joint letter expressing their
despair at the sweeping proposals. Jeremy Paxman and Kirsty
Wark, presenters on 'Newsnight' have also expressed anger at the
changes that will mean the introduction of five 'super editors' to
control all of the BBC television and radio news programmes.
Programmes as diverse as Radio Four's 'Today' and 'The World
Tonight', BBC Television's One, Six and Nine O'Clock News and
'Newsnight' will lose dedicated editors, and staff will be expected
to change between programmes regularly: I can't see it happening.

SUNDAY, 21 SEPTEMBER

At ten to four, Maurice and I are sitting in the Cattle Shed to watch
Chelsea v. Arsenal. Can Arsenal take three points this afternoon,
and prove to the neutral that they are good enough to win this
season's title? Briggy comes to join us. The three of us watch an
enthralling match. Chelsea command the first half, Arsenal the
second half. At half-time the score is 1–1, Chelsea scoring first
through Gustavo Poyet, the Urugayan, and Arsenal equalising
moments later when Ian Wright sets up Dennis Bergkamp to slide
the ball into Chelsea's net.

In the second half, Arsenal take the lead when Bergkamp
(surely already most people's choice as Footballer of the Year, and
the season is only just over one month old) fires in a rocket from
fifteen yards following a Chelsea defensive cock-up. Within

ninety seconds Chelsea have equalised. A magnificent curling cross from Mark Hughes, brought on as substitute to replace Gianluca Vialli, by-passes Bould and Seaman, and Gianfranco Zola runs the ball into the unguarded net – 2–2. Franck Leboeuf gets himself sent off when he trips Bergkamp, who is in full stride and heading towards the goal. It is Leboeuf's second bookable offence and he is already walking towards the tunnel before the referee takes out his red card. This changes the pattern of the game, with Arsenal dominating the final twenty minutes. With one minute left to play Nigel Winterburn, of all people, takes the ball from the halfway line to within twenty-five yards of Chelsea's goal, then fires a Brazilian-style rocket into the top left-hand corner of the net, giving Arsenal a 3–2 victory. It's an amazing match, full of excitement and technical mastery of the English game as we have come to know it. Arsenal move into second place in the division, and could go top on Wednesday night if they beat West Ham at Highbury, and Chelsea can some-how or other gain three points at Old Trafford.

Dennis Bergkamp is voted man of the match with a record ninety-three per cent of the vote. He is at the peak of his game, he is world class, he will join the Arsenal greats without a shadow of doubt. He seems to be getting better by the match. It's a privilege to have been around when he is at his peak.

WEDNESDAY, 24 SEPTEMBER

This afternoon both Maurice and I should have been off to London to watch Arsenal take on West Ham United, in a Premier League match. As it is, Maurice some months ago agreed to speak this evening to the Cheltenham Townswomen's Guild, and although he wasn't to know that this evening's talk would clash with an important Arsenal Premiership match, he is nonetheless very annoyed. So I go alone.

A special presentation is to be made to Ian Wright by club chairman Peter Hill-Wood, to commemorate his goalscoring achievement. Just before kick-off, children wearing the club colours of every team Wright has ever scored against come on to the pitch and form a circle. There is a tremendous roar of approval when the commentator announces that somewhere one of the children is wearing a Tottenham Hotspur shirt. Wright runs on to the pitch through an avenue of West Ham and Arsenal players to a colossal ovation, and on the big screens we see about forty of the 180 goals Ian Wright has scored for Arsenal. It is the most wonderful overture to the concert of football that is about to follow.

Although West Ham get the chance to score the first goal of the game when Seaman misjudges a cross from the left, John Hartson or Iain Dowie, I'm not sure which, fails to reach the ball in front of an open goal. Had West Ham scored just then it may have put a completely different complexion on this match. As it is, Arsenal start to dominate with their one-touch, Wenger-inspired football, turning on a show. Before too long Dennis Bergkamp, who else, puts Arsenal into the lead. Thereafter he puts on a world-class footballing display, as he seems to do each week now, and sets up Marc Overmars to score Arsenal's second goal, and his first at Highbury. Another giant ovation. This is becoming all too like opera.

A dubious decision by the referee gives Arsenal a penalty that Ian Wright converts nonchalantly, and this gives him his 181st goal for the club. John O'Neill (West Ham supporter and my music teacher) is adamant that there was never a handball in the penalty area by a West Ham player, least of all Rio Ferdinand, the rising young star. For John, the game has been ruined by an appalling decision by this referee, who up until this moment has been having a good match. The penalty, and of course the 3–0 scoreline, has knocked the stuffing out of West Ham. All they can play for now is their pride and to prevent a rout.

But just to add insult to injury, Bergkamp again turns on the style and sets up Overmars to score his second, Arsenal's fourth. Moments later, as Winterburn lies writhing in pain having been fouled by Hartson, the whistle for half-time blows and Arsenal return to their dressing-room 4–0 to the good, probably, no certainly, with three points in the bag and maybe a place at the top of the Premiership tonight. I suggest to John that teams that go in at half-time 4–0 up tend not to score in the second half; John believes Arsenal will score, and often, in this half and beat West Ham by 7–0. They don't, of course.

The second half is played at exhibition pace, with Arsenal giving a display of controlled and organised football, sometimes with high levels of flair. Although Bergkamp comes close to scoring the goals that would have made it 7–0, he doesn't convert any of the chances and the match finishes with a scoreline of 4–0. A dazzling display and as we leave we hear Manchester United have been held to a 2–2 draw by Chelsea. This means Arsenal are top of the League.

Thursday, 25 September

It never ceases to amaze me just what a popular show 'Birds of a Feather' is with an audience. I'm reminded of it this evening watching the recording of episode four, series eight of what must be described as Maurice's and my greatest television success. You can instinctively tell by the audience's reaction on being introduced to the stars of the show that this is one of those great rarities, a show that has become a classic. The applause and cheering is deafening, at least from where we sit. The girls take their bows and get on with it. From thirty seconds into the opening – it might not have been that long – laughter rings around the studio and everyone knows it's another winner. I feel a little detached from this series, probably as Maurice and I haven't written a single episode. Perhaps that's why we find it a little surprising that Pauline, Lesley and Linda say that this is the best series they have made for a very long time.

Friday, 26 September

We are going to Ealing Studios this afternoon to watch the first completed edit of 'Mosley', episode one, with Guy Slater, Irving Teitelbaum, Rob Knights and Peter Ansorge.

In the small editing suite, the lights go down, and the tape is rolled for our delight . . . or otherwise. First we have the choice of two opening titles, one in black and white and one in colour, but none of us comment on which we prefer until we have watched the whole of the first episode. It moves along very nicely, and if not with excessive pace, then fast enough for the viewer not to become bored by the complicated story. To be honest, I find it a little languid for my taste, what you might call a little 'Merchant-Ivory' in feel and look. However, when Jemma Redgrave comes on to the screen, the piece starts to come alight. One becomes engrossed in the blossoming love story between Tom and Cimmie, which is how it should be. I'm remarkably impressed by Jemma's screen presence, although, of course, it's Jonathan Cake who has to hold the attention in nearly every scene of this first hour.

I don't know what the Jewish viewers and Woburn House (the Jewish Board of Deputies) will have to say – a whole hour and not a hint of anti-Semitism to be seen.

TUESDAY, 30 SEPTEMBER

Tonight I'm going to London for three days, but first I have to watch tonight's UEFA Cup, second-leg tie between Arsenal and Salonika, being played at Highbury. Maurice and I opted not to go. We gave our tickets to Udi Eichler and Joshua, his son. This will be the first game either of them has been to. If Udi and his boy don't feel pampered after this experience, I give up.

Arsenal have to score two goals without conceding one in order to progress to the second round. Unfortunately, they fail to do it, and in the most cruel way for both them and their supporters. Having scored the goal that effectively equalises the 1–0 deficit from the first match, they just can't seem to score a second, although goodness knows they come so very close so very often. Bergkamp, of course, scores the masterly first-half equaliser. Parlour, Petit and Bergkamp himself come oh so close to adding to it, but nothing. Arsenal go in 1–0 to the good at half-time, and in the second half the Greek team come into the match far more and I fear the worst. I get the worst with just three minutes left of the game, when Salonika score a goal that means Arsenal must score two in three minutes. An impossibility. Arsenal go out at the first time of asking. Now even at this early stage of the season, they will surely have to concentrate upon the league title which will take them into the European Champions League, and bring in all that dosh.

SATURDAY, 4 OCTOBER

Before today's game against Barnsley I'm introduced to Michael Parkinson. Once the top chat show host in the UK and Australia, he finished up presenting a morning programme on LBC. BBC is

currently repeating some of the memorable Parkinson shows –
and many were memorable, I watched one last night – and the
BBC have decided to begin a new series of 'Parkinson' in January.
Turning back the clock isn't usually a very good idea and seldom
works, but as there aren't any chat show hosts who are journalists,
or who possess Parkinson's skill, I think this is different. It will be
a welcome change from the current crop of chat shows where the
star is not the guest but the host, who takes all the good lines and
whose object it seems is to make a total fool of his guests. No,
hurry back Parkinson, I think we might all need you. I ask him
who is the guest he most wanted and never got. He answers without thought, 'Sinatra,' adding, 'and Katharine Hepburn and Sir
Laurence Olivier.' I'm surprised he doesn't include Barbra
Streisand. The two greatest footballers he ever saw were Tom
Finney and George Best. He tells the story of Skinner Normanton,
a Barnsley hard-man of the 1940s, who came to Highbury with the
sole intention of breaking Jimmy Logie's leg. Alex Forbes, the
Arsenal hard-man, knew what Normanton was going to do,
warned Logie, and between them they devised a plan whereby
Forbes would 'do' Normanton. He did too. At the first throw-in
Forbes threw the ball to Logie, the little man jumped high into the
air, as instructed, Normanton went right through where Logie
would have been had he not jumped, and Forbes ground
Normanton's leg with his studs, putting him out of the game.

The match this afternoon is everything I imagined it to be. A
heavy Arsenal victory against the team that is probably the worst
in the Premier League. Arsenal win 5–0, with goals from
Bergkamp (2), Wright, Parlour and Platt. Arsenal's starting line-up
is probably their strongest: Seaman, Dixon, Adams, Bould,
Winterburn, Vieira, Parlour, Petit, Overmars, Bergkamp, Wright.
During the second half, when Arsenal are 3–0 to the good, Boa
Morte, Platt and Anelka replace Wright, Overmars and Parlour,
not because any of them are injured, but because Arsene Wenger
wants the players to stretch their legs and keep in tune with
Premier League appearances. It's a fine policy and it does mean
Arsenal are still unbeaten and top of the Premier League, having
scored twenty-eight league goals so far this season.

Dennis Bergkamp is playing at the top of his game and is far
and away the finest player in the Premier League, perhaps in
Europe, maybe in the world – what's more, he's wearing an

Arsenal shirt. It is astonishing to see him in action. Not since Liam Brady have we had a player who could win a game for Arsenal almost on his own. Barnsley are not the strongest or best-organised opposition, but nevertheless, this Arsenal team beat them 5–0 whereas Arsenal teams of the past might have scraped a 1–0 or 2–1 victory. It's becoming so that I can't wait for the next Arsenal home league match, such is the excitement it brings to me.

SUNDAY, 19 OCTOBER

Tomorrow Briggy and I set off for our annual holiday but this one's a holiday with a difference. We are going as travel writers, commissioned to produce 3,000 words for *Harpers & Queen*, with photographs, about four different Maldivian islands. I'm looking forward to it, as I look forward to every holiday. I feel ready to leave England and set off for sunnier climes. When I get back there's the big one, Arsenal v. Manchester United at Highbury. I do hope Arsenal win, although they'll be without Dennis Bergkamp. Yesterday at Crystal Palace the Dutchman was booked and this means he has accumulated enough bookings to constitute a three-match suspension. I wonder just how much this will dent Arsenal's championship ambitions.

SUNDAY, 9 NOVEMBER

Back for the big one! Maurice and I drive up to Highbury and on the way I tell him all about our holiday.

The match is about as unpredictable as anyone could ever have expected. First of all Arsenal are forced to field the following team, due to suspension and injury: Seaman, Dixon, Adams, Grimandi, Winterburn, Parlour, Vieira, Platt, Wright, Overmars and Anelka. It is the young Frenchman, Nicolas Anelka, who gives Arsenal the lead with the Gunners' first attack, and I have to admit that I am pretty amazed. When Patrick Vieira hits a stunning, bending shot from all of twenty or more yards, and Peter Schmeichel doesn't move, well at least not until he picks the ball from the back of his net, and Arsenal are 2–0 up inside twenty minutes, I begin to wonder what on earth is going on. If Arsenal continue on the rampage they could easily go down the tunnel at half-time three or even four goals to the good – but they do not.

No, instead Manchester United start coming back into the game and soon score the goal that just goes to highlight that Arsenal's defence, once so strong and bastion-like, is now getting older, slower and less communicative. Teddy Sheringham is left free inside the penalty box to score with the most simple of chances. With just five minutes to go before half-time, Sheringham scores again with a low ground shot, on the turn. I believe Seaman should have saved, or at least got his hand to it, but United equalise and now I fear the worst.

I don't recall anybody around me, and I mean nobody, saying that Arsenal will come out for the second half and take the game by the scruff of the neck, take United apart, and collect the three points. Arsene Wenger makes a half-time tactical change that pays dividends. He removes the influential Vieira (I hope he's not injured) and brings on Steve Bould to shore up the back. This works. When, late in this half, Arsenal replace Anelka with Wreh, another purchase from a French club, they begin to look as though they are going to, and want to, win this match. Wright could have scored had he hit a close-range shot truer, and Wreh misses two golden opportunities from inside the penalty area. However, Arsenal do score when Platt heads home another exquisite Ray Parlour (surely the man of the match) corner. Arsenal have scored with five minutes left to play, they are 3–2 ahead, and they don't look as though they will concede another goal. They don't, and take the most valuable three points so far this season.

Maurice and I are thrilled. We come home with smiles spread across our faces for there is no finer victory than to beat Manchester United. Besides, Arsenal haven't done so for five years. Does this mean we are their equal? I don't think so. They show a consistency that we do not, but we stay in second place (one point behind United) and from this position anything can happen. Arsenal's next four matches are their toughest so far this season – away to Sheffield Wednesday, at home to Liverpool, away to Newcastle United, and then at home to Blackburn Rovers. If we can take seven points from a possible twelve, I'll be happy. What I know is that I seem to be enjoying my football at Highbury this season more than I have for a very long time.

MONDAY, 10 NOVEMBER

A long time ago, Jack Hargreaves, former Pipesmoker of the Year, said, 'If a man can tell the difference between his job and his hobby, he's in the wrong job.' Therein lies what I feel, for I do regard my job as a hobby and I approach it with an eagerness that's only refreshed by a holiday.

What I have to look forward to in the twelve months before me, excluding the many surprises that obviously crop up in any given working year, is the writing of 'Patient A', our play about the relationship between Hitler and Freud, and a new series of 'Unfinished Business', the release of the first series of 'Unfinished Business', the umpteenth series of 'Birds' and 'Goodnight Sweetheart', and above all else, the release and response to 'Mosley'. All of this will keep Maurice and me at our desks for some long time and I find the prospect exciting, and perhaps the most exciting prospect is our entry into the theatre.

TUESDAY, 11 NOVEMBER

Briggy and I watch a Channel Four 'Cutting Edge' documentary, entitled 'Footballers' Wives'. The programme focuses on the wives of Ian Walker (Tottenham and England), Dean Holdsworth (Wimbledon) and Jason Lee (Watford). Each wife has a vastly different story to tell. Mrs Walker is a model, happy, in love, and exceedingly cautious about the company kept by her husband. Mrs Lee is most definitely unhappy, jealous, discontented with being nothing more than Jason's appendage, and wants to stay put in Nottingham, despite the fact that Jason is on the transfer list. And then there's Mrs Holdsworth, who has been cheated on by her husband (he ran off with a Page 3 topless model). She has thrown him out and taken him back, but realises that he's likely to wander at any given opportunity. All three women seem to live in luxury and have what appear to be superficially comfortable and exciting lives, but I know it isn't like that at all. Mrs Walker does seem to be genuinely in love with her Ian, but as for the other two, well, they seem to be embittered. Were it not for the high profiles of their husbands, and the luxury they can offer their wives, I think both of these marriages wouldn't have sufficient glue to hold them together.

Tuesday, 18 November

Exciting news! Channel Four have given us a definite transmission date for 'Mosley'. It starts on Monday, 9 February 1998 at 9 p.m – an excellent piece of scheduling. I think Monday is the best viewing night of the week, and February is the month everyone seems to stay at home. Guy Slater, who gives us the news, tells me that Channel Four will be promoting it as a political sex romp, and not a political study of a man who could have risen to the top but who instead sunk to the bottom. I suppose Channel Four want large viewing figures, even though I don't believe these viewers will be found. On BBC1 there's the Nine O'Clock News, and on ITV some minor blockbuster that usually attracts the major audience share of the night. I suppose that if 'Mosley' pulls in 3 million viewers, Channel Four will become ecstatic. I think I should be, too.

Wednesday, 19 November

Today's the day of the long-awaited luncheon with the BBC hierarchy. ALOMO are on the verge of signing a new three-year exclusive deal with the BBC and this is a 'shaking hands' meeting, a goodwill meeting, although the ink will not dry on any contract until it has been prepared to the satisfaction of both Pearson Television and the BBC. Today is a social affair. We do, of course, discuss in general what Maurice and I and our other writers might offer to the BBC in the next three years, and we listen to what they want more than anything else to make their schedules attractive. It seems that their greatest need is popular drama that can be shown in long runs, and return year in, year out, something like 'Casualty', or one of those series that the Americans do so very well. It almost goes without saying that quality comedy is required. This leads us to the debate about the quality of comedy on BBC at the moment. We all agree that we are not making our comedy (with very few exceptions) funny enough. We make it whimsical. We make it full of pathos. We make it unbelievable. We make it downright second rate.

More specifically, we discuss an idea that we have for David Jason and Richard Wilson. Maurice hadn't been all that keen on it, but Claire reminds us, thus earning her lunch, that we had a 'spin'

on the idea which made it attractive to all, and that was that it was
a renal failure that brought our two characters together. Maurice,
off the top of his head, calls the piece 'Sidney's Kidney', and everyone laughs. Now Maurice suddenly becomes excited by the
prospect and Alan Yentob wants a meeting arranged with David
Jason and Richard Wilson to discuss the project.

FRIDAY, 21 NOVEMBER

Today Maurice and I have started writing our very first play and
over the next weeks, perhaps months (although I hope not), we
shall focus all of our attention upon the events in Austria from
1905 to 1938. If we succeed we might have a wonderful experience
awaiting us in 1998, but there are many millions of computer keys
to be tapped before I can become in the least bit excited. I think it
might be a good idea for Maurice and me to turn off the office telephones and get our heads down to the task at hand.

SATURDAY, 22 NOVEMBER

For tonight's 'Match of the Day', I would happily pay 50 pence,
about twice the amount that would be asked were the BBC working on a pay-per-view system. Arsenal suffer a 2–0 defeat at the
feet of Sheffield Wednesday, Ron Atkinson's first match in charge
so something of a sensational start for him. Manchester United
give Wimbledon a 5–2 mauling at Selhurst Park and Blackburn
Rovers beat Chelsea 1–0, putting the Rovers into second place in
the Premier League. But the most remarkable result of the day,
perhaps even of the season so far, is Barnsley's 1–0 victory at
Liverpool. The victory takes Barnsley off the bottom of the
League, that place now occupied by Everton, with Tottenham
Hotspur, new manager Christian Gross and all, just three places
above them. It's all very intriguing, and the next four weeks will,
I believe, determine who will be fighting that dreadfully
long fight to save themselves from the big drop. I think I can
safely say that it will be Manchester United who will win the
championship . . . again.

SUNDAY, 30 NOVEMBER

Another bloomin' Sunday match at Highbury! I can't remember the last time Arsenal played on a Saturday, which is the day I associate with going to the football. Playing on a Sunday is for the benefit of Sky Television, but I would much prefer my soccer to be played on a Saturday afternoon, with a three o'clock kick-off. Arsenal v. Liverpool is Sky Sport's televised live match and there are moments when I ask myself why I want to make a 150 miles round journey when I could watch the game in the Cattle Shed. I suppose the answer is the reason football survives – it needs people such as I at the game, taking part in the excitement and creating the atmosphere.

There might well be atmosphere this afternoon as another capacity crowd fill the ever-diminishing stadium. I remember one foggy, cold, Tuesday night in 1958–59 when 67,000 packed inside Highbury to watch an Arsenal v. Colchester United FA Cup replay. I remember, too, one Tuesday afternoon in the 1973 season, during the three-day week, when what I believe to be 70,000 packed inside Highbury for an Arsenal v. Derby County FA Cup replay. Today's 38,094 needn't have bothered, for Arsenal's form is sliding. They go down 0–1 and never look like scoring.

Ian Wright has become an enigma. Since he scored the goals that beat Cliff Bastin's all-time Arsenal goalscoring record, Wright has scored only three times in league games. Something has happened inside his head that's preventing him doing what it is he does best. Bergkamp is back and I thought that his return would motivate Wright and goals would start pouring forth. Not a bit of it!

Steve McManaman scores a wondrous goal midway through the second half that wins the match for Liverpool, and leaves Arsene Wenger and Arsenal asking many questions. What has gone wrong? Where is that fabulous form they displayed for the first two months of the season? Can the exclusion of Patrick Vieira and Ray Parlour really make so much difference to the team, and if it does, is Arsenal's squad large enough to make a serious challenge for the championship? To this last question I suspect the answer is no. More players are required and quickly to give Arsenal a chance to qualify for Europe. Yes I know it's only the beginning of December but to fall too far behind the leaders at this stage of the season is to ask too much of a club throughout the winter and spring.

So Arsenal, playing bewilderingly below par, and as they have not played before this season, lose three points and will have to regroup and rethink. Two defeats don't put an end to a season, but there is something incongruous going on at this moment.

Of course, Arsene Wenger is in the rebuilding process, and all the fans expect the team to win every game, which is impossible. It will take Mr Wenger three years before he has the team he wants and not the team he has inherited. There is anything but a crisis at Highbury, they just happen to have lost two matches on the trot. If they win their next two (but this is asking an awful lot as they are away at Newcastle and at home to Blackburn Rovers) and Ian Wright scores three goals, all my worries will be meaningless and I'll wonder why we were all so concerned.

SATURDAY, 13 DECEMBER

I am determined to go to the Arsenal today, despite my cold and fever. Briggy stands at the kitchen door as I'm about to leave, saying, 'Are you really going to the Arsenal today? Is Maurice going?' I reply, 'Yes,' and 'Of course,' and I add that the Arsenal is the only constant in my life, something that links the 'other' Laurence to the present one, and how I will never want to miss an Arsenal game at Highbury if I can help it. I suppose one of the regrets of my life is that I never had a child of my own to take with me, to introduce him or her to that joy I was shown as a child, standing on the terraces of Highbury.

Can Arsenal win this afternoon against Blackburn Rovers? Goodness knows we need the points. In the first half it looks as though Arsenal have found the hunger for the game that has been missing over the past three or four weeks. They create several opportunities and Ian Wright is back at his sharpest – not that any opportunities fall to him.

Halfway through the first half Arsenal score. Parlour sends another long ball behind the Blackburn defence, Overmars attaches himself to it and lobs the ball over the advancing Tim Flowers and into the net. Arsenal are a goal to the good and will probably build on this lead, return to their winning ways and collect three more points, keeping themselves in contention for the championship. However, warning signals start flashing when I notice that Tony Adams looks anything but fit and well, and Winterburn is, as ever, proving a liability when the ball finds its way to his right foot. How can a professional footballer be so inefficient with fifty per cent of his professional equipment, and have got away with it for so long? At one point in the first half, Winterburn is in trouble because the ball falls on the right foot, so he sends a suicidal ball back to Adams. Usually so confident and authoritative, Adams stumbles, flails a short back pass and Kevin Gallagher latches on to the loose ball and has only Seaman to beat to equalise. Thankfully, he blasts the ball wide and Arsenal are let off the hook, at least until half-time. But this mess-up between Winterburn and Adams is indicative that Arsenal's back four are growing old together and that their pace is no longer equal to the younger strikers they are having to face week in, week out. They will be punished and punished badly in the weeks to come. Arsene Wenger must be seriously thinking about changing this marvellous back four who have been together since about 1987.

In the second half, Tony Adams's form goes from bad to worse and he seems to be playing as if he is suffering from the effects of too much drink or else a nasty hangover. He misdirects a ball he would clear with ease ninety-nine times out of a hundred, it falls straight at the feet of a Blackburn midfield player, and from him the ball goes to two players before finishing up in the back of Seaman's net. Then Kevin Gallagher scores with a sensational volley (reminiscent of McManaman's against us a fortnight ago), but here again Adams was out of position and late with a tackle that should have prevented Gallagher even getting in his shot.

Arsenal are, not to mince words, pathetic, and Maurice and I leave with five minutes to play, thus missing Steve Sherwood adding a third for Blackburn, giving them three points and effectively ending Arsenal's championship dreams. At least, that's what I believe. Maurice says the oddest thing, especially for someone with such common sense.

'Do you know,' he says, 'I think Arsenal will win the Double.'

'Why?' I ask.

'Because today will be the turning point.'

I wonder what Maurice has been taking. The way Arsenal have been playing these past five weeks, I think they will be lucky to

qualify for a European place. The big question is why have the
Arsenal become so disorganised and without hope? What has happened to the players who were performing so brilliantly during
the first month of this season? Is it solely down to confidence? I
believe it's something more fundamental. I think Dixon,
Winterburn, Adams, perhaps Bould and Seaman too, are past their
sell-by dates and can no longer cope with the speed and vitality of
the English Premier League. As George Graham had failed to consider that this day would eventually arrive, he did nothing to
replace these players. Now Arsene Wenger is left with the responsibility. He has begun a rebuilding programme that has brought
many fine players to Highbury, but I think he believed he could
manage with this ageing and very experienced defence for a little
while longer. It's now patently obvious that he cannot. In midfield,
Arsenal lack a creative talent, although Petit and Vieira are excellent. Upfront Marc Overmars has yet to settle into British football,
and something more than the excellence of Wright (maybe growing too old to survive week in, week out) and the brilliance of
Bergkamp is required.

Another world-class goalscorer is what Arsenal need. What I
also think they need, and I never thought I would hear myself say
this, is an organised and young defence. The season is now going
to be a learning curve for Arsene Wenger, and I anticipate week-
ends of frustration for the Arsenal fans. And Maurice believes
Arsenal will win the Double! Cloud cuckoo land! He ought to
place a bet on Arsenal for the Double; he could win a small fortune.

MONDAY, 15 DECEMBER

The news is very disturbing. It has a resonance of times past that
makes me think that Britain isn't the fair-minded country it pro-
fesses to be, and which we like to believe it is. Eleven promising
lines of inquiry have still not been followed up by police four
years after the racist murder of the black schoolboy Stephen
Lawrence at a bus stop, according to a report published today by
the Home Secretary, Jack Straw. The murder investigation suffered
from serious shortcomings and failed to operate to an acceptable
level, said the Police Complaints Authority in a preliminary report.

'Vital' witnesses were ignored, evidence linking suspects to other knife attacks was not properly followed up, while confusion in the handling of identification evidence may have meant one attacker was overlooked. The police lost the confidence of the Lawrence family at an early stage and were unable to regain it. Police claimed attempts to bring eighteen-year-old Stephen's killers to justice was blocked by a 'wall of silence', but the report said local people came forward with valuable information soon after the killing.

I wonder, just for one second, whether the same efforts were put into the investigation as perhaps there might have been had Stephen Lawrence been a middle-class, white lad who had been stabbed at a London bus stop. I so much doubt it, and if the particular police force investigating this case placed less value on a black life than they would have done on a white one, well, that is nothing short of intolerable. I'll say no more.

TUESDAY, 6 JANUARY

This morning is the press show for 'Unfinished Business'. During the course of it, I'm told that last night's 'Birds' episode got an overnight figure of 10.7 million. This probably means that when the final figure is published, it will be about 12 million viewers. This is unusual for a comedy programme and I don't know that we shall ever again create a comedy series that attracts this size of audience.

Maurice thinks the response to 'Unfinished Business' by the press is as good as any press show he has attended, and that the press were genuinely interested in the subject matter of the presentation. But, of course, you mustn't be fooled by what you're told by the press; they can say one thing and write another, and often do. We give honest interviews and what I do discuss quite freely is the censorship placed upon us by the BBC censorship department, should such a department exist. The word 'fuck' was removed, making Amy (Harriet Walter) not truly angry, and this took something away from the piece. Somehow I don't suppose the BBC thought about this; what they were thinking about were the few complaints that would arrive from those who cannot come to terms with the richness of the English language.

*

Sky's televised match tonight is the quarter-final of the Coca-Cola
Cup. West Ham United meet Arsenal on a pitch so bad I can truth-
fully call it the worst Premier League pitch I have ever seen. The
Somme springs to mind, with the pitch bearing the scars of the
colossal downpour we have had today – mud everywhere, divots
down the centre of the pitch, not the surface to produce a skilful
game of football, rather a wildly exciting one. Arsenal give away a
first-half penalty, or rather David Seaman gives away the penalty
by tripping Paul Kitson when he could have easily just dived on
the ball. John Hartson steps up to take the spot kick against his old
club and misses, or Seaman saves. What a let-off for Arsenal!

Not ten minutes later Arsenal take the lead. A very neat move
between Ian Wright and Dennis Bergkamp leaves Wrighty free to
shoot past Craig Forrest, the West Ham goalkeeper, and give
Arsenal a half-time lead. In the second half, a dreadful mistake by
Rio Ferdinand (still far too inexperienced to hold England's
defence together in this year's World Cup finals) leaves Marc
Overmars five yards from goal with only Forrest to beat, which he
does. Arsenal are 2–0 up and don't look as though they will allow
this match to slip from their grasp. Even though West Ham substitute Samassi Abou scores a goal when the ball bounces between
Keown and Bould, with Seaman well off his goalline, I still can't
see West Ham equalising. Arsenal win 2–1, becoming only the
second team to win at Upton Park this season. They were unquestionably the better team on the night, with Petit quite outstanding.

So Arsenal move into the semi-finals, as do Middlesbrough, and
tomorrow night two out of Chelsea, Ipswich, Liverpool and
Newcastle will join them. I do so hope Arsenal draw
Middlesbrough for I feel that this tie, over two legs, could see
Arsenal on their way to Wembley for the first time under Arsene
Wenger, and for the first time with the mercurial Dennis Bergkamp
in the team. Once at Wembley I don't really care whom Arsenal
have to defeat to lift the Cup, and their passport into Europe.

SATURDAY, 10 JANUARY

On how many January days have I gone to Highbury when there
is snow or frost on the ground, when the temperature is freezing

or below, and when I'm not too sure if the game is even going to be played or not? Too many that I can remember. Today is the day of my late father's birth, he would have been ninety-two years old and I wonder if this afternoon he would have been fit and well enough to have come to watch Arsenal v. Leeds? He died in 1975 so I shall never know the answer to that question.

I'm fully expecting the game to end 0–0, for I know only too well how disciplined George Graham's sides are at the back, and how little strike power Arsenal appear to have had these past two months. After a niggling first half Gerald Ashby, the referee, is booed from the pitch. He has had the most ghastly forty-five minutes during which he seems to be making bad decision after bad decision and getting in the way of Arsenal's forward runs. There is no score. Leeds, to be honest about it, had the two best chances of the half but missed them, and although Arsenal did much of the attacking they never really looked as if they could put the ball in the net. The Arsenal players started to lose their cool by the end of the half, and Petit is lucky not to have been sent off.

The second half is a different ball game altogether. Well, it isn't really, it's still football, but football of a much higher quality. Arsenal show intense commitment and start getting on top. After sixty minutes they score a wonderful goal. It comes from Marc Overmars who picks up the ball thirty-five yards from Leeds's goal, wanders with it from wing to middle, and there unleashes a ferocious shot that leaves Nigel Martyn helpless as it smashes into the back of the net. Arsenal almost go two up when a rebound hits a Leeds defender and the ball looks for all the world to be dipping underneath Leeds's crossbar, but somehow Martyn makes a magnificent save and the score remains 1–0.

This would be enough this afternoon, but the excitement of this second half continues and Leeds equalise through Jimmy Hasselbaink. Seaman parries a low hard shot into the Leeds forward's path and all Hasselbaink has to do is tap the ball into an unguarded net. It seems Leeds have earned the point they've come for. Not so. After a piece of quick one-two football between Bergkamp and Overmars, the little Dutch winger is through again, and this time from about fifteen yards he fires a low hard shot between Martyn's legs and into the net for the goal that gives Arsenal a 2–1 victory and three much needed points.

With the victory at West Ham on Tuesday night and this

afternoon's three points, perhaps Arsenal are beginning a roll and will be up there come the end of the season, although neither I nor anyone else around me in the upper East Stand can imagine that Arsenal will take the Premier League championship. At best, they could finish runners-up but even that I doubt. It's only Maurice who, for reasons best known to himself, and to everyone else's astonishment, still believes that Arsenal will win the Double.

WEDNESDAY, 14 JANUARY

Tonight it's the Port Vale v. Arsenal FA Cup third-round replay, following an appalling match at Highbury which ended goalless. The teams must battle it out to see who will go forward to meet Middlesbrough at the Riverside Stadium. Maurice said earlier in the day that Arsenal will win quite comfortably, an opinion I do not share. I think it will be an arduous battle with not more than one goal in it. We're both wrong.

Port Vale miss two golden opportunities to go 2–0 up by half-time (thank God), and Arsenal see an Overmars shot curl around Paul Musselwhite, the Port Vale goalkeeper, hit the inside of the post, roll the length of the goalline, nearly hit the other post, and then go away from the goal. I think a 2–1 half-time scoreline would have reflected the first forty-five minutes. In the second half, Arsenal begin to dictate the match, with Ray Parlour putting in as good a midfield performance as I have seen for many a season. Yet Arsenal cannot score and neither can Port Vale. Ian Wright heads the ball into the Port Vale net but the goal is disallowed for offside, a bad decision as the action replay shows. Wright has to go off with a hamstring injury and is replaced by Anelka. What can he do? Vieira is replaced by Grimandi who, to be perfectly honest, I don't hear mentioned again from the time he comes on until the match finally ends. The final score is 0–0.

Four halves of forty-five minutes have been played and not a goal scored, though so many missed, mostly by Port Vale, who should by now have been into round four. Extra time is played and with about four minutes left of the first period, Dennis Bergkamp scores a goal of exquisite calibre. I can't imagine anyone else in British football scoring such a goal. From twenty yards or further, Bergkamp, without so much as looking up, bends a fierce shot around the brilliant Musselwhite and into the top left-hand corner of the net. It's brilliant. It might even decide the game. I certainly hope so.

It doesn't. Port Vale equalise with about five minutes of the second period of extra time to play and this tie now goes to penalties. Lee Dixon takes the first. I'm on the edge of my seat. I've seen Arsenal lose penalty shoot-outs before . . . yes, in the final of the European Cup-Winners' Cup, 1980. I won't forget that in a hurry. Lee Dixon misses, or rather Musselwhite saves Dixon's shot. Same thing. Port Vale score, 0–1. Ray Parlour scores for Arsenal, 1–1. Port Vale score, 2–1. Dennis Bergkamp scores with such ease that the ball is in the net before Musselwhite realises the kick has been taken, 2–2. Then David Seaman saves Port Vale's third penalty, and when Boa Morte (on for the injured Overmars), the Port Vale player, and Stephen Hughes all convert their kicks, the score stands at 4–3 to Arsenal with the final Port Vale player ready to take the kick that will either prolong this shoot-out or else take Arsenal into the fourth round of the FA Cup. His shot flies over Seaman's bar and Arsenal have scraped through into the fourth round. Will they ever have a tougher FA Cup tie than this one has been?

SATURDAY, 24 JANUARY

'Unfinished Business' begins this evening. I cannot be objective about this first episode. Is it really good? Is it just run-of-the-mill? I don't think so. I don't believe anyone will think so. It's extremely well acted, nearly very well directed, and I think the writing is sharp and addresses the problems of 1998, which in itself is unusual for a television comedy. We'll have to wait and see what the viewing figures are and whether we can hope to call 'Unfinished Business' another of our hits. Fingers crossed.

After 'Unfinished Business' it's 'Match of the Day', and tonight's main match features the FA Cup fourth-round tie between Middlesbrough and Arsenal. Arsenal win 2–1 and go into the fifth-round draw. Also shown is Manchester United's demolition of Walsall 5–1; Coventry's victory over Derby County 2–1; and Wimbledon winning at Huddersfield 1–0. I would like to make a little wager that Arsenal draw Wimbledon in the fifth round of the Cup. I thought Arsenal would meet Middlesbrough and Paul Merson (who scored Middlesbrough's only goal this afternoon), but now I have an inner feeling that when the balls come out of the bag tomorrow afternoon, Arsenal will play Wimbledon. This will be the match of the fifth round and will be televised by Sky Sports. We'll see.

MONDAY, 26 JANUARY

I sit in the Clarges Street apartment this evening and watch the most sensational news story that I've seen for many months. The President of the United States, Bill Jefferson Clinton, angrily tells the world, 'I want you to listen to me. I did not have sexual relations with that woman, Miss Lewinsky. I never told anyone to lie, not a single time, never.' Mr Clinton briefly looked close to tears (an act I suspect, or sheer frustration for getting caught?) as he emphasised every word of his short statement with a jab of the finger, usually a sign of guilt. I wouldn't mind taking a small wager that Clinton, whom I believe has had 'sexual relations' with Miss Lewinsky, will be forced to admit this is so before too long. When a woman like Monica wants to get into your trousers, it takes a very strong-willed man to say go away. I don't believe Clinton to be strong-willed.

Earlier today in a dramatic development, Ms Lewinsky's lawyer emerged from a day-long meeting with his client and the special investigator, Kenneth Starr, with an announcement which could set the stage for a deal whereby she would defy the President and retract her denial of an affair.

WEDNESDAY, 28 JANUARY

The Coca-Cola Cup semi-final first leg is a match I believe the Arsenal must win by at least two clear goals to feel comfortable in the second leg at Stamford Bridge in three weeks' time. In the first half, Chelsea's defence is in disarray and they are without too much potency in attack, yet for all that Arsenal manage to take only a 1–0 lead down the tunnel with them at half-time. Marc Overmars is once again Arsenal's goalscorer, although it should be said that Bergkamp hits the bar with a header, and Parlour and Hughes come close with long-range shots on target. Is 1–0 enough for me, an Arsenal supporter, to feel contented? I think not.

The second half is five minutes old when a really expressive move between Anelka (the most bizarre and frustrating forward I have seen in a red-and-white shirt since Kevin Campbell) and Overmars puts the Dutch winger through on the left-hand side. Overmars' intelligent pass pulled back across the face of the goal finds Hughes running on to the ball and he slams it into Chelsea's net. Arsenal are 2–0 up and seemingly coasting. In truth, they could easily have been 4–0 to the good when Chelsea bring on Mark Hughes, something I always feel bodes ill for opponents. I wonder why Ruud Gullit, himself playing an entire match this evening, doesn't play Hughes from the start of every match. He must have his reasons.

Two incidents occur in sixty seconds that might determine the outcome of this semi-final. First, after another swift move between Anelka, Overmars and Petit (who this evening plays out of his skin) sends the ball into the path of Bergkamp who connects with a fierce low volley. Somehow Ed De Goey gets down to the shot and parries it away. It's a superb save and keeps Chelsea in this semi-final. Secondly, a fine cross by Gianfranco Zola finds Hughes, he sneaks in front of Adams and reaches the ball before Alex Manninger can get there, gets his head to it and nods it into an empty net. Arsenal 2 Chelsea 1 is how this first leg finishes, despite Arsenal's overall domination. It's a travesty really. As the big man who sits on my left says just before the final whistle, 'At 2–0 Chelsea would have had to score three times. At 2–1 it means they only have to score once, and they probably will!' I'm more optimistic. I believe Arsenal are so much the better side that they will go to Stamford Bridge and win the second leg and progress to Wembley.

FRIDAY, 30 JANUARY

A car takes us to Channel Four for a press showing and confer- ence of 'Mosley'. Once the first episode and excerpts from the other three episodes have been shown, Maurice and I face the press. We are asked some ridiculous questions that are fired at us from the floor, such as, 'Did you write this piece because Fascism is sexy?' Maurice lambasts the questioner, and when we discover another inane question has come from the *Mail on Sunday*, we remind them, much to the delight of other members of the press in the room, that it was the *Mail* that co-financed the British Union of Fascists.

We are asked if we are expecting a torrent of controversy. I answer this question by saying that I don't expect as much as we received after the first episode of 'Birds of a Feather', for I can't imagine that the duty office at Channel Four will receive 138 calls of complaint as the BBC duty officer did in October 1989. Everyone laughs but I'm being serious.

When we explain that our next project will be even more controversial, and tell the listening audience that it's a play that investigates the relationship between Hitler and Freud, someone asks if it will be on ice. We all laugh together. Maurice adds that we're thinking of writing a biography of Margaret Thatcher, the early years before she became a woman.

SUNDAY, 1 FEBRUARY

Our 'South Bank Show' is shown tonight, and earns, from me at least, a large seal of approval. I'm particularly impressed with the Hollywood sequences that are both funny (Muscle Beach and the drive along Sunset Boulevard) and sorrowful (my explanation of those months in 1985 when I was near suicidal, although I don't speak of them in those terms), and it's very good to see once more 'So You Think You've Got Troubles' and 'Get Back', the latter looking very much better than it did at the time. It's a videotape that I shall keep forever. It will be a reminder, one day, of those wonderful moments of joy and achievement.

When I fall asleep it is with the thought of success and how much publicity Maurice and I seem to be attracting of late, and what's it all for? Is all of this publicity making me happy? Is it making Maurice happy? Is this what we believed it would be like? And if we wanted success because we genuinely felt this would be a shortcut to getting beautiful women to do to us whatever we asked them to do, we find it's now too late. Maurice has settled down to happiness with his wife and two children, and I have, well, just settled down.

MONDAY, 2 FEBRUARY

Rik Mayall is one of the few people we have worked with whom I enjoy seeing socially. His contribution to last night's 'South Bank Show' was so good, and so amusing. Tonight Maurice and I are meeting him for dinner, and I greet him as I would no other man, with a hug. It's marvellous to be in his company again.

Of course, we recollect charged days and nights when we all worked together on 'The New Statesman', a show still warmly remembered by so many. More people remember it than ever tuned in to watch it. It was a cult, the movers and shakers watched it, talked about it, and encouraged others to watch it and talk about it.

Tonight we're here to talk quite seriously about a new project we are contemplating for Rik, about a private detective. 'Oh no, not another television cop,' is the usual reaction so we must make sure that whoever it is Rik plays is completely different from Hetty Wainthrop or Jonathan Creek. We must somehow find character traits and high humour in our projected new show that set it apart from any other. Rik, Maurice and I flit around the edges of the idea and come up with some interesting aspects of this new character – he lives with a gay milkman, who might be his brother or might be someone who takes a room in his house; he's an ace poker player who would like to become the world poker champion (à la Tony Holden); he's prejudiced; he has attitude. The show should be peopled with beautiful characters. We're not sure where to set the show. Rik's very keen on Cheltenham, and there's something Freudian about this choice – Rik, Maurice and I met in Cheltenham. Perhaps somewhere deep inside the three of us this evening, there is another, newer Alan B'Stard waiting to get out.

SUNDAY, 8 FEBRUARY

This afternoon it's Arsenal v. Chelsea once again, this time in a league match that both teams desperately want to win. Three

points would bring Chelsea to within one point of the league leaders, Manchester United, and would propel Arsenal back into the
title race. The battle between the two clubs at Stamford Bridge
earlier was the Premiership match of the season so far. Arsenal
have a strong line-up this afternoon, and are on a roll at the
moment. They haven't lost a league match since they were
defeated at home by Blackburn Rovers, and that was sometime in
early December. The team that takes the field is: Manninger,
Grimandi, Adams, Bould, Winterburn, Petit, Hughes, Parlour,
Bergkamp, Anelka and Overmars. Five of the eleven players are
foreign and I wonder whether Arsenal have ever fielded more foreign players in their team than they have this afternoon.

Within ten minutes Arsenal are one goal up, no thanks to
Anelka. The gazelle-like centre-forward is sent through the
Chelsea defence by a Franck Leboeuf mistake, and with only
the Chelsea goalkeeper to beat Anelka somehow manages to fire
the ball straight at him and fumble the rebound. When the ball
is cleared twenty yards to Stephen Hughes, the young midfielder fires into the back of the Chelsea net the most fearsome of
shots. This is Hughes's second goal against Chelsea in the past
fortnight.

The game becomes scrappy and ill-tempered with Gianluca
Vialli and Mark Hughes lucky to stay on the pitch after committing bloodcurdling fouls. But no one is more fortunate to be on the
field of play than Steve Bould, who pulls Vialli back when the
Chelsea striker is clean through on Manninger's goal. If the referee
awards a free kick to Chelsea, Bould must go. The referee does
award a free kick to Chelsea, but does not dismiss Bould. Nobody,
not even the Arsenal supporters around me, can understand just
why Bould is allowed to stay on the pitch. It's an extraordinary
decision but one that proves to be vital. Within twenty minutes of
this incident, Arsenal score a second. Stephen Hughes scores his
second! A beautiful cross from Bergkamp finds the head of Tony
Adams, who times a far-post run to perfection. Adams heads
across Chelsea's goalmouth and from nowhere Hughes comes in
to head his second goal of the match. Stephen Hughes is now on a
hat-trick, but he doesn't secure it.

The game becomes intensely bitter after that, feuding players
squaring up to each other, a catalogue of bookings, thankfully no
sendings off, but how I don't know. Arsenal are a hard bunch of

fellows and dish out as good as they get. Although Arsenal go in at half-time two goals ahead, as we learned in the Coca-Cola semi-final, to give a goal away in the second half can only put the Gunners under pressure. Halfway through the second half, Anelka is replaced by Ian Wright, much to the delight of every Arsenal fan in the stadium this afternoon, and Lee Dixon replaces Grimandi. Later on, Platt replaces an apparently out of sorts Marc Overmars, and Arsenal battle out their 2–0 victory. This means that despite the fact Manchester United lost at home to Leicester City last weekend, and could only draw at home to Bolton Wanderers this weekend (one point from six), no other of the chasing pack could make up points on United, for Liverpool and Blackburn seem to keep losing or drawing. Only Arsenal have done themselves any good by securing six out of six points. If Arsenal can win their two games in hand, they will find themselves just three points behind Manchester United, and suddenly the hope of winning the championship will be back on again.

Wednesday, 11 February

I would like to think that today will be the last day that Maurice and I become bogged down in the 'Mosley' publicity machine. We have to give three interviews today and then tomorrow the first episode is shown and I'm out of here as they say. Briggy laughs at this suggestion. She says that after tomorrow the recriminations begin and requests for interviews will start all over again. I know something – I don't think Maurice and I will ever again become so involved in a project from start to finish as we did with 'Mosley'.

The short interview for 'The Late Review' is perhaps the most amusing we've given for we don't take it seriously, which is perhaps the best way to give an interview. When asked for the 2046th time whether being Jewish helped write 'Mosley', I reply, 'I was only Jewish for the writing of the first episode. I was Moslem for the second episode, and converted to Catholicism for the third and fourth episodes.' The poor camerawoman-cum-interviewer doesn't really know whether I'm being serious or not, and the tone of the interview continues in this manner. Maurice tells her that we were brought up in Jewish houses. 'The houses were

Jewish, not those who lived in them . . .' I add, 'A man came around to take a slice from the roof. It wasn't so much a topping out, more a circumcision.'

THURSDAY, 12 FEBRUARY

For nine years I have been waiting for this day – 'Mosley' is being transmitted on British television. Everything has been building towards it, to unleash our serious work on the general public. Will they enjoy it? I don't know and I don't care. There will be many pigeon-holers gunning for Maurice and me. They will want to see failure so they can endorse their own feelings that those involved in situation comedy should stick to it and not attempt to cross the divide into drama.

For the second half of tonight's 'Goodnight Sweetheart' record-ing I have half an eye on the studio monitor and half an eye on the television. It's hugely exciting when the Channel Four announcer says: 'And now the start of our major new drama serial, from award-winning writers Laurence Marks and Maurice Gran, it's "Mosley".'

And when we come home we switch on BBC2 and watch 'The Late Review'. Tom Sutcliffe believes it's good, but we have set ourselves too many problems for everyone knows the ending; Mark Lawson and Suzanne Moore (who looks as though a gar-dener has turned her upside down and swept the grounds at Blenheim Palace with her) think it's excellent, the editor of 'Arena' patently doesn't understand what it is we're writing about and quite honestly makes a fool of himself on the programme. Furthermore, he misquotes Maurice and me and for this he should be ashamed of himself. But the general opinion is that this is a suc-cessful drama, written with style, elegance and pace, and I go to bed surprised by these critics' reactions, and on something of a high.

WEDNESDAY, 18 FEBRUARY

The Secretary General of the United Nations is going to Iraq today on yet another diplomatic mission. If Saddam Hussein does not accept what the United Nations put before him, military strikes on Baghdad will commence and who knows where this will lead? There has been talk that Iraq will strike back with attacks on the UK from bases in Libya and Algeria, but I don't know how reliable this piece of news is. I do know that all diplomacy seems not to have convinced Saddam Hussein so far. I can only hope that today's effort will be rewarded, for nobody, not even Saddam Hussein, can want war.

It's the ALOMO Christmas dinner – two months too late, but what can we do? Getting everyone all together in one place on one evening has proved to be extremely difficult, but tonight's the night. Of course, it's also the Coca-Cola Cup semi-finals second legs, and at Stamford Bridge Arsenal are playing Chelsea. They take with them a 2–1 lead from the first leg and will need all their guile and energy to go through to Wembley. Maurice and I listen to the first ten minutes of the match on the car radio, and we hear Arsenal go a goal behind in ten minutes. Now the game is all square. I wonder if Arsenal can hold out for eighty-eight minutes. I somehow doubt it. I wish I'd known before that the semi-finals were taking place tonight.

The tremendously enjoyable evening at Annabel's is marred when the receptionist tells us that Arsenal went down 3–1 to Chelsea tonight. Chelsea win 4–3 on aggregate and go to Wembley. Middlesbrough beat Liverpool 2–0 at their own ground, winning their semi-final 3–2 on aggregate. So the Coca-Cola Cup final will be a repeat of last season's FA Cup final – Middlesbrough v. Chelsea. Middlesbrough's result is far more impressive than Chelsea's. Most people will have bet on an Arsenal v. Liverpool final.

SATURDAY, 21 FEBRUARY

This afternoon I would usually be at Highbury; Arsenal have a home match against Crystal Palace (whom I saw at Highbury last Sunday), but for the second time in a month I have decided to put my wife before the Arsenal and miss the game. It is imperative that Arsenal (this afternoon playing with nine non-regulars) win and so maintain their chase for the title. At the end of the season, I think it will be only Arsenal that prevents this season's championship race containing just the one horse.

Arsenal do win, by the only goal of the game scored by Gilles Grimandi, and so move into second place, nine points behind Manchester United but with two games in hand, which as everyone realises must be won. In not too many weeks' time, Arsenal play at Old Trafford in what could prove to be the decisive match of the season. If Arsenal can go to Manchester and nick three points, they will be in a superb position to go on and take the title. Cloud cuckoo land again. No, I still think Manchester United will win the title. They are clearly the richest and best equipped club in the Premier League, and I don't think another club will remove United's mantle.

THURSDAY, 26 FEBRUARY

At just before midday Maurice asks me to go to Charlbury to collect Rik Mayall off the 12.11 train from Paddington. He's coming to talk about the new private detective series we discussed the other day. Maurice and I are going to propose it to the BBC. So off I go to Charlbury station – small and cute, like something out of an Agatha Christie. But when the train pulls in only about half a dozen people get off none of whom is Rik Mayall. Surely he didn't miss the train. With Rik, of course, anything is possible. The station master, seeing my confusion, asks me if I have lost someone. I tell him that I was expecting a friend and I'm certain he would have caught this train as this was the train we asked him to catch.

'He's probably missed his stop. He'll get off at Kingham. I bet you he's locked in the toilet. Lots of people do that, you know. That or else they fall off to sleep.'

After an exchange of emergency telephone calls, it transpires that Rik is at Kingham station. He locked himself in the toilet. Didn't realise that the train had passed Charlbury. Good to know that in one respect at least, Rik is like lots of people!

FRIDAY, 27 FEBRUARY

Yesterday Rik Mayall, today Adam Faith. Adam, whom it's always a joy to see, has come to discuss 'Grand Prix', a projected new drama series for BBC1. We would like to produce a 'Dallas'-like series with style, charisma, internationalism, excitement; a sexy weekly series that hooks both men and women.

We take Adam off to the Royal Oak – he has a penchant for puddings, both savoury and as a dessert, and they do magnificent ones there – to talk about the character he will play. We are looking for new characters for Rik and Adam that will play to their strengths yet be totally different from Alan B'Stard and Frank Carver (Adam's role in 'Love Hurts'). Is it possible? I don't know. I suppose it rather depends on the programme, and both are so very different in their styles and intentions. It is exciting though.

MONDAY, 2 MARCH

In London with time on my hands, I decide to revisit Selborne Road. On this wet, grey and lifeless afternoon, the memories come flooding back. Number 58, where I lived and worked for eleven years, hasn't changed very much, at least from the outside. Where I had blinds there are now curtains. Behind those blinds, my life went from a dishonest happiness to a full-blown depression and sadness; yet I have some delightfully happy memories, too. Now I find it small and sad. How grey and suburban it all is, but I never thought so when I lived there. I never felt that suburbia was getting me down; probably because I knew nothing else. My entire life had been suburban.

As I stare across the back gardens, I remember the view I had from my office window, and I remember the joys and traumas that occurred in that office-cum-bedroom, particularly with Briggy, not with Sue. Our traumas seemed to be confined to the front room. Oh, the memories and the tears left behind in Selborne Road.

Maurice and I are visiting our friends Alan and Jackie Field this evening for dinner and West Ham v. Arsenal. The four of us sit around the dining table and have what I would call a warm and Jewish weeknight supper. It's all very familiar, although it's been a long time since either of us was invited to such an occasion. West Ham and Arsenal battle out a tight goalless draw, although both sides have ample opportunities to score the goal that would have given them three points. Consequently, it seems like Arsenal have dropped two points rather than gained one. Upton Park has been a graveyard for visiting teams this season.

Manchester United sit comfortably eleven points clear at the peak of the Premier League and the betting has been closed for United to become champions again. Betting is open only for the runners-up place. Arsenal are favourites. Has Maurice put on his bet for Arsenal to win the Double? Mad fool! I think closing the betting is idiotic; United could lose two matches easily, Arsenal could win at Old Trafford. But it is Arsenal's away form, and the teams they have to meet (United, Blackburn and Liverpool), that has led bookmakers to believe that Manchester United are dead certainties.

SUNDAY, 8 MARCH

The lunchtime debating society – meeting up with a group of friends before the game – is often more interesting than the game itself, and today is no exception. It's the FA Cup quarter-final. Yesterday Leeds United were knocked out by Wolves; Sheffield United almost beat Coventry City and have a replay at Bramall Lane which they could well win; so Arsenal beating West Ham would make them favourites. But overcoming West Ham is not going to be easy – they haven't beaten West Ham in a Cup match since the War.

Manninger, Dixon, Adams, Keown, Winterburn, Vieira, Petit, Parlour, Overmars, Bergkamp and Anelka are the eleven who begin this Cup tie. The atmosphere is magnificent. The entire south end of the ground is occupied by West Ham supporters. Within a minute, Arsenal nearly score when Bergkamp fires in a viciously dipping free kick, but Bernard Lama, the French international goalkeeper, on loan to West Ham, makes a brilliant save. West Ham take the lead after twelve minutes – Ian Pearce scores when a West Ham corner isn't cleared and he shoots low past Manninger.

The Hammers break away, tearing Arsenal's defence apart, Eyal Berkovic takes a pass five yards from goal with only Manninger to beat, but can't control the ball. That should have been 2–0 and West Ham would definitely have gone through to the semi-finals.

As it is, Arsenal equalise with a penalty. Keown is chopped

down by Pearce, and Bergkamp scores with ease, even past Lama, probably the finest goalkeeper I have seen at Highbury all season long. At 1–1 I have to fancy Arsenal, but Anelka is really holding play up and is, to be brutally honest, a wasted player. In the second half he is replaced, and not before time, by Christopher Wreh, who is immediately far more effective. His running stretches the West Ham defence, but nevertheless the game finishes a dull and lifeless draw.

So West Ham and Arsenal are to meet again, for the fifth time this season, the third time at Upton Park. Arsenal have won one and drawn one – is it now time for them to lose one? I hope not.

The semi-final draw, made ludicrously before the start of the other quarter-final between Newcastle and Barnsley, pairs the teams thus: Coventry City or Sheffield United v. Newcastle United or Barnsley; Wolverhampton Wanderers v. West Ham or Arsenal.

Newcastle beat Barnsley 3–1. Who do I think will make it to the semi-finals? Well, I expect Coventry City and Arsenal to win their replays, and an Arsenal v. Newcastle United final, for the third time this century. Arsenal didn't win either of the other two, losing 2–1 and 1–0. But Wolves will be no push-over in the semi-finals, that is if Arsenal can win at Upton Park, which they won't if the lifeless and lazy Nicolas Anelka is chosen to lead the attack. I don't know what's wrong with him, why he feels he cannot perform in an Arsenal shirt. He has all the attributes of a great player; it seems to me that he wishes he didn't have to do this job for a living, such is his attitude.

WEDNESDAY, 11 MARCH

On my walk home from an evening engagement, I imagine Arsenal have won at Wimbledon by 2–0, and that Manchester United have been beaten by West Ham by the same result. Wishful thinking. When I arrive back at Clarges Street and check with Ceefax, Arsenal have taken three points from Wimbledon, winning 1–0, the goal scored by Christopher Wreh, and Man United have been held to a 1–1 draw by West Ham. This means Arsenal are now nine points behind Manchester United, with three games in hand (nine points, of course, should Arsenal win all of them).

On Saturday morning, Arsenal meet Manchester United. I'm

one of the very few who believe Arsenal can win this game. Why shouldn't they? If they do, they will be six points behind United with three games in hand and the title would be a real possibility. On the other hand, I can't see Arsenal winning all the matches they have left, especially away to Blackburn and Liverpool – although Blackburn got a 4–0 thrashing by Leeds United tonight. Most pleasing of all was to see that Barnsley have beaten Aston Villa 1–0 at Villa Park, and move closer to Premier League survival – at the expense of Tottenham Hotspur maybe? Oh, I do hope so.

SATURDAY, 14 MARCH

It's quarter-past ten in the morning and the throng of football fans standing in the enormous wasteland that is the home of Manchester United football club are behaving as if it were half-past two in the afternoon. They are eating fish and chips, they are supping pints of lager, cans of beer, and are in the liveliest of moods. I've been to Old Trafford once before but Maurice has never been here. This morning is not typical. How many fans get the opportunity to be guests of the directors of the club at any time in their lives, let alone on their first visit? We are the guests of Greg Dyke, non-executive director of Manchester United.

Greg takes us through the crowds to the door of the directors' entrance, and from there we make our way past commissionaires and security folk to the boardroom. Everyone is charming and friendly, and we are introduced to Peter Hill-Wood, the Arsenal Chairman, and renew our acquaintance with Ken Friar, the club's managing director and an 'uncle' to David Stanton, our old mate. Being there, in that atmosphere of welcome and kindness, is the most wonderful feeling. For reasons I haven't ever explored, Arsenal seems to have become a part of my family, like an old cousin I've known very well for the better part of my life.

I also get to meet Sir Bobby Charlton. There are hardly any people I would call 'Sir', but one is Bobby Charlton. As it happens I call him nothing at all. This man was perhaps England's greatest-ever footballer. He won everything there was to win – World Cup, European Cup, the league title, the FA Cup – and is England's all-time greatest goalscorer. Now he's a great ambassador for the sport, a boy who survived the Munich air crash and then blos-

Emmanuel Petit's goal against Derby County in the game I believe effectively won us the league title in 1997–98.

Briggy and me with the silverware. I wonder whether I shall ever again have the chance of being photographed with this collection of trophies.

Nicolas Anelka's goal against Newcastle, which took us to the Double.

The management. Above: *Bruce Rioch at the press conference announcing his appointment as manager in 1995 (left). Caretaker manager Stewart Houston in full voice in 1996.* Below: *A pensive Arsene Wenger (left) and his assistant, Pat Rice (right).*

Arsene Wenger parades his new signings Emmanuel Petit and Marc Overmars in June 1997.

Ian Wright celebrates his 179th goal, scored in the 4–1 win against Bolton Wanderers in the 1997–98 season, which topped Cliff Bastin's longstanding goalscoring record.

The magnificent back five that always served us so well. Opposite page: *Lee Dixon (far left), Nigel Winterburn (left) and Martin Keown (below).* Above: *David Seaman.* Right: *Tony Adams, pictured with the author at Arsenal's training ground in April 1999.*

David Platt's winning goal in the 3–2 victory against Manchester United at Highbury during our Double season . . .

. . . and Marc Overmars scores the only goal of the game at Old Trafford the following season in another success against United.

The players celebrate Alex Manninger's crucial penalty save against West Ham in the quarter-final of the FA Cup at Upton Park in 1998.

Lord Bragg of Wigton being searched by one of the 'uncouth' and ineffectual French riot police before the match against Lens in France in September 1998.

Arsenal vice-chairman David Dein and the author by the statue at Babi Yar, Kiev. For once football was the furthest thing from our minds as we tried to come to terms with the Nazi massacre of the Jews in this region.

COLORSPORT

The moment – the only moment – when I thought this could be our year in Europe: Dennis Bergkamp's flying header against Dinamo Kiev at Wembley.

I took the incredible Jennifer d'Abo to her first-ever football match: Arsenal v. Panathinaikos at Wembley. It was through her that my dream of sitting in the Arsenal directors' box came true.

Joshua Eichler, the son of my late, great guru Udi, pictured in his new Arsenal shirt in front of Wembley Stadium, where I took him to see Arsenal play Dinamo Kiev in the 1998–99 season.

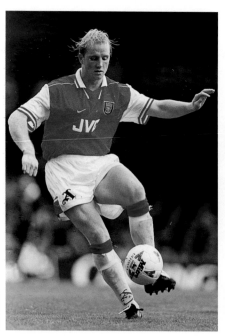

Among 'the ones that got away', the players Mr Wenger let go, were John Hartson (left) and Glenn Helder.

somed, a man who was never once booked in his lengthy career. We talk about this morning's match. If Manchester United win, they have virtually won this year's title; but if Arsenal win, the race is well and truly on. Bobby Charlton tells me how every match here at Old Trafford is an important one, with the same pressures for his team. He thinks it will be a very closely fought contest, and being far too wise about the game of soccer he doesn't predict a result and I don't ask him to. I just look at him and wonder, for a man who is much smaller than I thought he was, where did all his power come from? I suppose it was an inner desire to achieve everything there was to achieve. I don't believe I have often stood and spoken to a legend, so today must be a milestone for me. I have now met the two footballers who, more than any others, gave me so much delight as a schoolboy – Bobby Charlton and Jimmy Greaves – and so this schoolboy's dreams have been realised.

I savour the atmosphere of the boardroom and wonder what major decisions have been taken here, which managers' and players' careers made or destroyed. I imagine the conversations that took place in this room between Matt Busby and other managers of the club and Georgie Best. At one point the championship trophy is brought into the boardroom and two young boys are photographed with it. The child in me wants to be photographed with the trophy too, but the adult in me knows that to ask for such would be embarrassing. I wonder if Maurice feels the same way as I do?

I wonder, too, what it would have been like to be a young Manchester United player, signed from school and about to embark on what might be the most successful of careers, doing something that you love for a living. Would you be called into this room to sign your contract? What would you be told? What would life be like for you? I drift in and out of this fantasy – it is what I once wanted more than anything else in the whole wide world. What I became may be better, of course, but then, when I was thirteen or fourteen years old, football was the be-all and end-all of ambition.

Arsene Wenger is in the boardroom but nobody introduces us, and I can hardly be expected to go over and introduce myself. He is a tall, slim and fit-looking man, talking to a colleague in French. Ken Friar, who is so friendly and helpful when I ask him how I might obtain shares in the Arsenal Football Club, tells me a story that bears repeating. At Arsene Wenger's first press conference, having given a fairly comprehensive overview of how he would like the future of the club to move, a journalist asked him whether he speaks any other language? 'I am speaking yours', was the reply, and the journalist was put firmly in his place.

Arsenal have three excellent chances in the first half of the match. Two fall at the feet of Marc Overmars, who is by far the best player on the field, and he narrowly misses both. But the best chance for Arsenal to go in a goal to the good at half-time comes about when Ray Parlour breaks into the Manchester United penalty box, draws Schmeichel from his goalline, and then shoots over the bar. Mind you, United have two golden opportunities, both falling to Andy Cole. Lee Dixon, for reasons known only to Lee Dixon, plays a ball right into the path of Cole, with nobody around him, but Manninger, Arsenal's wonderful young goal-keeper, comes quickly off his line and makes a remarkable save. The next chance comes when an Arsenal attack breaks down, with Adams and Keown forward. The ball is played to Cole, whom Dixon and Winterburn believe to be offside (he isn't), Cole dashes forward and again Manninger foils him with a wonderful save. So although Arsenal have been the better team during the first half, a scoreline of 2–2 would not have been inappropriate.

Arsenal are in control for most of the second half. They may not attack as much as they did in the first half, but they are in control. Their defence and midfield never seem to be in any obvious danger, and Manchester United's danger men, Teddy Sheringham, Cole, David Beckham and Paul Scholes, are kept very quiet by Vieira and Petit. There is a period about ten minutes into the second half when United begin to look their old selves and I think that a goal is coming. Sheringham steps up a gear and becomes much more involved in the attack, but in truth Manninger doesn't have another serious save to make.

The breakthrough comes in the seventy-ninth minute. Anelka, who has been brought on for Christopher Wreh, nods a ball into the path of the ever-threatening Marc Overmars. The Dutch winger's speed takes him past defenders, into the United penalty box, and this time as Schmeichel comes off his line Overmars cracks a low shot past the goalkeeper and into the net. Arsenal have scored at a critical time in the match, and deserve to be in the lead.

Of course, from this point United throw all they have forward at Arsenal's outstanding defence – old but still formidable. There are one or two minor scares, not least when Keown brings down Sheringham on the edge of the box and is in danger of being sent off. He isn't, but United gain a free kick about fifteen yards from Arsenal's goal. Beckham, who is easily capable of scoring from this distance, steps up and sends his bending free kick over the bar. With ninety minutes long past (it seems when Manchester United are a goal down at home, every referee allows between four and eight minutes injury time, and so it is this morning) United gain a corner. Schmeichel comes up into Arsenal's penalty box to score the equaliser. He doesn't, and as the ball is cleared and he is running back towards his own goal, he pulls up and it is apparent he has damaged his leg. In fact he's torn his hamstring and will be out not only for Manchester United's European Champions Cup quarter-final against Monaco on Wednesday, but probably for the remainder of the season. The final whistle blows and Arsenal have quite remarkably, although deservedly, won. I think they are the first team since the Premier League was founded in 1993 to have beaten Manchester United home and away. The last time, I am reminded, that Arsenal won at Old Trafford it was also 1–0, the goal being scored by a foreign winger (Anders Limpar), and that season Arsenal went on to win the title. Is this a good omen?

I'm thrilled with the result. I did believe Arsenal would come to Old Trafford and take all three points. I also think that they will go to Upton Park on Tuesday night and go out of the FA Cup. Surely the Arsenal will not pull off the Double? All the Arsenal supporters and directors are overjoyed, while the Manchester United contingent are mortified, not just by this morning's score and the threat Arsenal now pose to United's championship hopes, but also by the loss of form (one point in three matches) and the prospect of the European Champions Cup match on Wednesday night, for Monaco are now probably favourites.

We're back at Euston by five o'clock and the first things we want to know are what is the Spurs v. Liverpool result? Have Everton beaten Blackburn? The answers turns out to be 3–3, and yes, 1–0. I think unless something goes drastically wrong Arsenal will finish this season as champions or runners-up, although there is still a long way to go. If they do, they will qualify for the

European Champions League and we should see some fun and games at Highbury next season.

Totteridge is this evening's destination to celebrate Linda Robson reaching the big four-O. The party is being held in the same large golf club where Linda and Mark had their wedding reception. The birthday cake depicts a sitting room with three figures on a sofa – Dorien, Sharon and Tracey. It's almost a shame to cut such a magnificent birthday cake and destroy all the careful work that has gone into making it.

Right Said Fred and Paul Young are providing the entertainment but Briggy and I are going home to Spring Hill, where we have not been together since the middle of the week, and at about half-past ten Briggy wants to go. Now this is a shame as the party really seems to be livening up, and the East End and Islington crowd really know how to party. I would have liked to stay around to see it alight.

TUESDAY, 17 MARCH

It's our neighbour Caroline's birthday today, and she and Duncan Wu invite us back to Sunny Cottage to enjoy a piece of her birthday cake. Out comes a huge chocolate cake. It's rich and delicious, and something we all know that we shouldn't be eating. In my case, it will add inches to an already expanding waistline. I'm often torn between eating what I like and thinking about my waist – I always eat what I like for one day I shall die and then it will be time to lose weight.

Over tea and cake, we discuss Duncan's book about writers and directors who form partnerships in the theatre. He has already interviewed Richard Eyre and David Hare, and I'm curious to know what was his first question to David Hare.

'What is your favourite colour?' Duncan joked.

I can't help expanding on this thought. 'Alexander Solzhenitsyn, world famous writer and Soviet dissident imprisoned from 1945 to 1953 for unfavourable comment on Stalin's conduct of the war, author of *One Day in the Life of Ivan Denisovich*, *Cancer Ward*, *The First Circle* and *The Gulag Archipelago*, winner of the 1970 Nobel Prize for Literature, the Templeton Prize for Progress in

Religion, and the Russian State Literature Prize in 1990 – who is your favourite Spice Girl?' It has Duncan in waves of laughter. It touches that funny bone and tickles it for several minutes, and as laughter is infectious, we all finish up eating cake, drinking tea, and laughing like drains.

Tonight Briggy and I go to the Comedy Theatre to see 'A Letter of Resignation', a new play by Hugh Whitemore. It's about Harold Macmillan, a man who in the rush of Swinging London seemed outdated and irrelevant, even though he was the Prime Minister, the last of the Edwardians, if you like. An Edwardian grandee lingering uncomfortably in the world of E-type Jaguars, Carnaby Street, the Beatles and TW3. Few were aware that his life was scarred by domestic unhappiness and sexual betrayal by his wife Lady Dorothy. This play explores the events that lay hidden behind the Profumo scandal and subsequent resignation of the Minister of War, and examines a complex web of personal and political morality.

Afterwards, it's straight home to Oxfordshire. At midnight, I'm in the Cattle Shed collecting the tape I hope has recorded tonight's vital FA Cup sixth-round replay between West Ham and Arsenal, and a minute or two later I'm alone in the living room glued to the screen, thankfully having no idea of the result. After half an hour, Dennis Bergkamp is sent off for elbowing Steve Lomas in the face after the West Ham player was holding on to the Dutchman's shirt. Why? Why did Bergkamp do this? Was something said to him? Right at the end of the first half, Arsenal score a brilliant goal. Vieira charges forward with the ball, it is interplayed with Anelka, and the eighteen-year-old fires in a spectacular goal from outside the West Ham penalty box, past the remarkable Bernard Lama. It is a goal of such international class that for just one moment I believe that Anelka might be as gifted as David Dein said he is. At Old Trafford last week, I asked David why Anelka was bought. 'He is brilliant from the toes to the nose. Once we get his head right, he will be superb,' was the reply. Anelka has certainly scored at the best possible time.

With only five minutes of the second half left to play, and with Arsenal defending quite magnificently and still leading 1–0, West Ham equalise through ex-Arsenal player, John Hartson. His low shot seems to find Manninger unsighted and the ball creeps in between Manninger's outstretched right hand and the near post. At full-time, it's West Ham 1 Arsenal's ten men 1. I sit with all eight fingers in my mouth during extra time, and when the final whistle blows no more goals have been scored. So as with the Port Vale v. Arsenal match, the game will be decided by penalties. Showing enormous restraint, I do not fast-forward but sit on the edge of my seat and pray that Arsenal score all five of theirs. I saw West Ham put out Blackburn Rovers on penalties and the Hammers were marvellous and very accurate. Stephen Hughes scores the first kick, and David Unsworth does likewise. Then Christopher Wreh misses his kick and I think Arsenal are out and bite down to the quick of my left index finger. However, John Hartson hits the post with his kick. Luis Boa Morte puts Arsenal 2–1 ahead, but Steve Lomas equalises. Remi Garde fires low and wide, but West Ham fail to capitalise when Manninger saves the next Hammers kick. After five kicks have been taken the match is poised at 3–3, each team having missed two penalties. Now it's sudden death. Tony Adams steps up and fires a low shot right down the middle of West Ham's goal, with Lama moving to his right, thank goodness. Samassi Abou steps up to keep West Ham in the game but hits the post!!!

Arsenal have won their quarter-final, but what a cruel way for West Ham to be eliminated. Abou is distraught, and the camera pans around to see West Ham supporters in tears. Arsenal supporters are ecstatic, and I'm in a state of near exhaustion. We are in the semi-final against Wolves, which we should win. The double is still a remote possibility, and with Arsenal having lost just one game in 1998 – against Chelsea in the Coca-Cola Cup – I think the bookmakers will reduce Arsenal's price drastically. I wonder what Maurice stands to win.

Tonight Sheffield United beat Coventry City by 3–1 on penalties, after the game finished goalless. Now Sheffield United, the most unlikely of semi-finalists, will play Newcastle United and who is to say they can't beat the Geordies. If they do, and Arsenal beat Wolves, we shall have a repeat of the 1936 Cup final. We can only hope for the same result – 1–0 to the Arsenal.

SATURDAY, 28 MARCH

We take our seats just in time for the kick-off against Sheffield Wednesday. Arsenal's team is: Seaman (back for the first time in about ten weeks), Dixon, Adams, Keown, Winterburn, Parlour, Vieira, Hughes, Wreh, Bergkamp and Overmars.

Arsenal dominate the first half, with Overmars giving the Wednesday defenders nightmares with his pace. Unfortunately none of his crosses seem to reach the unmarked Arsenal man in Wednesday's penalty box and so we do not benefit from Overmars's amazing skill. Wreh hits the bar with a header, Adams just fails to connect with a Bergkamp corner (this is Dennis's last game before his three-week suspension, and with him missing I can't work out who is to score the goals) and Parlour comes very close with a shot. With about ten minutes of the half left, Overmars once again receives the ball, moves forward to begin a run but instead opts for a cross that Bergkamp, sneaking into the Wednesday penalty area, reaches, controls and as calm as you like drives past Kevin Pressman, the Wednesday goalkeeper.

The second half is tense. Arsenal are unable to capitalise on their solitary goal and there are times when the defence goes to sleep, although they haven't conceded a league goal in eleven hours of football. Wednesday have two golden chances; one is blocked by Winterburn, the other flies just over Seaman's crossbar. Bergkamp nearly scores the goldenest goal of the season, but somehow or other Pressman gets his fingertips to the delightful chip, after Bergkamp has managed somehow to beat four surrounding Sheffield defenders.

There are no more goals and Arsenal gain another three points. Pity is, so do Manchester United and Liverpool – United win 2–0 at home to Wimbledon, but not without a struggle, and Liverpool win a bizarre match at Oakwell against Barnsley, 3–2. Barnsley have three players sent off and finish the game with eight men, and the referee decides to leave the pitch in the middle of the second half, without telling the players or his fellow officials what he's doing. There are pitch invasions and ugly scenes just before and after the final whistle, and were I a Barnsley fan I think I should have been incensed by the quality of refereeing during this match. If nothing else changes in the game of football, we must start training professional referees, and even having second opinions from neutrals, as there is in cricket. Perhaps two referees, or four linesmen?

I hear on David Mellor's 'Six–0–Six' that a Fulham supporter was murdered outside the ground at Gillingham this afternoon. Reports are scant at the moment, but the Kent police have confirmed that after running battles in the street, a young football fan was either kicked or stabbed to death. It has been a gloomy afternoon for football, and so close to the World Cup. Here is an interesting dilemma for the government. In Hyde Park, where 25,000 people turn out for a decriminalisation of cannabis march, there is no trouble at all, everyone no doubt feeling intensely mellow, while in Gillingham a young fan is murdered and at Barnsley there's a pitch invasion and the referee might have been killed had the Barnsley fans reached him, this behaviour fuelled by alcohol. Yet still this government, or any government, find it hard to realise that one (cannabis) is a good drug, and the other (alcohol) is a very bad drug.

TUESDAY, 31 MARCH

Tonight Arsenal travel up to Bolton Wanderers. Much to my amazement, they win 1–0, with a goal scored by Christopher Wreh. Martin Keown is sent off early in the second half for a second bookable offence, though I know not what it is, and Marc Overmars, injured in minute two of the first half, is deemed extremely doubtful for Sunday's semi-final against Wolves. So Arsenal might well line up without Bergkamp, Wright or Overmars. This is a damning blow and one can only pray that Overmars's injury isn't as serious as is now feared, that he makes a miraculous recovery and turns out on Sunday afternoon. Perhaps Arsene Wenger is playing a deep psychological game with the Wolves management, but somehow I think not. Whether we reach Wembley for the Cup final will rest heavily and squarely upon the shoulders of Nicolas Anelka, Christopher Wreh and Luis Boa Morte. Please God they don't let us down, and that they play so inspirationally that they will demand a place in the Cup final.

WEDNESDAY, 1 APRIL

Richard Wilson, a Scotsman from Greenock, bears little resemblance to his most famous character, Victor Meldrew. When we meet for lunch, he is elegantly dressed and elegantly spoken, but at the same time I can imagine him as Conrad Shakespeare, the character Maurice and I hope to create for him in 'Sidney's Kidney'. Maurice and I feel that Richard would be dead right for this part, for it must be the polar opposite of the old curmudgeon, Victor Meldrew. Richard tells us that nearly everything he gets sent to read these days is about grumpy old characters, and what interests him so much about Conrad is that this man is vivacious, with a love of life that will, undoubtedly, kill him in the end. And Conrad's life would go in the direction it is pointing were it not for the fact that nephew Sidney enters it and is more than a little protective of his donated kidney. I find Richard good company and I can imagine having a very easy and exciting working relationship with him.

This is a positive lunch; Geoffrey Jenkins, the BBC's Head of Comedy, is there too. It's positive in the same way that the lunch with Nick Lyndhurst was when we talked through 'Goodnight Sweetheart'. Nick is one of the most professional and talented men I have ever worked with, and his contribution to 'Goodnight Sweetheart' cannot be overestimated.

I look forward to meeting Richard again once the script is written, and listening to what notes he may have for us, for I always feel that is the truest test of all of an actor's instincts. I remember the brilliant working relationship we forged with Rik Mayall, quite unlike any other, and that produced comedy of the very highest quality. I should like to create another comedy that becomes a cult show; perhaps we might pull it off with 'Sidney's Kidney'. It feels to me as if it could be that type of show.

SUNDAY, 5 APRIL

FA Cup semi-finals day. I always look forward to it for I believe it to be the most exciting day in the football calendar, especially when one of the four remaining teams in the competition is your own. At midday (an unusual time to play a football match, but the

demands of television scheduling are more important than footballers' welfare) Arsenal meet Wolverhampton Wanderers, in a
repeat of the 1979 semi-final. At the more usual time of three
o'clock, Newcastle United take on Sheffield United. It is unusual
for two Premier clubs to be matched with two teams from the first
division, but perhaps that means that the gap between the two
divisions is closing all the while.

If Arsenal go through, it will be their first FA Cup final since
they won the trophy in 1993, and then only after a replay. I remember that night with clarity. Maurice, Briggy and I watched the
replay in Allan McKeown's Derby Street home, and we sat for 120
minutes watching a boring, goalless match, until in the final seconds Andy Linighan scored with a header and brought the FA
Cup to Highbury. The following season, Arsenal brought the Cup-
Winners' Cup back to Highbury too, and the fans all felt that this
would be the start of something big. Then George Graham was
found out, and a new unexpected beginning was thrust upon the
Arsenal which, as things have turned out, has led to a very exciting time.

Arsenal, with Overmars having passed a late fitness test, completely overrun Wolves in the first half. After thirteen minutes, a
bad clearance from Hans Segers, the Wolves goalkeeper, arrives at
the feet of Vieira (today's man of the match by a long chalk). The
lanky Frenchman runs from almost the centre circle into the
Wolves penalty area and slips a sideways pass into the path of
Christopher Wreh who, with all the coolness of a Brazilian, side
foots the ball around Segers and Arsenal are 1–0 up. Wreh must
surely be the first Liberian ever to score a goal in the FA Cup semi-
final. Wolves must score two to win the match, supposing that
Arsenal do not score again, which they almost do through Parlour.
I can't see Wolves scoring at all, let alone twice, especially against
a defence who haven't let in a goal for about thirteen hours. At
half-time Arsenal are in complete control, lead 1–0, and look as
though they will be at Wembley in May. In the second half everything looks so different. Have the Arsenal defence taken a nap in
the dressing-room and not quite woken up? Wolves nearly score in
the first minute when Steve Claridge steams in unguarded and
fires his shot straight at an unsuspecting Seaman. Moments later,
Seaman comes for what seems to everyone in the Villa Park stadium an elementary catch, but drops the ball right at the feet of

Don Goodman. The Wolves striker could and should have equalised, but a last-ditch tackle by Petit sends the ball for a corner. What a let-off!

When the final whistle blows, Arsenal are the 1–0 winners and must wait until twenty minutes to five to learn whom they will meet at Wembley. The Double is still a possibility but no more than that, although the bookmakers believe Arsenal can do it with more ease than Arsene Wenger believes is likely. I think Arsenal are 7–2 to win the Double. I suppose you could say that if they do no more than win the next seven matches, they will emulate the Arsenal team of 1970–71, but that is an enormous if.

It turns out to be an Arsenal v. Newcastle United final, and not for the first time. In 1932, Newcastle won 2–1, in that famous 'over the line' final, when a ball was crossed from which Newcastle scored a vital goal. Then in 1952, Newcastle won 1–0. Arsenal, playing with ten men for the best part of the final, fought bravely but lost to a George Robledo goal. Third time lucky? Well, everyone seems to think so. Football pundits feel Arsenal are by far the better team and with Ian Wright, Dennis Bergkamp and a fit (unlike this afternoon) Marc Overmars, Newcastle won't present too many problems. But Cup finals are strange events and nobody, not even the players, know just how they will react to playing on the famous Wembley turf. I think, and I hope I'm not pushing my luck here, that Arsenal will take this portion of the Double. An indication of how the two teams will shape up comes on Saturday at Highbury – Arsenal v. Newcastle United. It is astonishing how many times this happens. I won't predict a result for the Cup final. I just think Arsenal want it so badly, besides which, they are a damned good side.

SATURDAY, 11 APRIL

I'm stunned to hear on the 'Today' programme that Rik Mayall has been rushed to hospital, where he is now in intensive care with serious head injuries. His condition is described as 'stable', but the very fact he's in intensive care means his life could be in danger. It seems that Rik was out on a quad bike at their house in Devon, and while taking the bike at speed up a grassy bank, Rik lost control and it overturned. Now he's fighting for his life in

Devon and I'm deeply concerned for him, Barbara and their children. It is so infuriating when all you know is what you hear on the news, particularly when the news involves somebody who you feel close to.

At Highbury this afternoon, Maurice and I start off on the edge of our seats, but Newcastle pose little threat. The smooth, efficient and inspired team of Seaman, Garde, Adams, Bould, Winterburn, Parlour, Petit, Vieira, Anelka, Wreh and Overmars gets to work to finish off the Geordies as soon as possible. Newcastle, though, have the first marvellous moment when Steve Bould hits a back pass that's too hard for Seaman to control. He slips and with Shearer bearing down on him, has to pick up the ball, thus giving Newcastle a free kick seven yards from Arsenal's goalline and dead central. Arsenal form a wall on the goalline, and as Warren Barton taps the ball to Alan Shearer, the Arsenal wall charge at the shot and the ball flies away for a throw-in. Phew, that was close!

Anelka hits the post from an impossible angle, when he takes the ball past Shay Given, but the rebound runs away too fast and Anelka does well to reach it at all. After that, Anelka scores with a splendid low shot, reminiscent of Andy Cole's goal for Manchester United against Blackburn Rovers the other night.

Arsenal dominate the second half with as beautiful a display of football as I have seen them play since October – and this without their two star strikers, Wright and Bergkamp, which begs the question where will the two fit in when they return from injury and suspension? Fluent ground-passing takes Newcastle apart. When Ray Parlour (yes, he is the most improved player at Highbury, of that I am certain) cuts between Stuart Pearce and David Batty on a mazy run, he sends over a low cross for Anelka to score. Patrick Vieira scores Arsenal's third, and it must be rated as Arsenal's 'goal of the season at Highbury'. Vieira wins the ball near the centre circle, runs towards the Newcastle penalty area and, from thirty yards, lazily hits a fierce and swerving shot that gives Shay Given no chance at all. The ball flies into the top right-hand corner. This is truly continental and a joy to watch. I have to say here and now that I never thought I would ever see this quality of soccer coming from Arsenal.

Unfortunately, Warren Barton scores a goal for Newcastle United, thus putting an end to the possibility of Arsenal beating the club record of not having conceded a goal in thirteen hours of league play. Arsenal do, though, score a fourth, through Luis Boa Morte, but for reasons I can't fathom, the referee disallows the goal. Perhaps I'll understand why when I watch tonight's 'Match of the Day'. It's an easy 3–1 victory, and a most welcome three points. The situation now is that we're four points behind Manchester United with three games in hand.

MONDAY, 13 APRIL

At half past five, Maurice and I finish work and settle down in front of the office television to watch what might well turn out to be the match that decides whether Arsenal might really win the Premier League title. That we are thinking about this possibility at all is almost a miracle, for on Boxing Day Arsenal were thirteen points adrift of Manchester United. Should they win this evening, they will be one point adrift with two matches in hand. But Blackburn Rovers at Ewood Park isn't a game I relish at this stage of the season. No match at this stage is an easy game, it's just that some are easier than others.

At six o'clock, the teams kick off and at two minutes past six Arsenal are a goal up through Dennis Bergkamp. Much to Maurice's and my amazement, before the hands of the clock have reached quarter-past six, Arsenal are three goals up! Yes, three goals up! Ray Parlour bangs in the second, after receiving a pass made in heaven from Bergkamp, and on the fourteenth minute Petit fires his corner out of the Blackburn penalty area to Bergkamp, who shoots low and with venom. Alan Fettis, the Blackburn goalkeeper, can't hold the shot. The rebound goes to Parlour who smashes the ball high into the Blackburn net. Effectively, the game is over. There isn't any way in the world that Blackburn are going to score four goals without Arsenal adding to their total. With three minutes of the first half left to play, Winterburn sends a long and very accurate pass up the field, Anelka (improving by the minute – yes, I was wrong about the French teenager) latches on to the ball, runs with frightening pace between Colin Hendry and Stephane Henchoz, draws Fettis from his goalline, dummies him, goes round him and bangs the ball into the unguarded net. At half-time the score, quite unbelievably, to me at least, reads Blackburn Rovers 0 Arsenal 4.

The second half is played in a snowstorm. The white ball is changed for an orange one, so everyone can see the play, and there are moments when I think the match will be abandoned, which would be a travesty. Blackburn, who know they can't win this game, must play for their pride and to prevent Arsenal getting a record away win. Kevin Gallacher pulls one back for Blackburn ten minutes into the half, with the snow falling as you would expect it to fall in a Siberian winter. Arsenal regroup and play a holding game. At the end of ninety minutes, the game now being played in sunshine with no sign of snow, the score is Blackburn 1 Arsenal 4.

This is championship form and nobody, not even the most ardent Manchester United supporter, can deny Arsenal's right to challenge for the title Manchester United believe to be theirs by right. Arsenal have been the finest team in the country since the turn of the year. I think the reason for it is quite simply they are playing a style of football that has only ever been played in this country perhaps twice before. I don't believe it has ever been played by Manchester United, but Leeds United in the early 1970s and Liverpool in the late 1970s and early 1980s were playing it. It's quick, it's continental, it's fluent, and there are always options when it comes to releasing the ball. Arsenal's brand, in common with Leeds more than Liverpool, is purely continental inasmuch as the ball hardly ever leaves the floor – that green carpet, or in the case of tonight's match, that white carpet. Even at corners the ball is played along the floor rather than being pumped up into the opposing penalty area in the hope that some tall centre-forward or centre-half will reach it and head home a goal, much as Ronny Johnsen did for Manchester United against Liverpool.

Arsenal's game, which makes this Arsenal side possibly the most attractive to watch I have ever seen, is short, accurate passing, always to feet, at a speed that the English Premier League defences simply are not used to. Their finishing has now become clinical, and that all-important factor, the world-class spinal cord of the team, seems to be almost in place – Seaman, Adams and Bergkamp. While Dennis isn't strictly a centre-forward, there can be no doubt he is a world-class striker. With each of the players working this ever-so continental system, they will be better equipped than most English sides when they compete in Europe next season, although perhaps, to be frankly realistic, there is still some way to go.

Maurice and I watch 'Match of the Day' so we can see Arsenal's demolition job on Blackburn Rovers without the pressure of not knowing what's going to happen next. Trevor Brooking and Mark Lawrenson both say Arsenal's was as awesome a performance as they have seen from any team all season long. Brooking believes Arsenal will capture the league title; Lawrenson still thinks it will go to Old Trafford.

SATURDAY, 18 APRIL

Arsenal have not beaten Wimbledon at Highbury in seven seasons and Wimbledon have always proved to be a really difficult customer as far as Arsenal securing three points is concerned. Today they must secure three points to keep in touch. I'm sure they will, for this isn't any old Arsenal team; this might well be the finest Arsenal team ever to have pulled on a red-and-white shirt. They no longer lose matches to teams such as Wimbledon. Briggy and I take our seats in the upper East Stand and wait for play to start.

Arsenal, not to exaggerate the point, give a footballing exhibition. It is in many ways like a practice match, where fun is had and Emmanuel Petit is determined to score a goal. After twenty minutes, Arsenal brush Wimbledon aside as if they didn't exist. Adams scores with a looping header from a Petit corner (made by Anelka); Anelka breaks away, interchanges a series of passes with Overmars, who finds space and fires a low shot past Neil Sullivan, the Wimbledon goalkeeper, to give Arsenal a 2–0 lead; moments later, Anelka again turns the Wimbledon defence inside out, lays the ball into the path of Bergkamp who fires a hard, low shot past Sullivan for a 3–0 scoreline, certain victory, and a half-time result that will frighten the rest of the Premiership teams – not least Manchester United who are drawing at home 1–1 to Newcastle.

In the second half, Anelka receives a Bergkamp pass, sells a dummy to a Wimbledon defender, lays the ball to Overmars, who could almost certainly have scored himself but threads the ball sideways to Petit, who has once again joined in the attack, and the Frenchman rifles home an unstoppable shot from ten yards. Arsenal's fifth goal is scored by substitute Christopher Wreh.

Arsenal 5 Wimbledon 0. It's been another astonishing and masterly performance, and with Manchester United only able to draw
at home to Newcastle United 1–1, it means that for the first time
since October Manchester United have been deposed from their
position at the head of the Premier League. Arsenal have one more
point than United, and two games in hand. Statisticians have now
worked out that if Arsenal win three of their remaining five
matches, they are the new champions. *Magnifique!*

It is sheer joy to watch this side, more pleasurable with each
match. They may develop into one of the greatest English sides
ever. When I say English I mean the team, not the players, for
what Arsene Wenger has created here, in such a short space of
time, is a mixed team of French, English and Dutch who combine
to give us football that we haven't experienced before from our
boys in red. Arsenal will soon become fashionable, and many who
have until now supported Manchester United or Liverpool will
turn their allegiances to Arsenal, particularly if they win the
Double this season.

WEDNESDAY, 22 APRIL

Maurice and I go to Ladbrokes, not somewhere we often go, to
establish the price of Arsenal to win the 1999 European
Champions Cup. We think that at about 25–1, it would be a good
bet and are dumbfounded to learn that the bookies are giving no
more than 8–1. This has to be ludicrous as Arsenal haven't even
qualified for the tournament yet. While we're there, I decide to
have £10 each way on Nigeria and France to reach the World Cup
final. Maurice does the same but his teams are Denmark and South
Africa, which makes me believe that I have more chance of winning than he does. Maurice had a bet some weeks ago on Arsenal
to win the elusive Double and got about 7–1, which in retrospect
was jolly good odds. It would have been an even better bet had he
placed it when he said he was going to, after the home match
against Blackburn Rovers, when Arsenal must have been 50–1.
Now I suppose the bookies are giving even money.

Why am I more confident in 1998 than ever I was in 1971? It
must have something to do with the fact that this year Arsenal are
not chasing the leaders from many points in arrears, and the match

against Newcastle seems to be far easier than the 1971 Cup final against Liverpool; or is it that I'm older, wiser, have seen more, and believe that this Arsenal team is better than the 1971 Double-winning team?

Saturday, 25 April

While I'm driving around the neighbourhood – to Charlbury, to Burford, through Leafield, past Ramsden, all the local haunts where Maurice and I usually spend our lunchtimes – in the cause of recharging my damn car battery, I listen to Radio Five Live and Alan Green's first-half commentary on what is perhaps Arsenal's most important match so far this season. They are playing Barnsley. As they leave the match for a few minutes to go to Sandown Park for the horseracing, Arsenal score a goal. The horseracing is not interrupted but when it's finished the goal is played back in a type of action replay. Bergkamp has scored one of his wonder goals, his twenty-second goal of the season, and I ask myself will there be a more important one? Probably the next one, is the answer.

Arsenal seem to be all over Barnsley and, according to the commentary, should have scored three goals by half-time. In the second half, Arsenal apply more pressure and it sounds to me as if Anelka, playing another superb match, could easily have seized a hat-trick. Overmars misses two sitters, Lee Dixon nearly scores, as does Vieira, but it's still only 1–0 and anything can happen when the score is 1–0. However, with about ten minutes of the game left, Marc Overmars breaks through and slides the ball past the Barnsley goalkeeper, giving Arsenal a secure 2–0 lead which soon becomes a 2–0 victory. Arsenal's awesome play has produced their eighth consecutive victory, a remarkable twenty-four out of twenty-four points. They now stand proudly at the summit of the Premier League, having four more points than Manchester United with one game in hand.

Manchester United play on Monday evening, and if they lose to Crystal Palace, which is hardly likely, Arsenal could wrap up the championship by beating Derby County at Highbury on Wednesday night. If United beat Palace, Arsenal can secure the title next Sunday by beating Everton at Highbury, and I'll be there to witness what will be the most wonderful achievement by a side who looked in January as if they might not even qualify for a European place this season. It will more than ever show that football pundits and bookmakers really cannot foretell how a season will pan out, for many bookmakers closed their betting six weeks ago when Manchester United were leading the table by 12 points; some even paid out winnings. The fools!

WEDNESDAY, 29 APRIL

Arsenal take on Derby County at Highbury, knowing that three points will mean that they can win the title on Sunday in front of their own supporters. I've never seen Arsenal take the title at Highbury. In 1991 they knew before the kick-off against Coventry City that they were already champions, for Nottingham Forest had beaten Liverpool in a match with an earlier kick-off. Then in 1989, who will ever forget Anfield? And in 1971, Maurice and I were in a hall at London University having a band rehearsal when Arsenal went to White Hart Lane to take the two points they needed to fulfil the first half of the Double. Now it will all boil down to Sunday if Arsenal can win what is undoubtedly going to be a ferocious game this evening. Derby County were beaten comprehensively on Sunday afternoon and I'm quite certain that their manager, Jim Smith, will require them to fight as they have never fought before to regain their lost pride.

Kick-off is at 8 p.m. I don't know why; it isn't being televised. Perhaps the police believe the traffic is going to be so heavy that people are going to have trouble getting to the stadium. Maurice and I arrive at about ten-past seven and head for the shop to see what we might buy. Two shirts take my eye, both bearing Arsenal logos. One would be marvellous to wear on Cup final day. Maurice buys a Cup final tee shirt for a friend's birthday present and a photograph of Ray Parlour to use as a card.

Tonight is going to be very tense, and I should imagine Alex Ferguson, the Manchester United manager, will be monitoring the match every few minutes, hoping against hope that Derby can somehow break down the Arsenal defence and score vital goals. They usually beat us at Highbury, or give us an exceptionally tough match. In fact, they might be described as our bogey team. Arsenal field what I suppose is their strongest eleven: Seaman,

Dixon, Adams, Keown, Winterburn, Vieira, Petit, Parlour, Bergkamp, Anelka and Overmars. Derby County put out seven men across the back to protect Mart Poom, their goalkeeper, and from the first minute it is obvious to me that Derby's mission tonight is to intimidate the Arsenal players in the hope that one might get sent off. Parlour receives the first booking – and Arsenal's last; whereas Derby have six men booked and are fortunate not to have any of them sent off. I'm glad they don't lose a man or two, for ten or nine men seem so much more troublesome to play against than eleven.

By about minute ten it seems that the referee, N. Barry of Scunthorpe, has lost control of the game. Derby players are really going for it in a big way, kicking, pushing, tackling much too tenaciously when there's not a chance of them getting the ball. More importantly, they are denying Arsenal any room whatsoever in the midfield, something that no other team has succeeded in doing for several months, not even Manchester United. After thirteen minutes, good luck smiles on us when Anelka is deemed to have been fouled by a combination of Christian Dailly and Chris Powell and a penalty is awarded. Could this be the goal that begins the avalanche? Dennis Bergkamp steps up to take the kick, fires it hard, true and low to the goalkeeper's left but Mart Poom, the tall Estonian goalie, pushes the ball away and Arsenal have missed a glorious opportunity to take the lead. Is this to be a repetition of the game played at Pride Park earlier this season, when Ian Wright missed a penalty that would have given Arsenal a 1–0 lead, and Derby went on to score three goals and inflict upon the Gunners their first defeat of the season? I hope not, yet fear that this could be what happens. Oh God, I'm so nervous. Look, I'm sweating.

The game becomes rougher and tougher, but Arsenal can mix it and get stuck in hard. Mini-squabbles break out all over the pitch – Dailly and Adams (not a man I would want to face up to) square up, Winterburn is badly fouled by Dean Sturridge, Petit and Lee Carsley seem to be fighting a running battle – but it goes to show that this Arsenal team can add strength to their undoubted skill and if Derby wish to play the hurting game, then Arsenal are up for this too. What Arsenal want more than anything else is a goal, a victory, three points, and to finish this game with eleven fit men on the pitch. But Dennis Bergkamp, of all players, goes off with a stretched hamstring and who knows whether we shall see him play another league match this season, or indeed in the Cup final. That would be a crying shame; Wembley was made for Dennis Bergkamp.

Christopher Wreh takes Bergkamp's place, and is on the pitch for less than ten seconds when he is heavily kicked by a Derby defender with the ball somewhere up the other end of the pitch. After thirty-five minutes, Petit charges down the inside left channel, Wreh receives the ball in the Derby penalty box and quickly sets up Marc Overmars. Rory Delap dives in at Overmars in what seems more of an attempt to take the man than the ball, but Overmars manages to push to the ball back to Petit and from all of twenty-five yards Petit fires in a low, savage drive that gives Poom no chance. Arsenal are 1–0 up and at such a valuable time – although tonight any time is valuable. Vieira nearly makes it 2–0 before half-time. His shot is charged away by Poom and there's no Arsenal player nearby to turn the ball into the unguarded Derby net. Never mind, at half-time we are a goal up and perhaps in the second half we will relax and score another one which will wrap up these three points.

The second half must rank alongside the Liverpool match of 1989 as the longest forty-five minutes I have had to endure – although I should throw in the Arsenal–Manchester United Cup final of 1979, too. Although Derby County never threaten Arsenal's goal (I believe they have just one shot during the ninety minutes), they nearly equalise in the final four minutes. Arsenal keep attacking and come close to scoring through Anelka, who has another marvellous match and is the most improved player in the shortest amount of time I have ever seen, and I don't just mean in an Arsenal shirt. With four minutes left, after another Arsenal attack breaks down, Poom kicks a high, long ball towards Arsenal's goal. Keown hesitates, Seaman is rather late coming off his line (the story of his season), and Sturridge bears down on the bouncing ball ready to head into Arsenal's open goal. Winterburn gets there just in time and heads the ball behind for a corner, Derby's first of the night, although from where I'm sitting it looks as if Winterburn has turned the ball into his own net.

Eventually the final whistle blows and I feel as if I have played this match. I'm in need of a rub-down and a shower. I'm drained. This doesn't often happen to me. I believe all those around me feel the same way too, judging by the expressions on their faces and the difficulty they have getting up from their seats. This has been a tough night, but the reality is Arsenal have their three points and now must face Everton on Sunday, without Bergkamp but perhaps with Ian Wright, knowing that victory will also win them the Premier League. I suppose if tonight's match has been draining, Sunday's is going to be the nearest I have known to fighting in the trenches. Perhaps Maurice's beta-blockers will come in useful at four o'clock on Sunday afternoon.

Maurice and I walk to a nearby restaurant for the lucky Arsenal tee shirt recipient's birthday dinner. Fellow guests Melvyn Bragg and his wife Cate are already there. Melvyn didn't see the match tonight as he and Cate were invited to Windsor Castle by HMQ for what appears to have been an arts party. Really! What kind of supporter is Melvyn, I jest. Surely the Gunners take priority over the Queen? And why couldn't he leave Windsor Castle early and come to Highbury?

'I couldn't leave before Her Majesty,' Melvyn tells me.

'Why not? Surely she must know you're an Arsenal fan, and that they were playing their most important match of the season tonight! What a night to have an arts bash! Has the woman no consideration?'

Halfway through the evening, there is sudden uproar in the restaurant. Perhaps it's fuelled by Italian red wine, who knows? A party at another table, including Nick Hornby, all stand up and break into rapturous and heartfelt applause. Someone is being given a standing ovation. Then we see Arsene Wenger has come in with two other chaps. He acknowledges the applause as if he were an opera singer who has just sung the finest version of an Italian opera ever heard at La Scala. He smiles and waves. Does he realise that these people in the restaurant tonight love him, perhaps even worship him? Make no mistake, if Arsenal do win the Premiership title it will be Arsene Wenger's title, perhaps more than his players. His judgement this season has made me realise that we might moan and groan about team selection and who is bought to wear an Arsenal shirt, but Arsene knows and we don't. Who applauded his vision when he bought Anelka, Petit, Vieira, Garde, Grimandi and Overmars? Who could have dreamed that Arsenal would not be missing Ian Wright? Mr Wenger did and look where he has taken Arsenal in such a short space of time. If I was wearing it, I would tonight take off my hat to him.

SUNDAY, 3 MAY

'We are the champions, we are the champions. No time for losers
for we are the champions . . . of the wor . . .' Well, of the Premier
League. This song reverberates around my head at about three
minutes past six this evening as Tony Adams leads the glorious
Arsenal team back on to the field to collect the Carling Premiership
trophy and each of the players receives his medal. For Ian Wright,
Martin Keown and David Seaman, this is the first championship
medal they have ever won so perhaps they appreciate it more than
the foreign contingent in this wonderful Arsenal team. Yet it's
thanks to the foreign players that Arsenal have won the championship, for you can't overlook the enormous contributions of
Dennis Bergkamp, Marc Overmars, Nicolas Anelka and
Christopher Wreh in attack, Gilles Grimandi, Remi Garde and
Alex Manninger in defence, and the brilliantly gifted and industrious Partick Vieira and Emmanuel Petit in the midfield, the area
of the park where we have been so inefficient since the turn of this
decade.

This afternoon's match was always going to be difficult, perhaps
even tougher than Wednesday night's encounter with Derby
County. Everton required the three points as much as Arsenal and
I wouldn't have been surprised to see a bloody battle out there on
the magnificent Highbury pitch this afternoon. However, that's
not the way it turned out. The game attracted the largest crowd of
the season; every home match seems to have attracted a crowd of
38,000 and something, and today that something is 269. It's a
colossal pity that the stadium cannot accommodate more supporters. Danny Fiszman, an Arsenal director, told me some weeks
ago that he believed Arsenal could regularly attract a home gate of
55,000. A new stadium is definitely required, of that there can be
little doubt, but where is it to be built? Out of the north London
area? Will the Arsenal fans still feel that they are watching the
Arsenal? I wonder. As it is, their glorious Arsenal has very few
north London boys, if any, and in time this might well alienate the
fans, although not, I suspect, while they are winning titles.

A nerve-tingling match begins well with Arsenal setting out
their stall very quickly when Wreh fires in a fierce shot that
Thomas Myhre, the Everton goalkeeper, manages to push around
the post. Arsenal have come to win this match and win it well, that

is apparent, and after six minutes Arsenal get another corner kick. Petit takes it with his left foot and the ball flies over the packed penalty area to the far post where Tony Adams rises and heads the ball inside the near post for the goal that should do more than anything to relax the Gunners. When the action replay is shown on the big screen at half-time, it's clear that Slaven Bilic, the Everton defender, is the last to make contact with Petit's corner, and so it will go down officially as an own goal. Who cares?

The tackling becomes fiercer, particularly by Duncan Ferguson. I think he most certainly has a screw loose, for having been booked for scrapping, he commits two further fouls, right in front of the referee. He should be sent for an early bath, but the referee does nothing. Halfway through the first half, with Arsenal creating chance after chance, Vieira, who should have added two further goals to his annual tally, is badly fouled, and Petit seems to receive an elbow in his face. I didn't see the incident; neither did the referee. Petit is laid out cold by the players' tunnel, but the referee seems not in the least interested and allows play to continue.

When Arsenal break down an Everton attack, the ball is passed to Overmars who runs with it for what must be sixty yards, beats an Everton defender and fires in a low shot, not ferocious, that beats Myhre and rolls under his arms into the net to give Arsenal the goal that will surely bring the championship pot to Highbury. Well, actually it's already here, having red and white ribbons tied to it, but what I mean is that it is the goal that will mean the trophy will be presented to the Arsenal.

With about four minutes of the first half to go, and with David Seaman yet to make a save, an incident occurs which underlines for me the alarmingly low standard of refereeing that I have witnessed this season. Don Hutchison commits a two-footed tackle on Petit. On any other Saturday of the season, Hutchison would have been sent off immediately, regardless of whether he had already received a yellow card. As it happens, he has. The tackle leaves Petit on the floor in agony and the first fear is that his leg is broken. The linesman, or assistant referee, does not assist his referee in any way at all, and he's standing only yards from the incident. The referee isn't that much further away either but he does nothing about what has happened and allows play to continue until he blows his whistle for half-time. Meanwhile, Petit gets to his feet and I notice from row Q of the upper stand a horrible gash along his left shin. Platt replaces Petit, who throws his shinguards in the referee's direction as he hobbles from the pitch. Aren't referees supposed to guarantee players' protection? Not, it seems, this one.

So at half-time, Arsenal lead 2–0 and surely Everton can't come out in this second half and score three goals? The big chap who sits next to me still doesn't feel secure with this two-goal lead and I come to the conclusion that nearly all those I go to football with each Saturday, or Sunday, or whichever day Sky Television deems the match should be played, are eternal pessimists and don't like to believe that Arsenal can win the next game, let alone the championship. And this is half-time of the game that will give them the title!

In the second half, Everton replace three defensive players with three attackers in a last-ditch attempt to save a game that really can't be saved. Now the further forward Everton push, the bigger the gaps in their defence for Arsenal to exploit. And exploit them they do, although funnily enough not as much as they did in the first half. Tiredness sets in and players who haven't stopped running seem to slow down, but not the one-footed Nigel Winterburn, this afternoon playing his five hundredth game for Arsenal. He runs and runs and is a true hero. Nor Tony Adams, the rock on which this Arsenal team is built. He is once again magnificent, and if Arsenal do win the title it will be because of his inspiration and influence within this side.

Arsenal score a third when once again Overmars wins the ball as an Everton attack breaks down. I think Anelka feeds Overmars with the ball just on the edge of the centre circle and the flying Dutchman runs another sixty or more yards at high speed, being pulled further and further wide of the Everton goal, before unleashing a shot into the far corner of Everton's net and now Arsenal are the champions, surely? There you are, now I'm becoming a pessimist!

The biggest cheer of the afternoon before the final whistle comes when Anelka, surely the most important component of next season's challenge in Europe, is replaced by Ian Wright, who hasn't started a match in what must be four months. Wright seems bubbly, full of energy and passion, but it is soon noticeable that he lacks the speed and acceleration of Anelka. However, it's good to see him again and it would be terrific if he could score a fourth goal, but he hardly touches the ball and is obviously rusty. Ian doesn't have very much time to sharpen up before the World Cup finals, and he really wants to go as a first-choice player.

A fourth goal does arrive. Steve Bould, brought on to replace Christopher Wreh and play in midfield, chips a delightful forward pass into the path of Tony Adams of all people. The giant Adams takes the ball on his chest, moves a step or two forward, and from the edge of the Everton penalty box fires a brilliant shot past Myhre who is left stranded. This is a goal any Premier League centre-forward would have been proud to score. The perfect end to a sometimes-perfect season.

Hardly any injury time is played, although there should have been for Petit was badly injured right under the eyes of the referee. The final whistle blows, the singing, dancing, jubilation begins. Red and white flags wave in the sunshine, some even have 'Arsenal Champions 1998' printed on them – obviously produced by one of the few optimistic Arsenal supporters.

I'm thrilled, as is Maurice. I never thought this would happen. Maurice did. Now he tells me that in the front end of March he placed a bet for Arsenal to win the League and Cup Double. But neither of us dance and we haven't a flag to wave, or to stick out of our car window on our way home. I realise, though, that I have seen probably the finest Arsenal team I have ever seen, and each of them comes forward to collect trophy and medals. The entire squad and all the crowd are delighted to see Emmanuel Petit come out with a heavy bandage around his left leg and not plaster of Paris, which would indicate a serious injury. Then there is Dennis Bergkamp, seemingly as thrilled as all of us, and what an inspirational purchase was this by Bruce Rioch. He finishes the season as our top goalscorer, the sparkle of the team, the player everyone admires. No longer are we 'Boring, Boring Arsenal', rather we are 'Soaring, Soaring Arsenal', and under Arsene Wenger we have become the team in the Premiership who plays the beautiful game. Wenger seems shy and retiring as he comes out to congratulate each of his players with a hug, then faces the stadium holding the Premiership trophy above his head and taking tumultuous applause. It really is the most marvellous spectacle, as are the celebrations that are going on in the streets all around Highbury. This will be a night to remember, but I bet most will have very sore heads and have forgotten it by tomorrow morning.

I make my way home to Oxfordshire, singing to myself 'We Are

The Champions'. When I arrive home, honking my hooter in joy – goodness knows what the residents in Asthall Leigh must be thinking, for the Premier League championship is as far removed from their way of life as the Second World War – Briggy appears at the upstairs window and I call up to her 'The fat lady has sung!' This morning I said I thought Arsenal would take the title this afternoon. Briggy, another eternal pessimist, and not just about football, said to me 'It's not over until the fat lady sings.' In the house I'm congratulated as if I had a hand in Arsenal winning the title. I go straight to the fridge and remove the bottle of vintage Pol Roger 1985 I put in there this morning in anticipation. I'm so excited, but I wish my football-going friends were here to share it with.

Briggy and I watch a 'Match of the Day' special, concentrating on Arsenal's victorious afternoon and evening. The match highlights are shown, and afterwards several of the players are interviewed. There's also a long interview with Arsene Wenger, who speaks fluently and eloquently about what happened in the second half of the season to make the foreign imports and the home-grown players gel. They won 30 out of 30 points and set a new Premiership record, perhaps one that will not be beaten for many, many years.

Alan Hansen talks about this wonderful side, and adds that only a fool would bet against them to win the Double in thirteen days' time. He likens this Arsenal team to the Manchester United side of last season. He runs through the comparisons – United have Schmeichel, we have Seaman, the number one goalkeeper in the world; they have Pallister, we have Adams; in midfield they have the grit of Scholes and Butt, we have the grit and class of Vieira and Petit; they have the pace and skill of Giggs, we have Overmars; and then there was the brilliant, inspired football of Cantona, now we have Bergkamp. What Arsenal have that United do not, though, is Anelka, Wreh and Wright, all proven goalscorers. United continue to rely on Cole and he is just not up to it. Who will they buy in the close season? A foreign player maybe? Perhaps Dwight Yorke from Aston Villa?

I go to bed a happy, very happy, excited and delirious man. I have drunk too much champagne and I have to be up for work tomorrow. I would like to be able to rise without a heavy head, but I must celebrate this grand event. My team have won the champi-

onship in style and are without question the finest side in Great
Britain. Next season we shall see if they are the greatest side in
Europe.

THURSDAY, 7 MAY

We arrive at Teddington for this morning's final mass read-
through of 'Birds of a Feather'. I remember the first one in the
BBC rehearsal rooms in Acton as if it were the day before yesterday. Now, nine years and a lifetime later, during which time this
programme has secured Maurice and me a comfortable life, we are
to read what is being referred to as Series Nine, including three
scripts which are a hangover from the series we never completed.
I say a warm hello to Linda, Pauline and Lesley, and think just
what changes this series has made to each of their lives since 1989.
It will be difficult for them to appear in new comedies, for comparisons will always be made.

This year is the last for 'Birds' and after one final series of
'Goodnight Sweetheart', which will take us to the end of the
Second World War, we shall have a clean slate and we shall have to
fill it with programmes that are equally successful. We have four
projects in the pipeline – 'Grand Prix', 'Starting Out', 'Dirty Work'
and 'Sidney's Kidney'. All will require pilot scripts which we'll
have to write between finishing 'Unfinished Business' and the end
of the year.

SATURDAY, 16 MAY

Cup final day at Wembley. I did vow after going to this sixty-
years-out-of-date stadium to see England v. Italy that it would be
the last time I would ever set foot inside what people still refer to
as the most important football stadium in the world. Why is it so?
It might well be the most historical football stadium in the world,
but I can't imagine why it should be termed important. It's uncomfortable, expensive, lacking in the facilities you expect to find
when paying upwards of £50 for a ticket, and more important, it's
in a bitch of a location.

Maurice, however, thought that we should be there for this historic occasion. Maurice's bet that Arsenal would win the Double seemed absurd when he first wanted it, after Arsenal were defeated at home by Blackburn Rovers last December. Had he placed it then, he would have been given huge odds, but he waited until March and now stands to win something like £400 if Arsenal win this afternoon. I declined to place such a bet, for I never believed anyone other than Manchester United would win the championship, and when Arsenal were fighting to stay in the third round of the FA Cup during a penalty shoot-out against Port Vale, I didn't give them much hope of winning the Cup either. In fact, if my memory serves me well, I believe I thought that the Coca-Cola Cup was the only chance Arsenal had this season of qualifying for Europe.

The major cloud that hangs over this afternoon is the announcement made yesterday afternoon that Dennis Bergkamp, the players' Player of the Year and the Football Writers' Association Player of the Year, will not grace Wembley. His hamstring injury picked up against Derby County has not healed and Bergkamp is not even in the squad. This is an enormous pity, not because Arsenal require Bergkamp to win the Cup but because such a graceful footballer could have been on show to the world and everyone could have seen for themselves just why he has won everything that has been on offer this season. He even won the 'Match of the Day' goal of the season competition, with his masterly strike against Leicester City .

There was a time when, had a player who is as much a star as Dennis Bergkamp not been playing, some might have thought that it wasn't to be Arsenal's day. This Arsenal set-up is completely different. There are many stars, there is cover in every position, and there are no indispensable players – except perhaps Tony Adams. So Bergkamp's out and Wreh is in. And we mustn't forget that Arsenal could well win the Double playing most of the season without Ian Wright, the man every pundit and supporter thought was so vital to Arsenal's success. Even when David Seaman, rated as perhaps the world's number one goalkeeper, broke his finger and was out for twelve or more matches, young Alex Manninger came in and not only performed as well as could have been expected from Seaman, but didn't let in a league goal!

I remember the League Cup finals against Leeds United and Swindon Town. I remember the Cup finals against Leeds United

and Ipswich Town, both of which I attended, and the Littlewoods
Cup final against Luton Town, to which I took Briggy certain that
we would both see Arsenal lift the Cup, but we didn't. In fact, the
only Cup finals I have seen Arsenal win have been in European
competitions – the night at Highbury in 1970 when we beat
Anderlecht to win the old Fairs Cup, and the night in Copenhagen
in 1994 when we beat Parma to clinch the European Cup-Winners'
Cup. I think the Copenhagen experience was the happiest night of
my life as an Arsenal supporter; even more so than when we won
the first Double.

At Wembley Park station, Maurice and I walk out into the street
to see before us a sea, nothing less, of black and white, and red
and white. We stop to buy a couple of programmes (one for
Joshua Eichler) as a special souvenir of this great afternoon.
The Olympic Way is packed with thousands upon thousands of
Newcastle's Toon Army, some topless, with their black-and-
white striped shirts tied around their waists, many with tattoos,
all holding what appears to be the compulsory can of
Newcastle brown ale. In among them are Arsenal supporters,
wearing their Arsenal shirts, waving their Arsenal flags, sporting soppy Arsenal hats, but altogether far less anxious than the
Geordie supporters. I suppose it is the Geordies who are
making the greatest noise, singing at the tops of their voices,
and secretly trying to work out how their team will this afternoon win the FA Cup. I'm trying to work this out too, but the
Cup final has thrown up many surprises in the past and could
do so again this afternoon. At the stadium, we find our seats
north-west of the Royal Box among the players' wives and
other members of the squad who have not been selected this
afternoon. Remi Garde, one of Arsene Wenger's first purchases,
sits right behind us. I can't actually see the Royal Box but I
know where it is. What I can see from my most uncomfortable
seat are the thousands upon thousands of Arsenal fans who
have come to witness history being made. From my right, they
flow right across to the other side of the stadium, almost opposite where we sit. Then they stop and from there right around to
the right-hand side of the Royal Box is an ocean of black and
white. It seems to us that the Arsenal fans are far louder in
volume with their singing and chanting, but the PA system,

apparently turned up to near full volume, drowns out any ambient noise, so you feel as if you're at a rock concert rather than a Cup final. When the blasting rock-and-roll music stops, the bands of two guards' regiments – Welsh and Coldstream – take the field. Former lead singer of Spandau Ballet, Tony Hadley, takes the podium placed near the centre circle, and leads all 80,000 of us in 'Abide With Me'. Hadley's microphone screams out feedback and you can't hear the military band too well, but I suppose that's just typical of all that's not right at Wembley Stadium. Is it this summer that it's due for demolition? Not before time.

The teams, led by their managers, take the field to the most deafening roar I think I have ever heard. It is the most incredible sight, possibly because the teams' colours complement each other. The black and white and red and white give this occasion such brilliance that you feel as if you are inside some kind of dream sequence of a film. Psychedelia was never like this, at least not from where I laid on my back.

Arsenal have nearly their strongest team: Seaman, Dixon, Adams, Keown, Winterburn, Vieira, Parlour, Petit, Wreh, Anelka and Overmars. Ian Wright is on the bench with David Platt, Steve Bould, Alex Manninger and Gilles Grimandi. Can this team win the Double this afternoon? In the first half there is only one team in the game and that's us. Continuous attacks flow into the Newcastle penalty box, while Seaman makes just one save. Alan Shearer, the man we were all told to fear, is kept firmly under control by Tony Adams, the one man we simply cannot do without, as I have often said. No other Newcastle player makes an impression at all, and as far as I'm concerned it's only a matter of time before we take the lead. In the twenty-ninth minute, a well-weighted chip by Emmanuel Petit sends Overmars away. His speed takes him past Newcastle's defenders, he bursts into the box and, as Shay Given leaves his line as he has done so many times this season, Overmars slips the ball past him and into the net. The Arsenal end of the stadium goes wild. At the other end of the ground a silent black-and-white mass are motionless.

Two more opportunities fall to Arsenal during this first half. Ray Parlour makes an amazing run to receive a pass from Lee Dixon, breaks into the Newcastle penalty area and puts in a cross for Anelka. I think the young Frenchman should have scored, but he seemed to get underneath the ball and it flies just north of the Newcastle crossbar. I can't remember the last time I saw an Arsenal forward score with his head. Then with a minute to play before half-time, Overmars breaks down the left-hand side, checks, slides the ball into Ray Parlour's path and the most improved footballer of the season hits it first time but well over the Newcastle crossbar. So at half-time Arsenal are one goal up and halfway to achieving that coveted Double.

The second half is a far different story. Newcastle, who have now to go forward or else lose this final, begin attacking and continue to do so for what seems like twenty minutes. Dabizas hits the crossbar with a header, and about five minutes later there's near disaster, metaphorically speaking! A backpass to Keown is the start of it. In yards of space, Keown seems to be unsettled by Shearer closing down on him. Keown stumbles, the ball slips away from him and despite his efforts to recover it, Shearer is into the Arsenal penalty box, left centre of the goal with only Seaman to beat. He fires in a low, hard cross-shot that beats Seaman but hits the inside of the post and bounces out into play, fortunately to an Arsenal defender. What a let-off! Is this a sign from above that it isn't to be Newcastle's day? I think so. Shearer, who in my opinion should not still be on the field after an appalling tackle on Tony Adams at the end of the first half, is supposed to be the greatest centre-forward in the world, so it would not be unreasonable of me to think he should have put away this God-given chance.

Within ten minutes of that opportunity, the game swings Arsenal's way. A through pass by Parlour is reached by the electrifying Anelka, his speed frightening to behold if you happen to be an opposing defender. Anelka breaks away from his marker, and almost in one flowing movement fires a low cross-shot into the Newcastle net, giving Given no chance at all to cover the shot, so accurate and well timed is it. Anelka, in his own adolescent manner, instead of running towards his team-mates, who are in a state of near exhaustion (it is 95 degrees on the pitch this afternoon), runs towards the Newcastle supporters and waits there. Then noticing that no Arsenal player can reach him (he is after all the quickest player in the Premier League) he comes running towards his team-mates for hugs of congratulations; and how the young French kid deserves it. If his progress continues at the rate it has since March, Arsenal might have one of the best centre-forwards in the world. He is so reminiscent of Ronaldo, who cost Inter Milan £20 million.

There are twenty minutes of play left and I keep peering up at the timer on the scoreboard to watch the minutes run away, but they seem not to. Time is standing still now. The atmosphere is hotting up, the noise getting louder and more frantic. The sea of red seems to spread everywhere, and red balloons fly over our heads. Newcastle continue to attack, but not effectively and they are vulnerable to quick breakaways, so Arsenal could increase their lead. Parlour (later voted man of the match and described by Alan Hansen as having given the finest performance in any Wembley Cup final) breaks through twice with fast, strong runs. On the first occasion, he is ruthlessly brought down by Steve Howie (who should be shown a red card but isn't), and on the second he fires against the post from a very acute angle. Ray Parlour more than anyone else this afternoon deserves a goal; he has been magnificent, but then so have the entire team.

At the final whistle I breathe a huge sigh of relief, before jumping up and down as if on a spring. Arsenal have won the Double. But I don't feel the same jubilation I felt on that April day in 1971, when I sat with my dad, my brother Malcolm and my cousin David Mendelsohn in Malcolm's house in Gants Hill Crescent. There was something about that Double that filled me with so much excitement and pleasure. Perhaps it was because I was younger and football meant more to me then. This afternoon I applaud loudly, even cheer, but somehow, perhaps it's age and wisdom, I knew Arsenal would win this Double by the time they won the championship. I'm no less pleased they have because I knew they would. I stand on my seat and watch Tony Adams lead the team, substitutes and Dennis Bergkamp up the thirty-nine steps to the Royal Box.

I can't see the actual presentation, but I hear the cheers, sense the glory. Wouldn't it have been wonderful for Wembley to have had a giant screen, as we do at Highbury? The players bring the silverware on to the pitch and show it off to us all. The players wave continually in my direction, but they are waving at their wives, who don't appear to be as excited as I imagined they would be. There is high excitement and celebration going on at our end of the ground, though, and as I look down at the marvellous Wembley turf I think of all the mediocre teams I've seen over the last forty-five years (as I've said before, Arsenal is the only constant in my life) and that this is undoubtedly the finest Arsenal team I have ever watched.

SUNDAY, 17 MAY

In Islington, red and white flags will be fluttering all over the town hall. Last time Arsenal won the Double, teenage friend Lou Lester and I attempted to get as close as we could to the town hall but the massive crowds managed to keep us as far away as Highbury Corner. This morning I can only imagine what's going on. According to the news, 200,000 fans are crammed together, basking in the sunshine and the glow of Arsenal's finest achievement since 1971. I was twenty-two then and had the whole world and all my dreams in front of me. Those who mastered their hangovers this morning gathered outside Highbury from early on to await the departure of the traditional open-topped bus. In the end, there are two buses, the first team followed by the women's team who won the women's FA Cup and the League Cup. Players, wives and girlfriends left Highbury at 10.40 a.m. to drive through the backstreets of Islington, where every terraced house is decked with streamers and balloons and entire families hang precariously out of first-floor windows. The pavements along the route are a swaying sea of red and white, as much a joy to behold as yesterday at Wembley.

Just after midday the buses reach the town hall on fashionable Upper Street (it wasn't quite so fashionable when I celebrated the 1971 Double; in fact, it wasn't somewhere you would really want to live), more usually thronged with New Labour at lunch than New Arsenal on the march. Each player in turn lifts the trophy to huge applause, the biggest cheer reserved for Dennis Bergkamp. He may have been unable to play at Wembley because of a strained hamstring, but his wondrous goals helped Arsenal win the Premier League title. Although, as with me in 1971, few can get close enough to see anything, no one seems to care. There are fans on phone boxes, fans on top of vans and one group on the wobbling balcony of Islington's Pizza Hut.

Part of me wishes I was there, but mostly I'm glad to be down here in the peace and quiet of Spring Hill, with Briggy, Malcolm and his wife Doreen, who are Briggy and my house guests this weekend. As Malcolm later says, 'I shan't forget this weekend. I will always remember where I was the day Frank Sinatra died, and Arsenal completed their double Double.'

MONDAY, 1 JUNE

I telephone Udi at his Hampstead home to see a) whether he is still alive, and b) how he is faring? It is pointless to ask him the question I would ask anyone else: 'How are you doing?' He is dying. The telephone is answered by Hannah, Udi's daughter, and she tells me that Udi took a turn for the worse last Monday and has since been in a hospice. Udi told me he wanted to die in one so I presume we are now looking at his final days. I talk to Hannah, who is ever so pleasant and sensible about her father's imminent death, and she tells me that he was really sick last Tuesday, but since then he seems to be much better. She gives me the address of the hospice and I send Udi a card depicting an Italian scene, writing inside a poem of Siegfried Sassoon's, 'To Any Dead Officer'.

Meeting Udi was one of the most thought-provoking and marvellous moments of my life and now I want him to know just that.

THURSDAY, 4 JUNE

I decide to telephone Udi this morning to see how he is getting on. There is no reply from his mobile telephone, just a message telling me that the phone is switched off. I decide to call his home. Judith, his wife, answers and I tell her that I am sorry to call at what must be a difficult time, but I would like to know how Udi is getting on. She tells me she is sorry that she didn't call me yesterday, but Udi died at 5 a.m. His condition deteriorated between the time I spoke to him on Tuesday and throughout the rest of the day. I am saddened beyond even my expectations. I talk to Judith for a few minutes longer, telling her that I am partially glad he is no longer with us, for he will have to not endure any more pain. Yet I am devastated that what was so apparent has come to pass – his death. Life will be all the more empty for me and I don't think he will ever leave my thoughts. He was the wisest man I have ever met in my life.

TUESDAY, 9 JUNE

Tonight is the one hundredth episode of 'Birds of a Feather', a remarkable milestone. I don't believe any other British situation comedy series in television history has reached the century without cast changes. 'Last of the Summer Wine' has changed cast at least half a dozen times. I think, and I may be wrong here, that 'Doctor In The House' may have reached the ton, but they most certainly changed cast somewhere along the line. So if my presumption is correct, tonight's episode marks a little bit of television history. The episode features the wedding of little Garthy and the audience seems to have come from the most vociferous type one usually finds in Hollywood. Perhaps it indicates the enormous popularity of 'Birds of a Feather', something of a television phenomenon.

After the show we all retire to the Green Room for champagne and to cut a cake that has candles upon it, and just the inscription 100. Nothing more need be said. A few carefully chosen words are said by Tony Charles, the producer of this series, and Claire Hinson, the executive producer. Maurice and I are given special thanks for creating the monster, Gary Lawson and John Phelps, two of our most trusted team writers, are thanked, not only for the exceptional episode that was played this evening, but for their massive contribution to the show from the second series onwards. Pauline, Lesley and Linda are of course thanked, for it would not have been possible without them. I was rather hoping that one or other of them, perhaps all of them, might have said a few words of thanks to everyone else who has made the hundred episodes possible. As I'm leaving to drive back to Oxfordshire, Pauline comes over to me, kisses me, and says, 'I remember that day in the Albion, Islington, when you told us about this series, asked us to be in it, and said it would run eight years. Well, it has, hasn't it?' Pauline is delighted, of course.

I don't think it's unreasonable to have expected a 'thank you', if not some small gift. I mean, Greg Dyke, who is currently in Los Angeles, had the foresight to send Maurice and me a bottle of vintage Moët et Chandon, and a card of congratulations.

FRIDAY, 10 JULY

We eventually finish writing the final episode of this series of 'Unfinished Business'; is it the final series, too? I'm not certain that either Maurice or I know. We'll decide when we have distanced ourselves sufficiently from the concentrated writing and research in which we have been involved over the past months. We have lost the major instigator of the series, Udi, and it's his passing that makes me wonder whether I will want to write any further series, although it's been a most enjoyable exercise. Maurice feels that perhaps the story has reached its natural conclusion and that there's nothing more to say about Amy, Spike, Rachel, Toby, Tam and Ruth. Of course we could, if we wanted to, find more avenues for these characters to explore. The question is, do we want to?

SUNDAY, 12 JULY

World Cup final day, or should I say night. After five weeks of concentrated television watching, wherever and whenever I could, the day of judgement has arrived. Every newspaper I have read today says that there is only one winner, Brazil, with all their attacking flair, and no matter how fine the French defence might be there is no way at all that the French, even in front of their partisan supporters, will win this match and thus the World Cup for the first time in their history.

A drama ensues an hour before the match when the BBC panel receives a copy of the teamsheet given to the referee by the manager of each team. The Brazilian teamsheet causes the biggest news story of the World Cup finals so far – Ronaldo, the greatest footballer in the world, will be only a substitute. The press box, according to John Motson and Trevor Brooking, go wild and all telephone lines back to Brazil are jammed! What is going on? Nobody seems to know.

Speculation abounds in the BBC studio. Ronaldo did injure a knee in the semi-final, so perhaps this is preventing him from playing tonight. Further rumours trickle out, such as Ronaldo has been to the hospital in Paris to be given a thorough going over before being given the all-clear to play tonight, and he arrives at the stadium just forty-five minutes before the teams are due out on the pitch. It seems he has been given the all-clear and he will play. What is going on? Well, what the BBC and ITV panels believe is going on is that Mario Zagalo, the Brazilian manager, has a mutiny on his hands. In the Brazilian dressing-room a battle is raging between those who feel that an injured Ronaldo shouldn't play, for it will do nothing to enhance the Brazilian team, and those who feel Ronaldo's presence is vital if Brazil are to win this World Cup final.

Arsene Wenger said recently that you should never, but never, play any injured player, for he does the team a disservice, and it could do permanent damage to the player in question. He didn't play Dennis Bergkamp or Ian Wright in the FA Cup final because neither was fit. It would not have been fair to the players, or to the team. Mr Wenger, as ever, was right in his assessment and Arsenal won the FA Cup without their two star players.

However, as the teams take the field tonight, in front of 80,000 plus inside the Stade de France, and with over 2 billion television viewers around the world (who would have thought a football match would prove to be more of a spectacle than Diana, Princess of Wales' funeral?), it is apparent that the argument in the Brazilian dressing-room has been won by the pro-Ronaldo camp. He takes to the field, carrying whatever injury he may have.

The game kicks off and it becomes apparent very quickly that Ronaldo is not fit and that Brazil are carrying a player. Their mood, their attitude is wrong; desire and hunger to win this game appear non-existent, and this is the most unusual sight to see. France are really up for it and want to win. I think they will. Brazil create one good chance in the entire first half, a header from a corner, and Barthez saves it comfortably, although Ronaldo, on one of his rare sorties into the French penalty box, fires in a shot that causes Barthez some consternation.

What happens between Ronaldo's shot and the half-time whistle must have been beyond the wildest dreams of the average French supporter. From a corner kick Emmanuel Petit, having a wonderful game in midfield, curves a ball into the penalty area and Zinedine Zidane (can't be any other footballer with the initials Z.Z. – surely tomorrow's headline must be 'Z.Z. Tops'), seemingly unmarked, gets his head to the corner and plants the ball way beyond Taffarel's reach. So it's 1–0 to France, and furthermore it looks as though Brazil haven't too much intention of equalising, but I'm sure they have.

With two minutes of injury time played, France get another corner, this time from the left-hand side. Guivarc'h takes an inswinging kick and once again it's Zidane, unmarked, who steals into space and sends a low, fierce header beyond not only Taffarel but also Aldair and Roberto Carlos who are standing on the goalline. France 2 Brazil 0 is the amazing score at half-time, and to all those watching it doesn't seem likely that Brazil will pull this game around.

In the second half, and still with Ronaldo on the pitch but so obviously injured – Brazil have effectively been playing this match with ten fit men – Brazil step up their game. They dominate most of the second half, but don't look like scoring. Their one very good chance falls to Ronaldo, who makes space for himself inside the French penalty area, a little wide to the right, and fires a wonderfully hard and accurate shot that Barthez saves and holds. This incident makes me believe this is not to be Brazil's night, and there could be celebrations in France soon that compare with liberation night, 1944.

Halfway through the second half, Desailly is sent off. He had been booked for a forty-seventh-minute foul, and now he brings down Cafu, the Brazilian full-back, lunging for a ball that didn't matter. Said Belqola, the Moroccan referee, has little choice but to issue a second yellow card and off Desailly goes. Oh dear, what will this mean to France? Can they hold out with ten men and a two-goal advantage?

France withdraw Emmanuel Petit to centre-half and, in place of Djorkaeff, on comes Patrick Vieira, the second Arsenal Frenchman to operate in front of the French defence. With injury time being played, Vieira gets into the action. Brazil press forward in an impotent fashion, and with the minutes ticking away, and with all of the Stade de France, and probably all of France thinking about that magic moment when they become world champions, the ball breaks out of the French defence. It reaches Vieira who, in his regular Arsenal style, takes it close to the Brazilian penalty area, and then threads a delightful pass through to Petit who scores France's third goal and guarantees that they will be the 1998 World Cup winners. The atmosphere is fantastic, and only the lack of Brazilian penetration and heart mar the night.

What an amazing achievement! And what a season for Emmanuel Petit and Patrick Vieira. Double winners with Arsenal, now they have World Cup winner's medals to add to their fabulous collection. They are also the first Arsenal players to be World Cup winners, and I should imagine the reception that will be reserved for them when they take the field at Highbury for the Nottingham Forest match will have to be seen and heard to be believed. I can't wait.

Wednesday, 5 August

On the front page of the *Independent* there's a report that Rupert Murdoch is planning to exploit the multi-billion pound bid to lure England's top clubs into a European football superleague. He has joined forces with Silvio Berlusconi, the former Italian Prime Minister and media mogul, a Saudi Arabian prince and a German television magnate to set up a pan-European digital television network which could carry the games on a pay-per-view basis. Secrecy continues to surround plans for a superleague – given the codename Operation Gandalf by those involved – but it appears that assurances given by Arsenal, Manchester United and Liverpool over the future of their European football may be overtaken by events. So does this mean I could be watching Barcelona, Real Madrid, Bayern Munich, Inter Milan, Benfica and Paris St Germain regularly at Highbury very soon? Will watching the likes of Coventry City, Southampton, Sheffield Wednesday and Aston Villa be nothing but a faded memory?

Sunday, 9 August

Today is the official prelude to the 1998–99 football season, with the AXA Charity Shield being played at Wembley. The game is between Arsenal (the Double winners) and Manchester United (who won zilch last season). United have been especially invited to take part in this match as it's thought their appeal will generate the vast sums of money that it's hoped will be raised this afternoon.

Every pundit seems to think that Manchester United will not only win the Premier League title, but perhaps the European

Champions Cup as well. As for this afternoon, they will be out for revenge against Arsenal for taking away their title. I'm interested to hear Manchester United management, and the pundits, refer to the title as the divine right of United. It seems that nobody has stopped to consider just what a fine team Arsenal have become, and that winning the Double was no mean feat. Arsenal will want to win this afternoon's Charity Shield, for they have not won it outright since 1953, when they beat Blackpool. Furthermore, Arsenal will want to set out their stall for the season ahead, and while it's completely unrealistic to believe that they could win all they go in for, I expect them to win something, and I would like to it to be the Premier League title once again.

The difference in style between the two teams is immense. Arsenal play slow, controlled soccer, along the turf at their own pace, whereas Manchester United are all the time looking for the quick break. This usually arrives via a hefty punt upfield by one of their defenders, one of whom is now Jaap Stam, the most expensive defender in the world, bought for £10 million from Holland. Arsenal control the opening part of the first half, with United's forward movement never troubling the Arsenal defence. On two occasions, United do find themselves with an opportunity in the Arsenal penalty box, but on both occasions the player is offside.

With thirty-five minutes of the first half gone, Arsenal take the lead. As ever, Vieira collects the ball in midfield, casts Roy Keane aside as if he were a piece of furniture (Keane, by the way, is playing his first full competitive match in a year) and chips the ball forward. The electric-paced Anelka and Bergkamp move towards it on the right side of the Manchester United penalty area. Bergkamp back-heels to Anelka. Ronny Johnsen is there but Anelka somehow manages to take the ball off him and it falls into the stride of Overmars, who unleashes a ferocious shot which laser-beams into the top of the United net.

It's 1–0 at half-time and I haven't any doubt that we will win this Charity Shield, for we are playing by far the more controlled football. At the start of the second half, Christopher Wreh comes on for Dennis Bergkamp, who has felt the slightest of twinges in his hamstring, and nobody at Highbury wants a recurrence of this injury. Again Arsenal dominate, although United do have ten minutes when they throw everything forward in search of the equaliser, but as much as they throw forward, so Arsenal's magnificent defence deals with it. Dixon, Keown, Adams and Winterburn are about to enter yet another season as the regular Arsenal back four and they are every bit as good, if not better, than they were when Arsenal won the title in 1989 with Steve Bowd instead of Keown. In midfield we have the wonderful Petit, Vieira and Parlour (who would ever have imagined I would have used the adjective wonderful in conjunction with Ray Parlour?), and now upfront are Overmars, Anelka and Wreh. It's a finely balanced side, and about twenty minutes into the second half Arsenal score again.

Overmars goes on a forty-yard run with the ball, and not one United defender dares to commit himself to a tackle, for fear of being left on the deck. On the edge of United's penalty box, Overmars slides the ball to the ever-improving and impressive Anelka, who in turn glides the ball into Wreh's path, well inside the United penalty box. Wreh has only Schmeichel to beat, but that's a big only. Wreh's first attempt is blocked by Schmeichel, but the ball comes back to Wreh and with five United defenders around him, he manages to find the gap and slide the ball low and hard into the United net – Arsenal 2 United 0.

When Ray Parlour, picking up where he left off last season, drives forward through midfield, with not one United defender quick enough to stop him, he sends a curving pass, with the outside of his foot, into the channel that Anelka is running into. Jaap Stam is running into it too, but Anelka's frightening speed is too much for the £10 million man. Anelka gains a yard, takes a touch, and slams the ball past Schmeichel, who could never have expected such a quick shot and certainly not one as accurate. Arsenal 3 Manchester United 0 is how the match finishes, and Arsenal mount the steps to the Royal Box to collect the Charity Shield, their first trophy of the season.

On this display they seem far the most likely of the English clubs to win the European Champions Cup, but there is a very long way to go yet. I have mixed feelings about them playing their European games at Wembley. A wider and larger pitch and 75,000 fans screaming you on must make one hell of a difference. But if you lose the ball, how quickly can you win it back? And against the much faster European champions, that could well be the key to just how far Arsenal progress. Injuries will, no doubt, play their part too. Anyway, I believe Arsenal's victory this afternoon was overwhelming and comprehensive, as do all the commentators.

Arsene Wenger is his usual pragmatic self, whereas Alex Ferguson believes this was a good warm-up match for their first European qualifying match in Wodz, Poland, come Wednesday. It wouldn't surprise me were Manchester United to go out of the European Champions Cup at an early stage this season, perhaps even earlier than they did last season. I have a sneaking suspicion that this is a team past its best. This afternoon they met a team approaching its best. Perhaps Manchester United have had their great run, and all great runs, as we know, must come to an end.

And what of Arsenal? Well, one could not fault them on this afternoon's display. Anelka becomes more and more like Ronaldo, and Wreh is now playing with confidence, and I'm sorry to have to say this but not for one moment did I miss the presence of Ian Wright, who went to West Ham in July. I think it is Arsene Wenger's intention to buy another international forward, perhaps Henry from Monaco, or could it be Patrick Kluivert? Or what about the Nigerian, Nwankwo Kanu? I think Wenger will capture someone before too many weeks have passed, and then Arsenal will truly be a force to be reckoned with. I don't envy Nottingham Forest at this moment, for it is they who will face Arsenal at Highbury tomorrow week in what will be the start of Arsenal's defence of their title. I shall be there. I'm looking forward to it, even if Arsenal do not achieve the heights they scaled last season. But my real attention will be on Europe, and seeing just how far they can go in the toughest of all tournaments.

THURSDAY, 13 AUGUST

Peter Salmon, Controller of BBC1, wants to know more about 'Dirty Work'. After all our discussions with Rik Mayall, we've decided this is to be a comedy-drama, shot on location in Wales. Rik's character is Otto, an ex-cop, now a part-time private dick, when he can get the work. Otto's friends will feature prominently in the strong storylines. We want this show to be different from anything else on British television. No Miss Marple this one. Peter likes the idea. He likes it even more when we tell him that we could have all the six scripts ready by Easter 1999, which would mean shooting during the summer for transmission just before or just after new year 2000. That fits in with his proposed schedules and he would like to commission it. Great news! In less than an hour, we are to meet Rik Mayall at the Savoy. He will be delighted.

Oh, it's so good to see the big fella alive and apparently well. This is the first time I've seen him since his terrible accident. We hug. He's one of only two acting friends I've made since arriving in the industry in 1980. But Rik is a changed man. When he is not allowed into the Savoy's tearoom because he is not wearing a jacket (he is wearing a jacket, but it's made of blue denim, and carries the logo 'Bottom Tour 1993') and therefore cannot be allowed to sip his Earl Grey in the company of other worthies, Rik apologises for having the wrong attire. That's why he's a changed man. Pre-accident, he would have challenged the manager, making a scene, but Rik has always been a gentleman. He's lucky to be alive, so perhaps the accident has mellowed him; or perhaps it's nothing more than age. We are directed to the Upstairs Bar – yes, it's called the Upstairs Bar – and there we sit riveted as he tells what happened from the moment he arrived home on the afternoon of his accident until the moment he was given, if not the all-clear, the news that there is probably no lasting damage to his brain or any other important part of his body. He tells us how Rosie (his daughter) and her friend were on the quad bike with him before the accident, how it started to rain and so he asked them to get off the bike and go into the house, and how the next thing he remembers was being in hospital, very frightened, and with tubes sticking out of everywhere.

Rik was told by Rosie, who found him, that there was blood coming from his ears, nose and mouth, and his coat was covered in blood. Rosie rushed to tell Barbara who called the police. They said it would take them forty-five minutes to get Rik from home in Devon to hospital, so they called a helicopter and he was in the hospital seven minutes after being loaded up. That may have just saved his life. Who knows?

In hospital, Rik had a certain confusion with words. One time, he wanted to write a note and he remembers asking one of the marvellous team of nurses for 'a pencil and lesbian', which of course raised a huge laugh around the ward.

Another time his son Sid was visiting. Now out of intensive care and going to live, Rik wanted to make an escape from the hospital.

'Have you got the car keys?' he whispered to Sid.

'I'm only eight, Daddy'.

'Yes, but you can drive, can't you? We got to get out of here.'

'No I can't drive, I'm only eight. I haven't got a car. What's the matter with you, Daddy?'

'I'm in a catatonic biscuit!!!'

This sounds funny now, it must have been hilarious at the time.

As we hoped, Rik is delighted with the good news about 'Dirty Work'. The timing fits in perfectly with his schedule – he's making a guest appearance in a Jonathan Creek Christmas Special, and he's pleased to be able to tell us that with the help of Rosie he has been able to learn his lines. We think it might be a very good idea to visit Wales in September, when Rik has finished filming the special. We could spend a few days looking around, formulating ideas, coming back with a much clearer knowledge of the lie of the land, as well as who are our characters.

MONDAY, 17 AUGUST

For ardent and passionate Arsenal supporters, today is the beginning of our season – the champions and cup winners are at home to newly promoted Nottingham Forest. Of course, Maurice and I will be there, with our new season tickets. Will Arsenal have half as good a season as the last? It's asking rather a lot. Is the will still there to try to win the Double again, or the European Cup perhaps? I hope so, for this is the reason we do the 150 mile round trip for each home game, to see Tony Adams, our captain, lift a trophy and pass it down the line to all the other magnificent players in the eleven.

And so to our opening game of the 1998–99 season, the final season before the millennium. And to think that I've been coming here every season since 1953–54 when my dad used to bring me and my little blue stool, so I could stand down the front of the North Bank. No matter what, I've been coming to Highbury every season since, with friends, girlfriends, wives, brother, father, anyone who would go with me, just to watch the Arsenal. I believe I have had more exciting times inside this stadium than anywhere else in the world. Perhaps last season was the best, the very best, for we didn't just win the double, we won it with such style it was simply a joy to be here each Saturday, Sunday or Monday, or whichever night Sky Television allowed Arsenal to play.

Tonight the team is: Seaman, Dixon, Keown, Adams, Winterburn (ten years ago tonight he became an Arsenal player), Vieira, Petit, Parlour, Overmars, Bergkamp, Anelka. What a team! Surely favourites to win this season's title again. Nottingham Forest won the first division title last season. They are going to be a hard nut to crack. They don't mount any threat to Arsenal in the first half, but then, for all their sublime soccer, neither do Arsenal come close to scoring. The closest is when Anelka, with electric speed, brings the ball down on his chest, his knee, finds himself in the box with the Forest goalkeeper coming out quickly, and from a very tight angle hits the post. Unfortunately, nobody is following in to tap the ball into the empty net. Perhaps this is where we shall miss Ian Wright. So at half-time it's goalless.

Ten minutes into the second half, Anelka so nearly scores a typical Anelka goal. He just outpaces the Forest defence, and quickly sends in a low shot that scrapes past the outside of the post and goes off for a goalkick. Anelka did precisely the right thing, he was just unlucky. But Arsenal are playing a little edgily now, and their timing seems to be slightly out. Maurice describes them as 'ring rusty'. Surely they will score very soon, despite Forest's resolute defence containing nine men. The goal comes when Parlour, running through on one of his right-wing forays, is needlessly brought down and Arsenal win a free kick. Bergkamp (not having anything like one of his better games tonight) takes the kick, and from nowhere Tony Adams rises above the Forest defence and heads the cross against the Forest bar. From the rebound, before anyone else has moved, Emmanuel Petit heads the ball into the unguarded net. It's Petit's first goal since he scored the goal that won the World Cup final for France. Who would have backed Petit to become Arsenal's first goalscorer of the season?

Arsenal will probably win 1–0, or so all those around me think, but a lapse in concentration allows Geoff Thomas, a one-time England midfield player, to dance through the centre of Arsenal's usually so-secure defence, and send a curling shot around Seaman from about ten yards. So Nottingham Forest equalise with just twelve minutes of play left. I don't think Arsenal are going to collect all three points tonight, and here was I believing they would tear Forest apart with a three-goal victory. However, this Arsenal team do not lie down, they are not predictable, and all across the park are brilliant footballers, all of whom can perform the unexpected.

From a delightful pass out of midfield, Overmars (also not having one of his better games, although I can forgive this winger anything at all) begins a sixty-yard dash, as straight as an arrow through the centre of the Forest defence. As the goalkeeper, Dave Bessant, comes out I would bet my Arsenal handbook on Overmars sliding the ball past him for a goal, but his shot is saved by Bessant and the ball bounces chest high behind Overmars. Somehow, quite miraculously, Overmars seems to turn his body around, and in one brilliant movement hooks the ball back over the goalkeeper's outstretched arm and into the net – Arsenal 2 Nottingham Forest 1.

To say it's early days is to state the obvious, but three points are valuable. To have no points at this early stage of the season is worrying for a team such as Forest. They require all the points they can get because they'll be like gold dust come April. Arsenal will have to play with more fluency and better timing than they did tonight if they are to go to Anfield on Saturday and take three points against Liverpool. But the great thing about this Arsenal side is that you can always believe it's possible. They have the best collection of players in England, and by Saturday, the rumour machine tells us, they could have added Patrick Kluivert to their ranks. The man who sits behind me, who seems to know what's going on backstage, says he thinks Ronald de Boer might be another surprise purchase by Arsene Wenger. That would be magnificent. We've only got until Thursday to sign players who will be eligible for the European Cup matches. Still, in Mr Wenger we have the finest manager in Europe and he must know what he's doing.

THURSDAY, 20 AUGUST

This morning Maurice and I started out 'Starting Out'. This is to be our new BBC comedy series, and hopefully the successor to 'Birds of a Feather', although asking anything to be that is something of a tall order. Maurice and I spend the entire morning just discussing and writing down the characters, giving them histories, backgrounds and names. We knew about Samantha and Dean, but had no idea of the names of parents, brothers, sisters and friends. We also begin talking about the story for the first vital episode. We agree some of the time. This can be the most interesting part of the creative process.

Tuesday, 25 August

The news broke this morning that a European football superleague could be announced within weeks. It's likely to include Arsenal and Manchester United. Maurice thinks it will start as soon as the summer of 2000. Apparently, representatives from the Continent's biggest clubs met in London with Media Partners, the Milan-based marketing and sports rights company planning the league, to discuss the proposals. The clubs have been promised huge financial rewards for joining (and why else would they if not for money, for sport as we came to know it is no more), with some estimates being as high as £100 million per year per club.

At the moment, European club competitions are run by UEFA, European football's governing body, which also controls the distribution of the revenue. Europe's top clubs feel they don't receive a large enough share of this revenue – about fifty-five per cent goes to the participating clubs. They asked UEFA to do something about it, UEFA haven't done anything, so Media Partners is now offering an alternative. Good for them. What do UEFA do for their forty-five per cent, I wonder. When Maurice and I were in Copenhagen to watch the Cup-Winners' Cup final, we experienced at first hand the UEFA freeloaders swanning around and enjoying all the hospitality of the occasion, when outside were genuine Arsenal supporters looking for the odd ticket or two.

Could Arsenal or Manchester United play in two leagues, one domestic, one European? Would the average supporter want to watch, or indeed could they afford to watch, their team play in two leagues, and more to the point, how would the clubs manage to play in two leagues? It would mean having two teams, plus reserves, and that's not a viable proposition. Which of the Arsenal teams would one support? I think the supporters should be consulted by the clubs if they are to break away. It's a fascinating debate. Anything that moves or displaces UEFA and FIFA, both in my opinion questionable organisations, gets my vote and the sooner the better. But I wouldn't want it to cause the loss of the English Premier League, which I enjoy so much.

WEDNESDAY, 9 SEPTEMBER

Briggy and I wake in our beds in Tours this morning to the BBC World Service news that Rupert Murdoch is about to buy Manchester United football club as part of his strategy to control television football. His strategy isn't precisely clear just yet, but it seems that his plan to have pay-per-view soccer on BSkyB would be considerably enhanced if he were to control the club that everybody wants to watch. There are manifold problems from a footballing point of view, one being that he might allow the club to become a business rather than a football club, and I lie here this morning considering just what has happened to newspapers and television the moment Rupert Murdoch got his hands upon them. I think, and I hope I'm wrong, that should he acquire MUFC it will be the beginning of the end of football in England as I have known it since I started to attend matches aged five.

TUESDAY, 15 SEPTEMBER

When the mail arrives at Spring Hill this morning, the envelope postmarked 'N5' is not amongst it. This means that the tickets will not now arrive in time for us to go to Lens tomorrow to witness the beginning of Arsenal's European campaign. I telephone the stadium and get nothing more than a pre-recorded message – a young gentleman informing me that the next six home games are all sold out and no tickets are available. I try the main switchboard, allow it to ring for five minutes, but no reply. Perhaps it's too early, and the Arsenal employees don't start work until nine-thirty.

At nine-thirty I call again. The same pre-recorded voice gives me ticket sales information on the main switchboard number. It goes on to tell me all the Arsenal telephone numbers, which I know. I begin to wonder why Arsenal don't have a press office as Tottenham Hotspur do? As a last resort, knowing that I have to get through this morning if I am to have duplicate tickets issued, I telephone my old friend Yvette in the commercial and marketing department, and although I don't get through to her I do manage to ask whoever it is I'm speaking to to pass on to Ken Friar's secretary the information that I require some duplicate tickets because the ones that have been sent out have not reached me.

Half an hour later, a very nice woman from the ticket office calls me and I explain my predicament. She listens, understanding of nature, and says that Lens have specifically told the Arsenal that they will not issue duplicate tickets. That is why Arsenal Football Club asked supporters to come and collect their tickets by hand; the post is a risky business, particularly when one is up against a deadline. She does have four more tickets (which implies that Arsenal have not taken up their entire allocation for tomorrow night) and I could have these. However, I would have to buy them and also pay for the lost tickets. What else can I do? The tickets are £9 each and I agree that she should put four aside for me. I will have someone come and collect them.

When Maurice comes to work I tell him what has happened, what I have done. Briggy comes over and books a return ticket to take the car to Calais and return to Folkestone. Maurice opens the mail that has arrived for him during the week that I've been on holiday, and there in one envelope are the four Lens v. Arsenal tickets. They arrived on Saturday as promised! I didn't open, as I never do, mail addressed personally to Maurice. All the aggravation of not having our tickets was wasted energy.

WEDNESDAY, 16 SEPTEMBER

Today was a day of two halves. It was a pleasant day of anticipation as we drove to France for this evening's European Champions League match between Lens and Arsenal. It was an evening of drunkenness, aggravation, tension, and above all danger and fear, caused by nobody other than the French police. They had turned out for a riot, and if they were able to provoke one, it would have been a good evening's work. The trouble was that the Arsenal fans didn't want a riot, neither for that matter did the Lens fans. All everybody wanted was to watch a good football match and move about as and when they wished.

I don't believe I have ever been quite as frightened for my life as

I was tonight. It all began when we arrived in Lens. Inside and outside the pubs and bars and restaurants there was the usual sight, the English male holding a pint of lager, some very pissed, others merry, a few sober, but they were in good heart and voice. The police were there in force – riot shields, tear gas cartridges, long fearsome night sticks, guns, perhaps more equipped to deal with the stand-off in Tiananmen Square than a mere football match. I never sensed outside the ground that there was going to be any trouble, at least not of the making of the English football fans. The police had other ideas.

Melvyn Bragg and his son Tom have come with us to the match. We are directed to the end of the Felix Bolleart stadium by the police, courtesy of the fact that Melvyn is able to speak to them in French and ask them the way. Nothing is made easy for the Arsenal supporters. We have to walk a fair distance through the streets, then through what looks to me to be a factory forecourt. It's here that we are searched by armed police. I keep asking myself why armed? Maurice and Melvyn have mineral water in plastic bottles, and cans of Diet Coke which they are ordered to throw into a large skip. These are, I presume, regarded as offensive weapons. My Swiss army knife they allow me to keep!

We are then sent on a long walk to get into the north bank of the stadium, and at one point we walk through a funnel, or is it a tunnel, that to me spells disaster should there be a surge forward. On one side of us there's a concrete wall, on the other there's an enormous metal fence, and in between are large trees and police officers. In other words, there is no escape should anything untoward happen, and all the while I know that Maurice, Melvyn and I are thinking Hillsborough.

Once inside the stadium things seem peaceful enough. Good humour is evident again, Arsenal fans who don't know each other talking about tonight's match and how far we might get in Europe. I sit in my seat for the near two hours we have to wait for the match to begin. I've brought a book, Melvyn has a copy of *Private Eye* and a French newspaper and Tom is probably soaking up the atmosphere.

When the teams take the field, the entire end at which we Arsenal fans are supposed to be sitting to watch the game stand up. Most stand up on the seats they have paid £9 to sit upon. This crowd is not interested in sitting down. When the calls come for those in front to sit down, they turn around and ask how they are expected to see the match when those in front of them are standing up. And those in front of them are standing up because the advertising hoardings are so high they can't see over them unless they do. One young chap shouts that we shouldn't want to sit down, we should be here to stand and support our idols. He seems to think that this is some religious ceremony. I was under the impression that I had come to a football match. As I'm forced to stand on my seat, on which, I have to admit, I should much rather be sitting, so the first of many scuffles breaks out. The standing fans fall forward and some of us jump from our seats and manage to retain our balance. I can imagine what might have happened had we not. This is a dangerous situation. We are penned in. Behind the goal is a ten-foot fence, and although it has a large escape hatch, there isn't a solitary steward to be seen should a crisis occur. The conditions are there for a crush and the impression I get is that nobody cares. There are French police watching these events unfold, but they seem disinterested. Maurice shouts at the top of his voice for people to sit down for there could be a disaster looming, and some do, but most don't and another scuffle breaks out. I'm not entirely sure what the difference is between a scuffle and a fight; I mean punches are thrown, heads are butted, and in one instance I saw one lunatic try to bite off another fan's ear. He would probably have succeeded in so doing had he not been restrained. I believe this same guy, about sixteen stone of solid bone – from the neck upwards – was the cause of the first scuffle, and later pushed another fan down the stairs. He must have been exceedingly drunk, or just a plain, straightforward psychopath.

While all this is going on around us, an important European football match is taking place – not that I've seen very much of it so far because I can't see through the bodies of those standing in front of me and anyway, I've suddenly lost interest in what is going on as far as football is concerned. Unlike Bill Shankly, I don't believe football is more important than life and death.

With minutes of the match left to play, and with Arsenal winning by 1–0 thanks to a goal by Marc Overmars – whom I am told could have scored a hat-trick but for the woodwork and Anelka might have scored twice, and Bergkamp too – Melvyn suggests that we leave and get back to the car so we can make a relatively speedy exit. We parked it in the hospital car park! We leave our seats, with the match still presumably ebbing and flowing, and walk up the gangway, which is in actual fact a very narrow tunnel where all the fighting had been taking place. As we get to the exit we are confronted by about six riot police, all with riot shields at the ready, guns in holsters, hands on night sticks, and adopting the most aggressive stance. Both Melvyn and I ask them to remove the barriers for we should now like to leave. They do not. They will not. We have to stay until they are ready to move the barriers and that will not be until long after the game, even though they indicate with their fingers it will be in five minutes.

Where we are now is not the best place to be. We try to return to our seats but there isn't a chance of that. I do try, but the crowd is too thick and nobody is prepared to make way. I'm now stuck at the mouth of the tunnel, knowing that at any moment when the final whistle blows I shall be on the end of a surge forward of as many as 3,000 people. I have concrete walls either side of me about fifteen feet apart, I have armed police ahead of me and they have erected steel barriers to prevent anyone getting out until they are ready to remove the barriers. There is a set of concrete steps on the other side of one of the walls, on which stand three policemen trying to calm down the situation. Thankfully for the moment the crowd is not angry.

When four young women carrying children, aged between about four and seven years, reach the barrier and the police won't allow them out, then the crowd becomes angry. I imagine trouble is going to flare. Eventually, the police take the children and haul them over the barriers to safety, but what about the rest of us? Tempers fray and the crowd begin to scream at the armed police, whom I suspect are prepared to use their weapons. Chanting begins, 'Hillsborough, Hillsborough!' And, 'We are not Scousers!' I'm trapped in the middle of this crowd, but I don't feel as though I'm in need of fresh air, I just wish to get out and return to the car and leave France. But nobody is going anywhere! Eventually, the big push that was inevitable comes and the sheer weight of the crowd forces the six riot police aside, barriers and all, and we are able to get down the stairs to the exit – or so we think. By the gents toilet is a middle-aged woman in a state of shock, crying, shaking, having never experienced anything such as this before. Melvyn, Tom, Maurice and I try to comfort her and to convince her everything will now be all right, although we know only too well that it might not be.

I am concerned with getting down the steps and away from whatever further trouble might brew between the French riot police and the Arsenal fans. This entire evening is becoming like some of my worst dreams – being trapped, surrounded by fighting and death, and other dreadful images. We get to the bottom of the stairs, hoping that we have done some small thing to put the terrified woman's mind at rest, and move towards a large gate. Once through that, perhaps we shall be free of this maelstrom. Then we notice about thirty more riot police standing by the gate and ready for a fight. The police immediately shut the gate, locking us in a fairly tight space, although not nearly as tight as the space from which we have just escaped. I am fairly near the gate and move to within a distance of getting through it, but nobody is going to allow me nor anyone else to go anywhere. Maurice managed to get through before they shut it and so we lose him. The rest of us, Melvyn, Tom and I, stick together as close as possible but eventually we are split up. At one point the French riot police start waving their night sticks. I may not be dreaming, but this is a nightmare.

Never again. I shall never again travel abroad to watch the Arsenal. Somehow, after hundreds of fans find another way out through another gate, taking many of the riot police with them, I get out and as far away from these French thugs as possible. Fortunately, I meet up with Tom and Melvyn, but not Maurice. I don't know where he would have gone; hopefully back to the car. When we get back to the hospital, we find the gates are shut and locked. This means one or two of us will have to find the main entrance and get the car out. Tom elects to wait by the locked gate for Maurice; Melvyn and I take a long brisk walk around the perimeter of the hospital, find the entrance, and then attempt to find the visitors car park. There, standing alone, is the Bentley, and what a welcome sight!

We don't even discuss the football, the 1–1 draw, it doesn't matter. What matters is that we are never, ever again caught in such hell for the sake of watching a football match that we didn't even see. Who needs this? Life is too short. Life is far too important. What tonight has taught me is that I really do not have very much in common with some of those who were blocking my view this evening, some of those who feel a bond between us because we happen to support the same club.

What a shame it has been. What a terrible end to such a wonderful day. The drive to Folkestone that morning, in the sunshine, had been a delight. We could never have speculated how we would feel, what we should have experienced, just a few hours later. Well, when I get home to England I shall attempt, with Melvyn and Maurice, to make sure those in authority realise that a tragedy will occur once again and there will be blood on the hands of those who ignore the pleas we are about to make.

Please God, may I never go through such frightening moments again in my life.

SUNDAY, 20 SEPTEMBER

This afternoon Arsenal play Manchester United, at Highbury. Both teams played in the European Champions Cup this week, Arsenal away, United at home, so I suppose this gives United an edge. This is always one of the most important Premiership matches of the season, no matter their position in the table.

Melvyn shows Maurice and me the typescript of the thousand-word article he has written for tomorrow's *Daily Telegraph*. It's in the same vein as our letter to David Dein, David Mellor and Tony Banks, and I just hope that it provokes some response and a minuscule bandwagon starts rolling. I'm more than ever convinced that we must not allow the English football fan to be treated as a second-class citizen. I do so hope somebody in a position of power does something about it.

I predict a 3–0 victory for Arsenal today because their midfield is just so superior to United's. The sun is shining, the temperature is about 25°C, and it feels just as I always remember it felt at the start of a new season, except this season is already over one month old, and still Arsenal have not lost a game,

They haven't won many either, but something inside me tells me that they'll win this afternoon. They must also be aware of just what a psychological boost it would be to win against Manchester United for the fourth time running.

The fellow who sits behind me in the upper East Stand asks me if I would like his ticket for the Arsenal v. Panathinaikos match at Wembley, as the game is being played on Yom Kippur, the highest of Jewish holy days, and he will be in the synagogue and fasting which will prevent him going to the match. It's unusual I suppose to find somebody who places religion above football; on Wednesday I seemed to be in contact with those who believed football was religion.

Arsenal kick off and spring thrillingly into life. They dominate the first twenty minutes, and from where I'm sitting they make Manchester United look even more ordinary than Charlton Athletic. After fourteen minutes Lee Dixon is fouled, and not for the first time, by Jesper Blomqvist, and immediately Stephen Hughes goes over to take a quick free kick. As his cross comes in, Tony Adams rises effortlessly above Jaap Stam and Peter Schmeichel to head the ball into the unguarded net. The crowd go wild, yet Adams remains calm and begins his run back to the centre circle as if this is what a centre-half does in every major game. Well, Adams might, not many others do.

We have to wait until the forty-fourth minute before Arsenal take a 2–0 lead. What a wonderful time to score a second goal, and how demoralising it must be for Manchester United. Mind you, in between the first and second Arsenal goal, David Beckham crashed in a low fierce shot that beat David Seaman, hit the inside of the post, rolled across the Arsenal goalline, and seemed to spin away for a goalkick. I thought Seaman got his hand to the ball, but as the big screens showed in the replay, the ball had beaten Seaman all ends up. Anyway, in the forty-fourth minute, a marvellous challenge by Keown on the rampaging Ryan Giggs brings the ball into Arsenal's possession. Vieira allows Overmars to maintain the forward momentum, and the little Dutchman guides the ball over the statuesque Stam for Anelka to do what he does best, sprint on to the ball and score at his second attempt. I don't believe he missed at the first attempt. I believe he shot against Schmeichel to give himself a better angle, and when the ball came off Schmeichel's legs, Anelka crashed the ball into the empty net. George Best used to do that all the time, but when I suggest to those sitting around me that this was Anelka's intention, they think I'm joking. In the fifty-second minute, more disaster strikes United when Nicky Butt is sent off for a foul on Patrick Vieira, who was heading down the inside right channel towards goal and was tripped. I don't believe Butt was United's last line of defence, so he shouldn't have been sent off, but he is dismissed and now United, with just ten men on the pitch, have a giant, uphill struggle. Beckham, a player I don't think is as good as his publicity would have us believe, commits a very ungentlemanly foul on Stephen Hughes after Hughes had committed a lesser foul on Beckham. In my opinion, if anyone should have been sent off it's Beckham.

The game continues to run Arsenal's way and had Anelka and Bergkamp been sharper the score might have been 4–0 by the time Arsenal score their third goal. Anelka is substituted by Frederik Ljungberg, the Swedish international midfield striker whom Arsene Wenger bought earlier this week. He's reputed to be the quickest player with the ball in Europe. Ljungberg is on the pitch only for eleven minutes before he steals into space in the United penalty box during another Arsenal break, and when the ball comes towards him he lobs it over Schmeichel and it bounces into the net – Arsenal 3 Manchester 0, as I predicted. I knew that Arsenal would beat this United team; their midfield of Beckham, Keane and Butt flatters to deceive. Maurice and I are thrilled with this result, and with the three points – it's Arsenal's first victory since the opening game of the season. They've drawn all of the other games.

FRIDAY, 25 SEPTEMBER

Socialite and businesswoman Jennifer d'Abo has never been to a football match so Maurice and I invite her to watch Arsenal v. Panathinaikos on Wednesday. We thought her first should be at Wembley. We tell her how we get there before Maurice thinks to ask her if she has ever used public transport before. 'I went on a train once . . .' she tells us. Well, we shall go on a train again, unless I can find a driver to deliver and collect us. 'You must feed me,' Jennifer demands. We shall, if we can find somewhere to go. We explain to Jennifer the type of atmosphere she must expect, the rowdy language, the chanting, and she is thrilled at the prospect. I think she feels about going out with us two the same as did Frankie Howerd those many years ago – but for entirely different reasons.

WEDNESDAY, 30 SEPTEMBER

Whatever else Wembley Stadium might be, what it most certainly is not is a Football League home ground. I don't believe I'm making a rash judgement here. It's based on having visited many league club grounds. There's a certain atmosphere, a familiarity, a closeness to the players, an empathy between players and fans that just seems to be missing this evening. Arsenal are playing Panathinaikos of Athens in their first 'home' European Champions Cup tie at Wembley. Highbury is too small, both in capacity and size of pitch, and, apparently the advertising hoardings around the ground do not meet with the European Football Association's specifications. That seems ridiculous. I believe it will hand the advantage over to the away team. Of course, as with most everything else in football, it has really to do with money, and if Arsenal believe they can make very much more money by playing their matches in a larger stadium, that's what they will do. I wonder, had they taken a referendum amongst their fans, what the overall vote would have favoured? But since when has football been democratic?

Jennifer's sporting activities so far have taken in anything with a horse, a hound or a gun, I suspect. Of course, I might be doing her a grave injustice and she might be a ball person, but when I do eventually ask her whether she attends or used to attend sporting events, it turns out that the only one which is played with a ball is tennis, and she found Wimbledon 'faint-makingly terrible, so much better to watch it on the television'. I wonder what she will to make of tonight's match at Wembley?

Maurice and I have no routine of going to Wembley – we did go there for the England v. Italy World Cup qualifying match, and the FA Cup final, and I went to the Euro '96 Cup final – so we are not sure of our timing. If tonight's match were being played at Highbury, as I believe it should have been, we would know to the half hour just how long it would take us. But Wembley? On a weekday evening? Who knows?

The kick-off is delayed because of the traffic, and the teams come from the tunnel at about five past eight. It isn't like a Cup final or an international match. The atmosphere is unusual – neither fish nor fowl. There were no national anthems, no introduction to royalty, and the teams stood in front of the Royal Box not quite knowing what to do. Music played but I think this was the Champions Cup theme for the benefit of television. The crowd is much larger than I imagined; in fact, 73,455 constitutes Arsenal's biggest-ever 'home' gate, but I know, and those here tonight know, that this isn't really a home game at all.

Jennifer is consumed by the atmosphere, all around us are cheering at the top of their voices, as are all the Arsenal supporters all around the stadium, yet the noise doesn't seem to be going anywhere. I wonder whether the players are picking up the support? At half-time the score is 0–0, with Panathinaikos only having one scoring chance.

Jennifer is enjoying the match, even though she cannot make head nor tail of the rules, some of which I try to explain. I keep well clear of the offside rule – there are many, including several referees, who don't seem to comprehend that one. She loves this atmosphere and asks me how many people are here. I guess at 70,000, and she remarks that she has never been anywhere with so many other people. So I can boast that I have introduced a first into her full and rich life. She asks me at which point Arsenal score. I wish I knew.

'Perhaps they won't', I say.

'But then it won't be any fun, will it?' The answer is no, it won't, and we mustn't anticipate this outcome.

The second half is much more vibrant than the first. Nineteen minutes into the half we are on our feet, even Jennifer, although she isn't fully seized as to why. From a Petit corner, the Panathinaikos goalkeeper, Wandzik, goes for the ball, covers the ball, drops the ball at the feet of Vieira. He passes it to none other than Tony Adams, who has been making sorties forward all night long, and the captain smashes the ball into the back of the net from all of six yards.

Now Arsenal power forward and in the seventy-third minute they score a second. The stadium is by now buzzing with noise, although it doesn't appear to be travelling in my direction, it's locked in the bowl of the pitch. Once again, Petit swings in a corner and at the near post Martin Keown glances a header that finds its way straight into the net. The stadium erupts, except for the green and white section that houses about 5,000 Greek fans. Surely, I say to Jennifer, Arsenal will not concede two goals in the final twenty minutes? Surely they can pretty much bank on the three points tonight, as they must have done in Lens? But football, I have come to realise, is an unpredictable game and anything can happen. Arsenal might score two more goals, they might concede two goals. Who knows?

What happens is Patrick Vieira is booked for the second time in this competition (just two games old), and this means he will miss the next home match against Dinamo Kiev, and the Panathinaikos substitute, Mauro, pulls back a goal in the ninetieth minute to give us a nail-biting finish. No, please Arsenal, don't do this to me twice in two European Champions Cup matches! Don't give away an equaliser. It will make it nigh impossible for you to qualify if you do. But they don't, and Jennifer and I leave the stadium with smiles upon our faces. I have introduced Arsenal to a new fan.

SUNDAY, 4 OCTOBER

These days, Arsenal v. Newcastle is always a bright and open football match, although it never used to be. In the seventies, it was always a dour 0–0 battle; if either team did ever win it was never by more than one goal. I remember in Arsenal's first Double season (listen to me, first Double season!) we met Newcastle towards the end of the season, when two points were a vital requirement, and the game was as much of a stalemate as it was possible to be. One moment of inspired genius by Charlie George (who else?) gave Arsenal the two points that were so valuable to their championship hopes. It's funny, I remember that match as if it were last Saturday. I have clearer memories of that match than I do of the Arsenal v. Newcastle Cup final last May.

I remember standing on the North Bank and willing Arsenal to score. In those days Arsenal's victories meant so much more to me than they seem to today. Perhaps I had very little else in my life other than the Arsenal, and now there's more to worry about, and enjoy. Arsenal is a leisure pursuit, not a pseudo-religion as I thought it once was. If Arsenal lose these days it does not wreck my weekend as it once did. I get on with my life. If they don't win this week, they might win next. I suppose I'm not what you might call a fanatical supporter. I just want to see as near to the perfect team as possible, and for them to be my team. I suppose the Spurs Double team of 1961 was just such a team, and the Leeds team of the early 1970s, and the Liverpool team of the late 1970s. I don't think Manchester United have had such a team since the European Cup in 1968, and of course the Busby Babes of 1956–58, although I can't remember them too well.

Today Arsenal play some lovely football. They field a team that to me must rank as the strongest side that has taken a field at Highbury for as long as I can remember: Seaman, Dixon, Adams, Keown, Winterburn, Vieira, Petit, Ljungberg, Bergkamp, Anelka and Overmars. What a beautifully balanced side! And we win. We win 3–0 once again, the same score by which we beat Manchester United. Bergkamp scores the first goal he has scored since the 'made in Heaven' goal for Holland against Argentina, and his first Arsenal goal this season. Mind you, he should have had two before he breaks his duck, and when he does score it isn't a spectacular Bergkamp goal, as we have come to expect, but one that is fashioned by Anelka, who sends a slide-rule pass into Bergkamp's path. The striker slips the ball past goalkeeper Given.

About eight minutes before Bergkamp scores his goal, he runs twenty yards to make a defender's sliding tackle (untypical of him – Bergkamp is too dignified to become involved in scrapping), wins the ball, and sets up an attack for Anelka. I turn to the chap who sits on my left, and whose name I still don't know, and say, 'That tackle will be seen as the moment when Bergkamp's season springs into life'. He laughs and doesn't take me seriously. When Bergkamp does score the first goal, I turn to him again. 'There you are'.

Bergkamp's goal lifts not only the Dutchman, but the whole side. When he breaks down the inside-left track, latching on to an Overmars up and under pass, he races towards the Newcastle goal and could easily have slipped the ball past Given. Instead, he slides it across the face of the Newcastle goal to Anelka, as if returning the compliment for the superb pass that made the first goal, and the teenager taps the ball into the empty net. Arsenal 2 Newcastle 0. Alan Shearer doesn't get a look-in all afternoon; neither do any other of the Newcastle forwards, although in the second half a wicked deflection from a Nolberto Solano shot brings the save of the season from David Seaman. I'll stand by what I've always said of Seaman – he's a brilliant shot-stopper but not so great at coming to collect crosses, high or low.

At half-time, Ruud Gullit has much work to do to try to encourage his Newcastle players to find their way back into this match, but Arsenal don't let up and keep going forward in search of more goals. What happens is that they start sending passes astray, Vieira and Petit go off the boil a little, and they allow Newcastle into a game that should really be dead for them. When

Arsenal mount another attack – Ljungberg replaced by Alberto Mendez, playing his first-ever league match for Arsenal – it is Anelka who delivers a precision pass, this time to Overmars, and the flying Dutchman dashes past defender after defender into the Newcastle penalty area and is brought down by Nikos Dabizas. Arsenal are awarded the penalty and Dabizas is sent off. The guy who sits behind me says, 'When was the last time we saw a match finish with twenty-two men on the field?' Bergkamp steps up to convert the penalty, scores his second goal of the match, and season, and gives Arsenal a 3–0 lead.

With about five minutes of the match left, Bergkamp is tackled from behind in the Newcastle penalty box, and although he scoops the ball into the net, the referee points to the penalty spot and Arsenal are awarded yet another penalty. Bergkamp fires a low, brutal shot into precisely the same position where his first penalty kick beat Given. This time the goalkeeper out-guesses Bergkamp and stops the kick, denying the Dutchman his hat-trick and also preventing Arsenal from winning this match 4–0, although had it been 6–0 it would have flattered Newcastle.

So another three points take Arsenal into third place in the Premier League, behind Aston Villa, the surprise leaders, and Manchester United. I wouldn't be at all surprised if this victory marks the start of a fine run by Arsenal, and I wouldn't mind a small wager with whomsoever wants to take it that Arsenal will be top of the League by the end of November. I do hope so! I wonder, if Arsenal do win the championship this season, where will they play next season's home European matches? They can't play at Wembley because it will be nothing more than a building site. So where, then? Cardiff Arms Park? No, surely not. Twickenham? Possibly. I can't think where else could accommodate the size of crowd Arsenal seems to be attracting these days.

Saturday, 10 October

For all the excitement and thrills of this afternoon's England Euro 2000 match against Bulgaria I needn't have stopped reading my *Times Literary Supplement*. England have just one shot on target throughout the entire match, and Bulgaria have none. Seaman hasn't a save to make. England come close on three

occasions, but on none of them do they force the Bulgarian goalkeeper to break sweat. The final score is 0–0, and England have
just one point from six, not enough to qualify for the finals.

I sense that the press are baying for Hoddle's blood, or if
they're not they soon will be. Certain tabloid football reporters
think it's time for Glenn Hoddle to leave his position as head
coach of England, and yet nobody I have read has offered a
suitable alternative. I'm reminded of the words of one broadcaster who said to me a while ago that the Football Association
will allow Hoddle to destroy himself, then they will replace
him with Howard Wilkinson and David Platt. I wonder if these
words will come true. I suppose it's possible. I wonder just how
long Hoddle's tenure will last. If England were to lose to
Luxembourg on Wednesday night, the axe would certainly
begin to swing. But perhaps what interests me more than anything else to do with England's football team is the fact that the
press seem to believe we have a God-given right to win all we
go in for. What they fail to see (and perhaps I'll ask the question
when I travel to the Ukraine in three weeks' time in the company of some of the press) is that England are nowhere close to
being among the best ten teams in the world, and probably not
among the best six teams in Europe, yet the press believe that
we should win every game. At least they have stopped trying to
pick the team for the coach. Is the truth that we believe our
players are better than they really are? Just because Michael
Owen scores a fantastic goal in the World Cup finals, it might
not make him a world-class striker. Alan Shearer ditto. I think
we are inclined to delude ourselves, and the press are living in
another era.

WEDNESDAY, 14 OCTOBER

I watch the highlights of England's ignominious victory over
Luxembourg by 3–0. Owen, Shearer (pen) and Gareth Southgate
score England's goals, but they have a lucky escape when David
Seaman brings down an oncoming Luxembourg forward in the
fifth minute and gives away a penalty. A Luxembourg part-timer,
probably a banker during the day, steps up to take the kick and
blasts it high over Seaman's crossbar. I wonder what would have

happened had Luxembourg scored. England now have four points from three games (surely not good enough to qualify, especially as both Poland and Sweden win this evening, and both have maximum points). Rio Ferdinand is by far and away England's most illustrious player. I do hope he retains his place for the next England matches, he certainly deserves to. Glenn Hoddle, though, is nothing if not unpredictable.

TUESDAY, 20 OCTOBER

After the theatre (Alan Ayckbourn's 'The Things We Do For Love') Maurice and I go to Joe Allen, where we sit at a table next to a couple straight out of an Edward Albee play. For the entire meal he seems to be verbally abusing her (is she his wife? I suspect so), and she keeps threatening to get up and walk away from the horrendous scene. But she doesn't, and so he continues to abuse her, and everything about her. It is dreadful to listen to, and Maurice and I ask each other why she would want to stay with him. I presume they have a marriage that suits each of them, and in all truth it's probably a better marriage, based on mutual contempt, than most of the marriages I know.

WEDNESDAY, 21 OCTOBER

I am sitting in my car reading when I hear the chanting of 'Arsenal, Arsenal, Arsenal' coming from a child's voice along the street. I look up to see Joshua Eichler, the young chap about whom I have heard so much. Udi told me a few weeks before he died that he would miss Joshua more than anything else in his life, and that he loved the boy more than he has ever loved anyone before, and would I please take him to watch the Arsenal.

On the journey to the stadium I get to know Joshua. I talk to him about school, and he asks me all about my own school and whether caning was on the agenda. I tell him that it most certainly was. Joshua asks me how long I have been watching Arsenal, and I tell him that I attended my first game in, I think, 1954. Joshua can't comprehend 1954. He refers to the 'olden days' as if I were a relic of the Great Fire of London. I tell him that I am not *that* old, to which he replies that I am.

He tells me that he has only ever been to two 'live' games, both of which he attended with Udi (he refers to his late dad as Udi), and he thanks me for letting him have Maurice's and my season tickets. He describes one match he went to at Highbury when, with ten minutes of play left, and with the score at 1–1, his dad thought they should leave to avoid the traffic. When they got home, Joshua learned that Arsenal had won the match 4–1 and he had missed three goals. He was really upset about it. I hope this doesn't happen tonight.

Sometimes I find it hard to believe I am sitting with a nine-year-old in the passenger seat. I have no children and I am not used to being in the company of them, but Joshua is like a little adult and nothing about his conversation belongs to someone who has spent only nine years on this planet. I find it intriguing, and begin to realise some of the pleasures to be derived from having chosen to have a child.

We walk across the Wembley Industrial Park and go into a giant sports warehouse, in which I buy for Joshua the latest Arsenal first-team shirt. He can't believe his good fortune. 'Now I've got a brand-new Arsenal shirt, I'm going to wear it for the match, all I want now is for Arsenal to win! Don't we all, Joshua?

Just before the game commences, the chap who sits next to me tells me that some of his City friends have informed him, most reliably, that Arsenal are going to buy Alan Shearer for £18 million. The sale has been agreed, and the delay in the announcement is to do with the Newcastle United share price. My neighbour (how come I have been sitting next to him for over a season now and still I do not know his name?) tells me that the last time he received information from this same source was many months ago when he was told that George Graham would leave Leeds United and join Tottenham Hotspur, which of course came to pass.

By half-past seven Wembley stadium is almost full and the noise level is deafening, although I'm still not convinced that this is really the best place for Arsenal to play their European matches. Arsenal are tonight without Vieira and Petit, the engine of their midfield, and the teams are read out to us: Seaman, Dixon, Keown, Adams, Winterburn, Parlour, Hughes, Garde, Overmars, Anelka and Bergkamp; Shovkovsky, Luzhny, Golovko, Vashchuk, Dmitrulin, Kaladze, Kossovsky, Shevchenko, Rebrov, Gusin, Belkevich. Dinamo Kiev are probably the finest team I have seen live playing in Europe. They are wonderful. They have such pace. Arsenal do not. It becomes all too apparent that Arsenal's midfield is not going to cope with the speed and skill of the outstanding Shevchenko and Rebrov. It's only the magnificence of Tony Adams and Martin Keown at the back that prevents Kiev going in at half-time 2–0 up. What's more, if and when Dinamo Kiev score a goal, Arsenal will not penetrate this defence. In truth, Arsenal are run ragged. I haven't seen this happen to an Arsenal team since the arrival of Arsene Wenger. Yes, I know they are missing Petit and Vieira, but I wonder whether they would have made such a big difference.

Arsenal drawing 0–0 at half-time is something of a bonus for them. In the second half, as against Panathinaikos, they find some rhythm but, unlike against Panathinaikos, Arsenal fail to create a solitary goalscoring opportunity. In fact, I can't recall them having one shot on goal. Then with sixteen minutes of play left, Arsenal do what nobody in the stadium can imagine them doing tonight, they score a goal. And what a wonderful goal it is too, a goal to grace any European Champions Cup match. Parlour once more finds the ball and some space in midfield (something of a rarity for most other Arsenal players tonight), and he sends a diagonal ball to a rampaging Lee Dixon, who has up until now had a poor game. Dixon shows marvellous touch, speed and persistence, crosses the ball on the run, and Bergkamp, eluding Kaladze, flies at the cross and heads home before the goalkeeper can move. The stadium erupts. Against the run of play, we could take the three points. But there's a quarter of an hour of play left, and Arsenal have let in a goal in the ninetieth minute against both Lens and Panathinaikos, so who's to say they won't do it again?

Anelka is taken off and Vivas comes on, as Mr Wenger shores up his defence. Just before Bergkamp's wonderful goal, Shevchenko scored what looked to me to be a perfectly good goal but the referee disallowed it for offside, which it most certainly was not. I don't think this Dinamo Kiev side deserves to be a goal down. Even when they are, they continue to play some beautifully flowing football, and still, even at this late stage of the game, they play with a speed that Arsenal cannot match. Then in the ninetieth minute, with everyone about to leave for home, Rebrov places a low shot past Seaman and the Polish referee blows his whistle for offside. Everyone knows that, like the first incorrect decision, Rebrov is onside. After consultation with his linesman, the Polish referee gives the goal, and for the third time in three European games Arsenal let in a goal in injury time and they give away two points. This might prove to be their undoing. Dinamo Kiev are far too good and classy to leave tonight with nothing from a match they have dominated. I think they will win the European Champions Cup. I haven't seen a better European club side this decade.

Thursday, 29 October

Fred Street was Arsenal's 'sponge man' for as long as I can remember. He was in fact a physiotherapist, and whenever an Arsenal player collapsed in a heap, there was the bald-headed figure of Fred Street running from the dug-out on to the field with the task of making a writhing wreck of a man perfectly upright and fit again, and all in a matter of thirty seconds. Fred Street was as important to Arsenal's success back in the early 1970s as was Bertie Mee or Don Howe. I'm certain that he did very much work that was never reported in the national newspapers, or spoken about in pub football gossip; just a man in a tracksuit, sponge bag at the ready, who performed quietly and efficiently outside the glare of publicity. When Don Revie was England manager, Fred Street was asked to become England's physio, which he remained until a few seasons ago. Every major British player's injuries were assessed and treated by Fred Street.

This evening at the Royal Lancaster Hotel, Briggy and I attend Fred Street's testimonial dinner. We are early so we can have our photograph taken with the FA Cup, the Championship trophy and the FA Charity Shield. This collection, rarely seen together on the same table, on loan to the same football club, is the collection that every football club and football fan dreams of winning.

In the reception area, women who look as though they would be better suited to serving in a lap-dancing club are circulating and selling raffle tickets for a variety of prizes that I personally would not wish to win. They are 'wish fulfilment' prizes, all meaningless to me. Nevertheless, as the money presumably goes to Fred Street, and it's his night, I buy a line of tickets at an exorbitant price.

There are people here wearing the most bizarre clothes that

might at a stretch be passed off as evening wear, and then there are others who make no concession whatsoever to following any dress code. One of these is Eric Hall, a football agent. Tonight he appears wearing a mid-blue sports jacket, red shirt, tie and funny shoes. What footballer in his right mind, which perhaps many are not, would choose this man to look after their professional affairs? Not me, that's for certain. And yet he may well be brilliant. He may have incredible flair. He may be inventive. But somehow I doubt it. I don't think I could trust a man who could not read an invitation.

Pauline Quirke and Stephen Sheen are there. Pauline says that Nicholas Lyndhurst won last night's 'People's BAFTA Award' for best actor in his role as Gary Sparrow in 'Goodnight Sweetheart'. Amanda Redman pipped Pauline to the post, both being up for the best actress award. I didn't know it was being televised, nor do I know quite what it's supposed to represent.

When dinner is announced, Briggy and I make our way to our table to be welcomed by Sammy Nelson, one half of one of Arsenal's famous full-back partnerships. Pat Rice and Sammy Nelson are synonymous. Both came from Northern Ireland, both were nearly the same age and came to Arsenal at about the same time, both played for their country, and both enjoyed enormous success at Highbury. Indeed, Pat Rice is still doing so as assistant manager to the great Mr Wenger. Throughout this dismal meal, at which you are hard-pushed to hear yourself speak, Sammy Nelson tells us of his life and times at Highbury. George Best and Johan Cruyff were the best players he ever played against – no surprise there – and what made them the best was their unimaginable pace over a short distance, an attribute that was part of Paul Gascoigne's game. He also describes some of the antics the Northern Irish team got up to when Best was in the side, mostly to do with women. Sammy stopped playing for Arsenal in about 1983 and went to coach Brighton and Hove Albion. This of course meant going to live in Hove, which Sammy still does, commuting to London to work for Allied Dunbar selling insurance policies.

Sammy doesn't conform to the stereotype of your average foot-baller. Here was a young man, about my age, who had just taken his GCE O levels when Billy Wright, then Arsenal manager, announced to the young Irishman that he wanted to sign him on professional terms. Sammy, a football fanatic as we all were at six-teen, didn't know what to do. He was keen to take his A levels and realised that if he signed professional terms for Arsenal he would not be able to further his education. He asked the great Billy Wright to telephone his parents in Belfast and explain the situation to them. Sam's dad answered the phone to be greeted by, 'Hello, this is Billy Wright, the manager of Arsenal . . .' Sammy says that to this day he wishes he could have seen his dad's face. Anyway, between them they decided that here was a once-in-a-lifetime offer too good to pass up. Sammy signed for Arsenal and had a wonderful career wearing the No. 3 shirt.

An interesting side note to this story is that Tommy Youlden, the captain of the team for which I played at Holloway School, signed for Arsenal at about the same time, and played in the same position as Sammy Nelson. Because of this, Sammy played on the left wing rather than at left-back, and it was only when Tommy Youlden was injured that Don Howe moved Sammy to the left-back position where he performed so formidably that it effectively finished Tommy Youlden's Arsenal career. I'm going to see Tommy Youlden for the first time in thirty-three years at the end of November, as he is the guest speaker at the Old Camdenians dinner. Spooky!

Sammy is married with grown-up children. He keeps in touch with many of his old colleagues, and he's just ten pounds heavier today than he was in his playing days. I wish I were. He's a typical Irish joker, with a gleam in his eye every time he tries to assess whether you realise that he has just spun you a yarn. He has great recall of those moments in his life that all of us around this table (perhaps with the exception of Briggy) would so much have liked to experience. I ask him what he might have done with his life had his father told Billy Wright that he wanted his son to stay on at school and do his A levels. Sammy lets out a long sigh and turns up his hands; either he has no idea at all, or it's too ghastly even to consider. The young Irishman was paid to see the world while performing the task that he most wanted to perform. Nobody could ask more than that from his life. Sammy says that he knew his time was up playing for the Arsenal when, during one home match as he made an overlapping run down the left wing, he was passed by the linesman. Then he grins that wicked grin, and I know that once again he is sending me up.

The evening races along. Gary Stevens, the former-Brighton full-back, is the master of ceremonies and doesn't seem to know how to use a microphone. No, it isn't that we can't hear him, rather that his voice floods the room. Somebody might just have cared to turn down the volume of the PA system. There's a table raffle where the prize is a football signed by England's World Cup squad. Then there's a game called Heads and Tails where for a fiver you get the opportunity to win a £250 travel voucher. Of course, nobody at our table does so. Then there's what seems like a non-stop auction, in which a plethora of Arsenal and England football shirts come under the hammer. Like the Rod Stewart and Tina Turner imitators singing at Wembley before the Gunners' match against Dinamo Kiev, I wonder if they are what they say they are.

Around me I see faces of people I once thought were gods – Terry Neill, Bryan Robson, Gary Lineker, George Graham, Geoff Hurst, Graham Taylor (well, I can't remember thinking of him as a god), David O'Leary, Pat Rice, Tony Adams and Martin Keown. But of course they are far from being gods; they are mere mortals, fallible and certainly unglamorous in this setting. They belong on or around a football pitch. Take them away from that location and they become ordinary.

TUESDAY, 3 NOVEMBER

The flight to Kiev goes from Luton airport. I'm the last to check in.

The first familiar faces I see are Mike Ingham's and Alan Green's from Radio Five Live. With them is tomorrow evening's guest commentator, John McGovern, the former Derby County and Nottingham Forest midfield player. He followed Brian Clough, going to each club Clough went to with the exception of Brighton. He offers me a wine gum, suggesting this is about as good as the food will get in Kiev. It seems the press have heard that food is short in Kiev and we will be hard pushed to get an adequate meal. Arsenal have brought their own. I wonder where this rumour about food shortages originated. We are going to a civilised nation, not Kosovo.

Once on board this charter flight, I'm seated next to a gentleman whom I later establish is Martin Thorne of the *Guardian*. Rows of empty seats act as a barrier between the press and supporters on this executive trip (although I'm still trying to establish what's 'executive' about it) and the players and directors of Arsenal Football Club, who sit closer to the front. Apparently, there's an unwritten pact that the press don't talk to or associate with the players. Any questions are put to Arsene Wenger and he answers on behalf of hid team.

Martin Thorne is a Scunthorpe United supporter. He's from Scunthorpe. I don't believe I've ever met a Scunthorpe United supporter before, so I make the most of the opportunity. What's it like to support a club that you know, most definitely know, is not going to win anything in any given season? What do you live and hope for at the stadium? He tries to explain that it's the hope of a victory on that day, you can't look any further ahead than that. A good Cup run means getting to the third round before being knocked out, and a good league position means not being relegated. My word, it takes some dedication to support a club like that. Who really would go on a wet Tuesday night in mid-February to watch Scunthorpe play Lincoln City and be beaten by the odd goal?

Some Arsenal players leave their seats and venture down to this end of the aircraft. David Seaman even stops and talks to some of the fans, and seeing that he has done so Lee Dixon and Martin Keown follow suit. There's no Tony Adams, Marc Overmars or Dennis Bergkamp on this flight. There's no Dennis Bergkamp on any flight, for Dennis has a pathological fear of flying. Anyway, I believe he has a back injury and would not have been playing even if he could have somehow found his way to the Ukraine. Adams and Overmars are injured and were ruled out yesterday.

We arrive at Borispol Airport, Kiev on time, hitting only one short spell of turbulence on the way. While I'm waiting in the arrivals hall, hoping my luggage will soon appear on the carousel and generally gazing around, Ken Friar comes over. This kindly and charming gentleman thinks I'm looking alone and isolated He's due to retire at the end of this season, after fifty years as an Arsenal employee. He joined the club the year after I was born. What absolutely amazing loyalty and service! Ken says that most who work for the Arsenal stay a lifetime, and even the newcomers have been there for ten years. Arsenal must be a wonderful employer, that's all I can say. Of course, we mustn't overlook the cachet attached to working for the Arsenal, and the perks that must come with the job – and I don't mean the George Graham sort of brown-paper-bag perks.

On the coach to the hotel, I find myself sitting next to John

McGovern. His playing career began at Hartlepool United, progressed to Derby County, briefly Leeds United (during Brian
Clough's forty-four day reign as manager), and then the finest
side McGovern played for, Nottingham Forest. He says you could
not get a better apprenticeship in the game than at Hartlepool,
where there wasn't even enough kit to go around for all the players. Ambrose Fogerty, a Hartlepool player of note, always used to
arrive at the ground for training and for match days in a very
good suit, shirt and tie, unusual in footballing circles. One day he
was late for training and there wasn't any kit left for him to put on.
So on he went in his suit, shirt and tie and began doing his jogging,
sprints and stretching exercises. When the five-a-side match
began, Fogerty joined in, not caring a jot that he happened to be
dressed as if he was about to go for a day in the office, which in
effect he was. A very well-turned-out footballer indeed.

John has recently been dismissed from his post as Woking manager, because he was not getting the results required of him. There
was no money for new players, and with a small squad it meant
any injuries made it nigh on impossible to field a full side. Now he
finds himself out of work and contributing to Radio Five Live
football commentaries, when and if asked. I ask him who would
want to be a football manager. He says it's a question he has often
asked himself.

I can't resist asking him what it was like working for Brian
Clough and Peter Taylor, for McGovern was the mainstay of each
of their teams. John says Clough was very dour and direct, without any sense of humour or fun. He gave you a job to do and by
hell you did it. There was no discussion, criticism or consultation.
He said, 'You do this,' and that was law. Taylor, on the other hand,
was full of humour, wit, quick one-liners, and the players really
liked him. Together, they formed a magical partnership and won
championships for more than one club, and the European Cup
twice – quite astonishing achievements and each of their teams
was captained by John McGovern. What outstanding memories he
must have.

The Hotel Rus has twenty-two floors and each floor has about
thirty rooms, so you work out the size of the hotel for yourself. I'm
on the thirteenth floor. The lift seems to take an eternity to come
and while waiting I get chatting to a gentleman called Jonathan
Metliss, a lawyer friend of David Dein's. I saw him coming

through the customs desk reserved for Arsenal directors and wondered who he was. On hearing my name, he asks if I'm Jewish.
What an unusual question so early in the conversation. He introduces me to the two people he's with, Arnold and Alan Dein.
Dein? Arnold is David Dein's brother, and Alan is Arnold's son,
David's nephew. Arnold is charming, and asks if I would like to
join them at a kosher restaurant in Kiev this evening. This might
well turn out to be an interesting adventure, so I agree. 'Yes, thank
you, that would be . . . unusual.' Arnold books a table for four at
the only kosher restaurant in the whole of Kiev (Judaism was
banned until the turn of this decade), Restaurant Haifa on
Konstantinovskaya Street.

   The $10 taxi ride takes us to what, in the dark, seems to be a
broken-down area of Kiev, not even in the Jewish quarter. The
kosher Restaurant Haifa is empty. Two beautiful waitresses and the
restaurant administrator (she speaks English) greet us and soon we
are perusing the menu to see what's recognisable to us Jews from
England. The journey in the taxi gave Jonathan, Alan, but particularly Arnold, a chance to establish who I am and what I'm doing on
this trip. It soon became apparent that they know my name and yes,
I am the author of 'Birds of a Feather' and many other television
programmes that have given them hours of pleasure. I am now
introduced into the Jewish Supporters Club of Arsenal. Hooray! We
have a wonderful evening of laughter and food. Arnold tells me all
about his brother David and how he became involved in the
Arsenal. David is nine years younger than Arnold, but they think
the world of each other and still talk on the telephone twice a week.
Arnold lives in Temple Fortune, Alan in the East End, Stepney
Green to be exact, and Jonathan in Muswell Hill, although that's
Highgate if you're selling. I tell them a little about myself, but soon
the interrogation ends and we get along like a house on fire. I forget
that I'm sitting with relatives of the Arsenal vice-chairman; they are
fellow Jews who want a taste of the city their grandparents, or in the
case of Arnold and David Dein, their father, was born.

   This splendid and totally unexpected evening could have gone
on for hours longer, but tomorrow David Dein has arranged a
tour of Jewish Kiev, including Babi Yar, an emotive destination,
where thousands of Jews were shot dead by the Nazis. Back at the
hotel, well made-up hookers linger by the lift. Arnold can't take
his eyes off them as we sit in the lobby.

'What a business, eh? You got it, you sell it, and you get it back. That's the type of business I should be in.'

'Yes, Arnold,' I respond, 'but you haven't got what the buyer desires.'

Wednesday, 4 November

A very beautiful and charming tour guide, a young woman of thirty-four who doesn't look a day over twenty-six, comes to collect our party in a private minibus belonging to Intourist, to show us around the sites of Kiev. I'm delighted to be asked to join the expedition and we set off through the streets of Kiev on a grey and wet day, perhaps the ideal setting for what we in England imagine the old Soviet Union should look like. But this is not the Soviet Union any longer, it is Kiev, and the guide talks us through what we see around us, often using the word 'free' when referring to the state of Ukrainians' lives since 1990 when . . . well, when they became free from the shackles of communism.

The centre of Kiev is much more attractive than I ever imagined. I thought it was all but totally destroyed by the Germans in 1941, but here around us are grand and beautiful buildings, with architecture that puts much of central London to shame. Jonathan says it reminds him of Shanghai, but I think in places it bears a striking resemblance to Manhattan. I believe my maternal grandmother came from this area. You can't help but think of the people and their plight in leaving what must have been horrendous pogroms in this city in the late nineteenth century.

Our first port of call is the Caves Monastery – at least that's what our tour guide calls it. Actually, it's the Kiev Percherska Lavra Monastery built in 1051 by two monks, Antony and Feodosiy. The primary aim of the monastery was to spread the newly adopted Christian religion. Monks worshipped and lived in the caves beneath this church, and were also buried in these caves. The combination of the cool temperature and humid atmosphere allowed the bodies of the dead to mummify, and today the monks remain almost perfectly preserved, as we see for ourselves as we walk around the caves. There's no lighting, and to see anything at all you need a candle, which you buy by way of an entrance fee. We all take a candle and, mingling with some Russian Orthodox priests, we wander down the stairs into the caves. Arnold finds this not at all to his liking, feeling claustrophobic. David Dein stopping at one of the mummified bodies wrapped in whatever mummified monks are usually wrapped in, turns to me and says, 'Now I know what happened to Gus Caesar!'

Everyone wants to visit one of Kiev's two synagogues and Babi Yar. Indeed, Jonathan would like to see Babi Yar more than anything else here in Kiev, including tonight's football match. He's a Chelsea supporter! So we get back in the minibus and head off to a large park on the outskirts of the city – Babi Yar.

While we are driving along the Street of the January Uprising 1918 – yes, that is the name of the street – our tour guide tell us a little about day-to-day life in Kiev and the Ukraine. There's five per cent unemployment in Kiev. Doctors earn about $50 dollars a month, which is nothing more than a pittance as they are stretched to the extreme to live one week on this money. What is required to live, let alone live comfortably, is $200 a month. To earn this sum is to be considered middle class. Teachers and miners have not seen a Hryvna in wages for months and so they have withdrawn their labour until their wages are forthcoming. It's a dreadful state of affairs that doesn't look as though it can ever get better. Ukraine just doesn't have the money to pay most of its workers.

At Babi Yar, there's a giant memorial at the top of a flight of steps overlooking the scene of the most ghastly atrocity that took place here. Babi Yar used to be a deep ravine on the outskirts of Kiev. Occupying German forces changed all of that in September 1941 when they ordered 35,000 of Kiev's Jewish residents to gather their belongings and march to Babi Yar. They were told they were being transported to Germany to work for the Reich, and instructed to bring three days' worth of food and a suitcase. They did as they were told, and along the edge of the ravine the Nazi firing squads proceeded to shoot them. To save precious ammunition, the Einsatzgruppen SS lined them up in three rows in front of each other and used one high-powered bullet to pass through three bodies. Efficient were the Nazis, weren't they? They didn't bother with bullets for babies and small children, they just smashed in their skulls with clubs and rifle butts. The bodies were thrown into the ravine where they still lie buried. Very recently, when the Kiev building department were digging for a new underground railway station, they started to come across hundreds of skeletons and stopped their work. Throughout the Nazi occupation of Kiev, Babi Yar was used for mass killing. In all, over 100,000 people, including partisans and members of the resistance, but mostly Jews, were killed here. This giant monument was erected in 1991.

None of us can imagine what it must have been like to have been a Jew in the Ukraine in 1941. Perhaps we should sometimes stop thinking about football and give a thought to how very fortunate we are to have been born after the Second World War, and in England where being Jewish does not mean persecution. I think we all feel the same. It is a moment of profound sadness.

From Babi Yar, we are taken to the synagogue on Yaroslavska Street. I didn't know before that Ukraine contains the third largest Jewish community in Europe, and the fifth largest Jewish community in the world. Ukraine boasts dozens of organised religious and cultural events, day schools, yeshivot, Hebrew and Sunday schools, too. There appear to be just two synagogues. Under the Soviet regime, one of them doubled up as a puppet theatre. The other one, the one we are to visit, is a hundred years old this year, the older of the two. It's situated in a very run-down district of Kiev.

The synagogue is red brick and looks as old as it is. During the last war, the Nazis used it as a stable for their horses, but nobody seems to know what happened to the Torah. Somehow or other it managed to survive Stalin's time and the Soviet era, when religion, especially the Jewish religion, was *verboten!* The rabbi speaks English, as do some of those in his office, and the Deins go to look at papers and records relating to their family. I am particularly moved by the official stamps issued by the Metropolitan Police each time a family moved from one street in London to another. It clearly proves just how carefully monitored were the Soviet Jews who had escaped to England.

A young rabbi describes how the shul operates today. He gets about thirty-five people attending prayers on a Friday, many more for high days and holy days. He drops into the conversation that he is a big Dinamo Kiev fan and is promised a ticket for this evening's match. I get the impression that David Dein really enjoys being in the position he finds himself today. As vice-chairman of one of the greatest football clubs in the UK, he has every right to feel proud. He's supporter turned executive and still thinks as a supporter. He wants to make Arsenal the best club in the world. In the synagogue this morning, the other side of

David Dein is on show, the caring and approachable side of a patently good man.

On the way to a smart-looking restaurant called Guest House, nothing more, for lunch, we drive through the district of Kiev where all the government buildings are located. Outside the main government building, we come up against the coal miners' strike. A protest march has come to a halt there. Miners, dressed in their working clothes and carrying a coffin to represent the death of the mining community of the Ukraine, wave banners and placards. Their messages say they have not been paid in months and something must be done. Under the old Soviet regime, these men, and there must be over two hundred of them, would have been arrested and worse. Now the people of the Ukraine are free, as our tour guide keeps reminding us. The miners are free to protest, and the tour guide is free to pass an opinion about the way her country is being run and how she is less than happy with it. This is a magnificent sight. Then the thought occurs that the cost of one top-class footballer is probably more than the entire Ukrainian mining community could dream of earning in their lifetime. There's something unjust about that.

After a surprisingly good lunch of chicken Kiev – yes, really – we resume our tour, driving past the very elegant house in which Leo Tolstoy stayed, now a library, on the way to St Sophia's Cathedral, the St Paul's of Kiev. Later we come to the Dnieper River, from where we gaze out over the city, thinking of the history and tragedy that has gone on down below. It's misty and getting dark very quickly, which I suppose has something to do with us being so far north. I like this view of Kiev. Not so far north is Chernobyl, where in 1986 the world's worst nuclear disaster occurred. Even now, some twelve years on, farmers in the area are unable to sell their produce, for who in their right mind would want to eat nuclear contaminated wheat? I think I might have liked to see Chernobyl. What is there to see there I ask the tour guide. 'Desolation,' is her reply. No thank you. If I want desolation, I'll visit Tottenham.

Back at the hotel, a ticket for tonight's match in the VIP box is waiting for me. It means travelling to the game with the directors in their private minibus, attending the pre-match reception, using the directors' check-in at the airport and flying at the front of the aircraft. Excellent, thank you David. Of course I won't talk to the players, win, lose or draw, for they will wish to be left alone, but who would really want to talk to the players anyway? What would I have to say to them?

Arnold, Alan, Jonathan and I pack our bags and head off to the Hotel Imperial where the directors and players are holed up. Around the front door to the hotel – and by now it is pouring with rain – are a crowd of young Ukrainian football fans, wanting Arsenal souvenirs. They even ask me for 'pin, Arsenal pin'. I don't have one, I tell them, but still they ask. When David Dein comes out on to the front steps and starts handing around pins he is besieged by these young children. It's all reminiscent of Father Christmas – the children certainly enjoy him playing that role.

As we stand in the lobby, talking to Arsenal representatives wearing their dark blue blazers, white shirts and Arsenal ties, someone volunteers the information that Nicolas Anelka will not be playing. Last night he had a sore foot, a corn between his toes, and did not report it to anyone. This morning his foot was sore and extremely swollen, and when it was examined by Dr Leonard Sash it was found to be septic. Anelka could have played had he but told someone about it last night. He didn't think. He was given a shot of antibiotic, but this morning was twelve hours too late, and now his foot has swollen to such proportions that he cannot get his training shoe on. Arsenal are down to the bare bones – no Anelka, no Bergkamp, no Overmars, no Tony Adams. Who, we all wonder, will be in the side? Gary Lewin, the trainer, says to me, 'Are you any good?'

We leave the hotel in the directors' minibus, accompanied by police escort, although they are more for the benefit of the team bus than for us, but oh how very different from my Lens experience. At the stadium we are taken through to a reception for – well, I don't quite know who. There are most definitely Arsenal directors, supporters, Dinamo Kiev executive club members and a fair spattering of what look to me like heavyweight Mafiosi. Stale bread sandwiches, wonderful Nutella pancakes, Amstel beer and some soiled fruit is the fare on offer – not what I would call the way to make Arsenal directors feel at home. To make matters worse, there are 'No Smoking' signs everywhere. I'll have to wait for the game to begin. The 100,000 seater stadium is uncovered – it's raining buckets.

I talk at some length to Peter Hill-Wood about Arsenal and their move away from Highbury. He tells me that a few weeks ago he and his fellow directors went on a bus tour inspecting possible sites for Arsenal's new stadium. Brent Cross was unsuitable. As was Northolt. King's Cross could be very good, but the club could not have it until the year 2008, and Hill-Wood explains to me that he wants to be living when the club moves, and he may well not be in 2008. Wembley is still a possibility, and all efforts are being made to negotiate a move to Wembley; furthermore Hill-Wood is slightly optimistic. And finally he tells me that Finsbury Park must not be ruled out. Talks have taken place with Islington Council, and not only is there much space for building in the rather raggedy park, but it is in Arsenal's current catchment area. Well, I never! Finsbury Park. The very place where I spent my misspent youth.

The Arsenal directors are seated in a corner of the VIP enclosure where the rain gets in, while behind what looks to me to be bullet-proof glass sit the Dinamo Kiev directors and the Mafia. In front of where I'm sitting, there's an enclosure that houses what seems to be Dinamo Kiev's Chassidic fan base. In their frock coats, wide-brimmed, fur-edged hats, ringlets and long beards, they are here to cheer on their team and become as excited as those around them as wave after wave of Kiev attack threatens Arsenal's goal. I can't for one moment imagine the Stamford Hill Chassidic community attending a midweek evening match at Highbury. It's just another wonderful image in two days of startling images I have experienced here in Kiev.

As the game begins, the bullet-proof glass behind me comes down electronically and slowly so the Mafia have a clear view of the game. The stadium is nearly at capacity, and the roar and noise is quite unlike anything I have ever experienced at any sporting event, or indeed any event at all. It is truly deafening. Is this what it was like at one of Hitler's Nuremberg rallies?

Arsenal announce a very makeshift team: Seaman, Dixon, Winterburn, Vieira, Bould (captain), Vivas, Keown, Parlour, Petit, Wreh and Boa Morte. Well, there's no pace there, and I wonder where the goals are going to come from? In fact, this Arsenal side make an excellent start and could have scored three goals inside the opening quarter of an hour. But Boa Morte scuffs his shot when presented with a great chance in front of the goal with only the goalkeeper to beat, Wreh misses an equally fine chance, and

Keown has a header well saved by Shovkovskyi. The inevitable happens in the twenty-sixth minute, and Arsenal are punished for not taking their chances. The right side of Arsenal's defence has been constantly sliced up by the sheer pace of Dinamo Kiev's forwards and midfield operators, and on one such break the dangerous Rebrov breaks into the Arsenal penalty area only to be brought down by Keown. Dinamo are awarded a penalty, Rebrov takes the kick, Seaman saves partially, but the ball flies over his shoulder, off the post and into the net. Arsenal are in big trouble now. Then Steve Bould clashes heads with a Dinamo forward and has to go off to have four stitches in an open head wound. While he's off, Dinamo become increasingly dangerous. This doesn't look good. I'm not enjoying this.

It's Dinamo Kiev 1 Arsenal 0 at half-time. Can Arsenal equalise and hold on? I think that would be deluding ourselves. This side are so superior to us that if we manage to lose by just the one goal, we will have had a fair result.

In the sixty-second minute, Kiev score another goal. It comes after Nigel Winterburn trips an on-rushing Kiev midfield player and from the free kick, Olexander Golovko leaps and heads the ball down past a static Dave Seaman. If Bould had been on – he was replaced by Gilles Grimaldi at half-time – he may have had Golovko covered. As it is, Dinamo Kiev have a commanding 2–0 lead, which means certain victory. They score a third when the brilliant, magnificent Andrii Shevchenko – the best player I have seen for many a season – scores directly from a fierce, bending free kick. Seaman seems to watch the ball as it curls around the Arsenal defensive wall.

Stephen Hughes scores a late goal for Arsenal and the stadium falls into funereal silence. But 3–1 does us little good. When Christopher Wreh heads in a Parlour cross (and Parlour is Arsenal's most industrious player on the field this evening) I think at 3–2 we have a chance of equalising. But no, the goal is disallowed. I don't know what for. The linesman seems not to be flagging for an offside decision, so I can only presume that Wreh handled the ball. Still, in truth it would have made little difference. The game is Dinamo Kiev's. They deserve it. I think tonight they have put us out of the European Champions Cup, but David Dein thinks not. 'If we can win our last two games, at home to Lens and at Panathinaikos [who, incidentally, win this evening 1–0 against

Lens, and thus are top of the group], we shall have eleven points and we should qualify.' Yes, but not if this wonderful Kiev side win their last two games, and there is more reason to suppose that they will than we will.

WEDNESDAY, 11 NOVEMBER

Every time I've been to Highbury, and I believe I've attended well over a thousand matches, I've always looked up at the directors' box and wondered who was sitting in there this week, and how one becomes a director of a club such as Arsenal. As a child, I thought that was where the rich and famous people sat; when I was a teenager, I wanted to know whether being a director of Arsenal was open to anyone, or was it a family-run business? Now I know precisely how it works. If you are acceptable and have huge bundles of dosh, you might just become a member of this élite group. Tonight, for the first time since I was brought to Highbury forty-five years ago, I'm sitting in the directors' box. It's the apogee of my supporting career. It is, to be honest, a dream come true. I never believed that it would be me sitting in the front row of the directors' box, a guest of the chairman. Neither did Maurice. I wonder whether tonight there's a child on the North Bank looking up and thinking who are those people sitting in the Arsenal directors' box. If my father were alive and sitting here today, would it mean as much to him as it does to me?

Jennifer d'Abo, Maurice and I walk up the steps of the main entrance of the grade two listed East Stand, and are shown into the inner sanctum of the boardroom where we are welcomed by the Arsenal chairman. The boardroom has wood-panelled walls and thick Arsenal logo carpet. Chairs line the walls and I'm told that the high-backed chairman's chair has five legs. I can't work out why. I savour the atmosphere of this fine old room and wonder what momentous decisions have been made here, and by whom. What must it be like to attend an Arsenal board meeting? What's discussed? What's said that the fans will never know? I bet they're as boring as every other board meeting I've ever attended.

A buffet and bar is laid out for the guests, including Chelsea's chairman, Ken Bates, and other Chelsea people. This evening Arsenal play host to Chelsea in the fourth round of the

Worthington Cup, the latest alias of the League Cup. It's not an important trophy, even though it takes the winner through to the UEFA Cup. Perhaps if a club is in the European Champions Cup, they should be exempt from the Worthington Cup. It doesn't really matter what team Arsenal field tonight. When the team sheet is handed around, it reads: Manninger, Vivas, Grimandi, Upson, Grondin, Ljungberg, Hughes, Garde, Boa Morte, Bergkamp and Wreh. Can this team beat Chelsea? I doubt it. Surely it's a matter of by how many goals we are defeated.

From our privileged and exquisitely comfortable padded seats, we watch Arsenal do battle with a Chelsea team that I wouldn't call its second choice. They field: Kharine, Petrescu, Babayaro, Leboeuf, Goldbaek, Poyet, Vialli, Duberry, Di Matteo, Flo and Nicholls. There are only four British-born players on the field. I wonder what my father would have made of that! Tonight would have been an utter confusion to him. I light a cigar, for Mr Hill-Wood has given me permission to smoke in the box, and watch the match unfold in front of us; not that the match really matters too much. I mean, it does, but I'm here to savour all around me, to glimpse what it must be like to be a director.

It looks as though Arsenal might win. They mount all the early attacks, and after one magical dribble through the Chelsea defence by Fred Ljungberg, after which he fails to fire his shot on target, it seems that Arsenal could pull off a surprise here. Luis Boa Morte misses a chance he really should have put away, and Dennis Bergkamp fires in a fierce free kick that Dmitri Kharine saves admirably. But apart from these chances, Arsenal's attack is all a little too impotent and I start to feel that Christopher Wreh and Luis Boa Morte are never going to score. There are some good defensive performances, particularly from Matthew Upson and Gilles Grimandi, but they fall apart when Chelsea are awarded a dubious penalty. A tackle by Gilles Grimandi fells Gustavo Poyet but the referee allows play to continue inside the Arsenal penalty box. When Chelsea's attack comes to nothing, David Elleray blows for a Chelsea penalty and the Arsenal defenders are furious. Franck Leboeuf steps up and crashes his shot into the net – even if Manninger had gone the right way, I don't think he would have heard it, let alone seen it.

At half-time, Chelsea look the better side. They are faster, more skilful, more experienced, and it seems, more determined to progress in this tournament. In the second half, Chelsea run riot. Remi Garde is replaced by Alberto Mendez, but this makes little difference to Arsenal's attacking qualities, and soon Chelsea score a second goal through Gianluca Vialli, and the game is over, though not for Chelsea. They score three more times through Vialli again, and Poyet, twice. So it's Arsenal 0 Chelsea 5. When was the last time Arsenal suffered such a heavy home defeat? Nobody around me can recall such a mauling. I remember Spartak Moscow beating us 6–2, and Manchester United beating us by the same score, but on both those occasions we did at least score twice. But five-nil! In fact, this is Arsenal's worst home defeat in seventy-three years, which means that somebody (nobody can remember who) won by this score against an Arsenal team in 1925. Is there anyone in the stadium tonight who remembers that last crashing defeat? I suspect not. I wouldn't mind betting that Fabian Caballero, the young Uruguayan who made his Arsenal debut tonight as a substitute for Bergkamp, won't forget it in a hurry.

Jennifer is mortified, more so than Maurice and me who realise that Arsenal did not have the desire to win tonight, and that their elimination from the Worthington Cup will prove to be a blessing in disguise. Some of the Arsenal directors feel this way too. The question being asked in the directors' lounge this evening is would Arsenal have been beaten had Mr Wenger put out his full team? Almost certainly not, but we shan't know, the scoreline will forever be in the history books, and it will remain Arsenal's worst home defeat in my lifetime. Yet why am I so unconcerned? Because it doesn't matter. Now if Arsenal lost 0–5 on Saturday to George Graham's Spurs, I shall be as perplexed as Jennifer is tonight.

SATURDAY, 14 NOVEMBER

This afternoon, after their midweek mauling at the hands of Chelsea, Arsenal field almost their strongest side: Seaman, Dixon, Adams, Keown, Winterburn, Vieira, Petit, Parlour, Ljungberg, Anelka and Overmars. Spurs of course come to Highbury with their new manager, George Graham, the man whom many believe to be the finest Arsenal manager since the War until Mr Wenger. I believe this too. There are also many Arsenal supporters who feel grossly betrayed by George Graham, not because he has become the manager of our greatest rivals, Tottenham Hotspur, but because he put money that belonged to Arsenal Football Club into his own bank account, and was then surprised that he got his marching orders. Why was GG surprised, I wonder? Did he think what he did really was this side of legal? He must have convinced himself that it was. So while the Arsenal fans unquestionably admire Graham for his managerial skill, they despise him for his dishonesty.

Today he returns to Highbury and chooses neither to sit in the directors' box, nor be entertained in the very boardroom where he was told he was to be dismissed. He sits in the dug-out with his coaches and watches his improving Spurs team take a real drubbing from a far superior Arsenal team that, despite a dozen goal-bound efforts, cannot put the ball into the Spurs net. Anelka has the best chance of the match when his speed takes him past all the Spurs defenders, but his shot, for which he had time, is fired wide of the near post – it was the accurate cross shot that Anelka usually performs so well that was required. Other Arsenal attempts are long-range shots, all of them admirably saved by Bardsen.

In the first half, Spurs have just one opportunity, perhaps it is the best opportunity of the entire game, and it falls to Allan Nielsen. But when through on Arsenal's goal with only Dave Seaman to beat, he fires the ball straight at the goalkeeper's hands. In the second half, the pattern of the game is the same, with Arsenal creating all of the chances but taking none. Spurs mount one serious second-half attempt but the meaty shot by Nielsen goes well wide of Seaman's goal. Anelka is injured and replaced by Boa Morte, and Mr Wenger brings off Ljungberg and replaces him with Christopher Wreh, but these substitutions make little difference to the pattern of the game, except that Overmars, who has been playing central midfield, returns to his left-wing position and creates consternation amongst the Spurs defence. Arsenal fail to score, and the match, for the second season running, is a 0–0 draw. Arsenal have effectively given two points away in their championship bid. Arsenal are finding it nigh on impossible to score the number of goals they were scoring last season. I don't believe it's down to the loss of Ian Wright. Yes, of course Wrighty scored netfuls of goals for Arsenal, but last season goals were coming from all positions, even the back four. Bergkamp (injured for this afternoon's game) and Overmars were scoring goals into double figures. Parlour, Vieira and Petit were scoring too, as were Anelka and Wreh, vital goals. Now they seem to have dried up right across the park and I wonder why this should be. I suppose you could put it down to confidence, or the lack of it, but the system being played, with Anelka upfront on his own, doesn't seem to me conducive to a flurry of goals. On the other hand, Arsenal are making more than their fair share of goalscoring opportunities. They are just not taking them. Their defence is as solid as ever, but a series of 0–0 or 1–0 matches is not what the 38,000 regular fans have come to expect, or want, under Mr Wenger.

I suppose it's all too easy for a fan to suggest that what Arsenal need is a new striker. Who? No English striker immediately springs to mind. The idea that Shearer, Owen, or – I can't think of another I should like to see – would want to play their football at Highbury is pure fantasy; besides which, Arsenal would never pay the silly money that would be asked for these forwards. There's no guarantee of them scoring any more goals than are being scored at the moment by the players in the team.

All right, so it's a dip in confidence that is to blame, and it's come at precisely the wrong time – not that there would ever be a right time. The goals will return. After Mr Wenger led us to the Double last season, surely we must allow him time and space. The man is masterly, and far be it from us, the spectators, the fans, the enthusiasts, to criticise anything the Frenchman does. So Arsenal drew 0–0 following a 0–5 home defeat – so what? We have been supplied with a dazzling display this afternoon. We have players in our team who must be the envy of every other English club. Which other fans get to see the heavenly skills of Petit, Vieira, Bergkamp, Overmars, Anelka and Adams, week in, week out?

TUESDAY, 17 NOVEMBER

The news comes through that the overnight viewing figures for last night's 'Birds of a Feather', the first of what is to be the final series, is a staggering – and I mean staggering – 11.2 million. If a show nowadays receives a viewing figure of 7 million everyone is walking around with smiles on their faces, so to receive 11.2 million, possibly with more to add, is nothing short of astonishing. It means that 'Birds' can still pull in massive audiences. It must be one of the very few comedy shows, if not the only one, on television that can do this. There was a time when 'Only Fools and Horses' and 'One Foot in the Grave' were able to command such figures, but both of these classics have now retired and so 'Birds', for the moment, is the only show left. Perhaps 'Goodnight Sweetheart' might be able to emulate these figures, but even that I doubt. What it does tell me, though, is that there *is* an audience out there that loves to watch a damn good comedy. And it might mean, too, that all these 'people shows' that seem to be a favourite form of cheap television amongst the executives, just might be coming to the end of their natural life.

Saturday, 21 November

An hour after the final whistles have blown around the country, the news seeps through from Ewood Park that Roy Hodgson, Blackburn Rovers' manager, has either resigned or been sacked. In May, Blackburn Rovers finished in the top six and qualified for Europe. The pundits thought that, under Hodgson, Rovers really stood a chance of winning the championship. Nobody imagined that six months later Rovers would be holding up the division. Who will replace Hodgson? Where will he go? A Celtic supporter on the David Mellor phone-in believes that Hodgson, a hugely well-respected manager, will be managing Celtic by the middle of next week. Wishful thinking? And some are talking about Kenny Dalglish returning to manage Blackburn, the team he led to the championship. That's wishful thinking, too.

There is certainly no job security as a football manager. Hodgson has been doing a good job at Rovers, but I believe, with no inside knowledge at all, that the players disliked him, and did not play to the best of their abilities, thus letting him down. Will the same thing happen to Arsene Wenger, I wonder, or has he become, even after two seasons, a Highbury legend? I suppose you could have thought the same of George Graham, but the time comes for every manager to move on to pastures new, and inspire a different set of players. It will be no different for Mr Wenger. At the moment he must be wondering what it is he has to do to inspire his forwards to start putting the ball into the opponent's net. The goals have well and truly dried up. After last season's displays with goals coming from every quarter, Ian Wright was considered dispensable. Now we are beginning to wonder. If what I have heard is correct – that Wright was let go to West Ham so Rio Ferdinand could one day hold the Arsenal back four together – it was a long-term plan. If it's just gossip, losing Wright could well prove to be costly. In any case, Arsenal must soon find their goalscoring touch or else they're going to find themselves in mid-table and out of the European Champions Cup. I can't at the moment see from where the goals are going to come. We mustn't blame Nicolas Anelka; he is being asked to do alone what should be shared amongst his fellow forwards. It's Bergkamp and Overmars who are not pulling their weight.

WEDNESDAY, 25 NOVEMBER

I'm writing this a few hours after returning from Wembley with Maurice. It was a most disappointing evening. I should say here and now that Arsenal lost tonight's decisive match to Lens 1–0, which is no more than the Frenchmen deserve, and the defeat means that Arsenal are now definitely out of the European Champions Cup. I suppose it's as far as they went when they last appeared in this tournament, under the managership of George Graham. I remember clearly the evening Benfica came to Highbury and gave us a lesson in European counter-attacking football, and although we did manage to win the European Cup-Winners' Cup some years later, I don't know that we have ever managed to close the gap on the greatest of European teams.

I suppose when the draw was made and we found ourselves not in the same group as the big name clubs, but in a league alongside RC Lens, Dinamo Kiev and Panathinaikos, we untutored Arsenal supporters thought this must be our year and we had drawn an ace card. We thought we would have no difficulty whatsoever finding a way through to the quarter-finals of this most prestigious of competitions. Arsene Wenger knew better and always believed this would be a very tight and difficult group (actually, there's no such thing as an easy group in this competition), and that we would have to win each of the three home games that we would play. As it turned out, we beat Panathinaikos, drew with Dinamo Kiev, having been comprehensively outplayed for the better part of the game, and tonight we lost to RC Lens. The match in Athens is now academic. Maurice is going and it still will give him the opportunity to experience the fantastic atmosphere that European fans are able to conjure up in front of their own team. It seemed tonight that Arsenal fans were completely subdued, as if we were playing an away game. The vocal support provided by the RC Lens fans was loud. Arsenal supporters were quiet. When on the way home I heard the commentators on BBC Radio Five Live speak of the 'fantastic atmosphere at Wembley tonight', I wondered whether they had been at the same Wembley.

As for the game, well they say that a team gets only two chances to score at this level of soccer, and must convert one of these chances. Arsenal's two chances came early in the first half. As early as the second minute Christopher Wreh, standing in for the once-more injured Dennis Bergkamp, managed to chest down a magnificent Ray Parlour cross, and with the goal gaping in front of him, miskicked his shot as the recovering defenders flew in. About ten minutes later, Anelka latched on to a fine Christopher Wreh through ball, and his ferocious pace left the Lens defence in his wake. Warmuz, the Lens goalkeeper, came off his line but was never going to get the ball. Instead of shooting low past the goalkeeper, for reasons best known to himself, Anelka decided a subtle chip over the goalkeeper was called for. Unfortunately, he chipped the ball too high and it went over the bar. So Arsenal's two chances had gone.

Lens' goal came in the seventy-second minute. Only a magnificent display by David Seaman meant that the game was still goalless, and that Arsenal still had a remote chance of winning. The ball reached the left wing, and the excellent Smicer turned Dixon one way and then the other, and then back again, and sent in a hard, low drive across the face of Seaman's goal. The ball certainly evaded Seaman and it seemed to me as if there was no other Arsenal defender there to clear it, they were standing in a line ahead of the ball appealing for offside. The referee and linesman were having none of it, and Michael Debeve, Lens' right full-back, came in at the far post and slid the ball into the empty net. Perhaps, I wondered, the Arsenal had for a moment forgotten they were playing in blue shirts (their third team strip) and did not recognise one another. Who knows? What the 74,000 of us watching did know was that Arsenal wouldn't find a way back into this match. Two goals in eighteen minutes? No. They've scored only three goals in the past six matches, and it's 444 minutes since they scored their last goal.

One more chance did fall to Overmars, last season's most reliable goalscorer. In the final minute, Overmars found himself in the Lens penalty box with only Warmuz to beat. The goalkeeper easily saved his weak lob and Arsenal's final chance to equalise had gone. That's when Maurice and I left the stadium, so we missed the sending off of Ray Parlour and Tony Vairelles in separate incidents, but except for maintaining discipline, these sendings off didn't matter. Arsenal already knew, in their collective head, that they were out of Europe.

So Arsenal must now turn their attentions to retaining the English championship in order to qualify for Europe next season. They will have to be far better equipped than they were this season. Arsene Wenger probably knows those players he would like to add to the Arsenal squad, allowing him to give the likes of Overmars, Bergkamp, Adams, Vieira and Petit a rest from football, rather than having to play them carrying injuries.

Was playing European home games at Wembley a success? Well, financially, I expect so. It enabled the club to sell a good proportion of tickets for £10 each, a terrific gesture to the fans, which also meant they could get twice as many supporters through the turnstiles as they would have been able to do at Highbury.

For the players, the experiment most certainly wasn't a success. I felt from game one that when they lost the ball they had tremendous difficulty in retrieving it, being much more used to a narrower and smaller playing area. For the supporters, I believe that Wembley was alien to them. It never felt like home, largely because we were not sitting amongst our regular companions. Tonight, for instance, instead of being with our comrades from East Stand, block C, we were surrounded, some might say invaded, by Lens supporters. Why was this? It was as if we were at an away game. I wonder whether this feeling was transmitted through the stands and on to the pitch, to the Arsenal players? I never once felt, in any of the three home games, that Arsenal were receiving the support that is so essential to them, and the entire atmosphere was somehow or other false.

So for me, the Wembley experience was a failure. I'm not saying this because Arsenal are out of the tournament, but because I believe that we didn't use our home advantage properly. Yes, it was a novelty at first, coming to the national stadium to watch your team, but Wembley has never been my favourite stadium, and it certainly doesn't work well without the pageantry, of which there is none during an ordinary club match. I do so hope that Arsenal decide not to pursue their ambition of making Wembley their regular home ground. Highbury may only seat 38,000, but it does at least feel like home, which I suppose begs the question, would Arsenal have progressed into the quarter-finals had they played their three home matches at Highbury? I doubt it. After not being able to dispose of Lens in France, when Arsenal could and should have won by at least three goals, everything thereafter was going to be a steep uphill struggle. I can clearly recall the sentiments of Marc Overmars after the Lens v. Arsenal match. He said that not scoring the chances that fell to us, and allowing Lens a last-minute goal, would be decisive. He was right.

It was also those last-minute goals that we conceded against Panathinaikos and, much more importantly, to Dinamo Kiev that were our undoing. Our defence, consistently so impenetrable, seemed to lose concentration and made it so unutterably difficult for themselves. Anyway, all of that is history right now, a learning curve. What I have learned is that if we are to do very well in this competition, we require a vastly enlarged squad of experienced and international players. We need players who have played regularly in this competition, and very much more discipline from those who haven't, who through suspension have rather let the side down. And we need another Dennis Bergkamp with no fear of flying, who doesn't mind travelling across Europe. Without a player of his inspiration, the team suffers.

There's still the Panathinaikos match, and perhaps we might win this game and learn a little more about playing at the highest level, where you get few goalscoring chances, and very little space to use the ball. I doubt we shall win in Athens, and that will mean we finish bottom of a group that everyone except Arsene Wenger thought was our passport into the quarter-finals. It just goes to show what little we English supporters know of European football, and perhaps what little our players know, too. Since the Heysel tragedy, we have failed to make an impression on the European Champions Cup.

THURSDAY, 26 NOVEMBER

I don't think I have completely got over the disappointment of
Arsenal failing to qualify for the quarter-finals of the European
Champions Cup, and part of that disappointment is to do with the
fact that they did not deserve to go any further than they have. I
suppose when Arsenal won the FA Cup final at Wembley earlier
this year thus pulling off the Double, I believed, as many others
did, including the bookmakers, that they really did stand a chance
of going all the way in the competition from which they have just
been eliminated. Then again, the team I watched earlier this year is
not the team I was watching last night. So many vital players were
not on display, and those that were are not playing as they did last
season. We shall just have to pick ourselves up, dust ourselves
down and start all over again – a rather good maxim, I believe.

WEDNESDAY, 9 DECEMBER
(aboard the ship *Seabourn Spirit*)

We have a fine evening, classical guitarist George Sakellariou
being excellent company, and his face lights up when I tell him
that had I not been on a ship tonight I would have been in Athens.
'Why?' asks George. 'Well, I would have been watching Panathinaikos playing Arsenal, my football team, in the European
Champions' Cup.' I look at my watch and add, 'It is now half-past
ten in the morning in London, so it is half-past midday in Athens.
In eight hours' time they will be kicking off and I want to know
what is going on.'

I realise that I can't watch the match on board ship, for there are
only four television stations, none of which are in the least bit
interested in what is going on anywhere other than on board or in
the USA. The only way I can follow the game is if I can receive
BBC World Service on my shortwave radio, or by going into
Bangkok at about three o'clock tomorrow morning. I consider this
possibility, but decide that it would be beyond the call of duty.

However, I now find that my radio doesn't work. This is the first
place I have ever been in the world where I couldn't pick up any
sort of reception at all. As for going to Bangkok, I suppose the
chances of me being picked up, kidnapped, sold for sex slavery,

and never again appearing before those I know and love are probably less great than the chances of Arsenal scoring a goal tonight.

THURSDAY, 10 DECEMBER

Okay, let's get our priorities right this morning. Where's the
paper? While I was asleep (getting my first full night's sleep, does
this mean the jet lag has at last left me?) Arsenal were playing
their final European Champions game of the season in Athens,
and I'm desperately keen to know by how many we were beaten.
I had read that they were without thirteen of the first-team squad
so goodness knows what team they were able to put out. Much to
my amazement, I see in *Britain Today* that Arsenal beat
Panathinaikos by 3–1. The brief report doesn't mention the
goalscorers, or the team that was fielded, but it does describe
Arsenal's performance as their finest of the season, and says that
had they played this way in their other matches they would have
by now qualified for the quarter-finals. They must now rue those
nights when they simply did not take the chances that fell to them.

MONDAY, 21 DECEMBER

. . . So here I am in a hotel room in Hong Kong, lying in a queen-
sized bed, watching live football from Highbury. The temperature
looks freezing. Nicolas Anelka wears gloves and everyone in the
capacity crowd is wrapped up against the cold. Here it's warm,
perhaps even very warm, and I can't imagine what it must be like
in London N5. It's quite extraordinary watching a football match
with a commentary in a language I can't begin to understand. I
can't make out one word; even the pronunciation of the players'
names is unintelligible. The pre-match, half-time and post-match
analysis is gobbledegook, and the translation into Chinese from
English of the players' thoughts about the match is mystifying. I
remember some years ago I watched Arsenal play Chelsea from
my hotel room in Cape Town, but on that occasion the commentary was in English and it was rather like being at home. Tonight
it seems as if the Chinese speak ninety words to the dozen, which
perhaps they might, and the commentary is far too frantic for the

action. The Chinese commentators become wildly excited when Arsenal win a throw-in forty yards from Leeds' penalty area. One would have thought Arsenal had just won the championship. It's amusing though, and certainly an experience to add to my Arsenal encounters.

The match, as it happens, is as exciting as any I've seen at Highbury or Wembley this season. Arsenal field what must be something close to their best available team: Manninger, Dixon, Vivas, Keown, Bould, Petit, Vieira, Ljungberg, Bergkamp, Anelka and Overmars – players, on their day, to beat any team. Arsenal start very fast and very well, but it's Leeds who spurn the greatest opportunity when David Hopkin misses what might be termed at this level of football an open goal – a let-off for Arsenal, who could then have fallen two goals behind if a better final pass by Harry Kewell had found Jimmy Floyd Hasselbaink. Instead, Arsenal take the lead through a goal so simple that I don't at first realise they have scored. Bergkamp seems to float the ball past Nigel Martyn, whose desperate dive takes him nowhere near it. The ball enters the Leeds net as if it were a balloon, and Bergkamp seems to have returned to his goalscoring ways.

In the second half, after about eight minutes, Arsenal increase their lead with a marvellous goal by Patrick Vieira. He bursts through the Leeds massed defence as if it didn't exist, and fires a low, hard drive into the corner of the net. This goal is as exhilarating as Bergkamp's was simple. Jimmy Floyd Hasselbaink's goal is even better than Vieira's. He scores with a twenty-yard, low, vicious drive past Manninger, and this goal must give Leeds hope. I can picture a scenario whereby Arsenal give away a late goal and Leeds take a point that they truly never looked like taking. But then comes the best goal of the game, and maybe Arsenal's finest of the season. Lots of passing in the midfield – this match really seems to me, 8,000 miles away, one of the highest quality – delivers the ball to Bergkamp's feet. He looks up and sends a delightful ball into open space behind the last line of Leeds' defence. Emmanuel Petit arrives from nowhere and without looking up, and all in one movement, shoots the ball wide of Martyn. It hits the inside of the post, but Petit has turned around ready to celebrate before the ball actually finds its way into the net. A masterly goal, and very European. A goal one would not encounter at Gillingham on the average Saturday afternoon.

SATURDAY, 26 DECEMBER

Back home in cold Oxfordshire after the warmth of the tropics, I am in the Cattle Shed. Kick-off at Highbury is at midday and we listen to the second-half commentary. Arsenal are playing West Ham United in the match that must have been billed as 'The Return of the Native' in the broadsheets, or 'Ian Wright Comes Home' in the tabloids. It seems that Arsenal have had almost all the play, and could easily have gone in 4–0 at half-time, as they did last season. As it is, they are a solitary goal ahead, scored in the seventh minute by Marc Overmars, and Nicolas Anelka has limped off with a damaged ankle. Christopher Wreh is his replacement.

In about the tenth minute of the second half, Arsenal nearly score a second goal, and it comes from, wait for it, wait for it, Alex Manninger! Yes, the goalkeeper! It's described by the commentator as 'nearly a Christmas madness goal'. Manninger takes a goalkick that travels high in the air towards the West Ham goal. Shaka Hislop, the Hammers' goalkeeper, left his line when Manninger took the kick, and from what I can interpret, the ball just flies over Hislop's head (obviously aided by the gale force wind) and is heading goalwards. When it reaches West Ham's goal, the ball goes just over the bar. That would have been one for the headlines. It would have been the first goal scored by a goalkeeper at Highbury for as long as I have been attending matches. When was the last time a team had every member score a goal in a football league season? Not Arsenal this season – so far only about four players seem able to find the net.

The second half continues to be all Arsenal yet they just can't score a second goal, which the commentator and I are sure would wrap up this game. Then with about five minutes left to play, West Ham surge forward in search of an equalising goal. Arsenal appear to be holding on by their boot straps rather than walking away with the match, and when the fourth official, as he is now called, tells us that there are four minutes of injury time to be played, I can see West Ham nicking a point. Arsenal hold on for the three points, which must move them up the Premiership table. They have taken six out of six points, and now that their foreign imports are beginning to play as they did last season, perhaps we might have a repetition of last New Year?

SATURDAY, 2 JANUARY 1999

Alan Hansen, Trevor Brooking and Desmond Lynam make their
FA Cup predictions. Lynam plumps for Aston Villa, Hansen for
Tottenham (who win impressively 5–2 against Watford this afternoon), and Brooking chooses Liverpool. I have a sneaking feeling
for Tottenham Hotspur, even though there isn't a 1 at the end of
the year. Who else? Well, don't rule out Arsenal or Chelsea, but if
I had to go for an outsider I think this might be Leeds United's
year.

MONDAY, 4 JANUARY

This is the start of the nineteenth year that Maurice and I have
worked together as full-time television writers. Where have all
the years gone? I remember that first year clearly. It began on 10
March, not 4 January, and we had ambitions to climb the ladder of
situation comedy history and be up there one day with the immor-
tals – Galton and Simpson, Clement and La Frenais, Took and
Feldman, Croft and Perry. Some are kind enough to say we made
it. Now nearly two decades later, we are to embark upon two new
situation comedies and a comedy drama series. What else comes
along during the year we shall have to wait and see. You can never
be sure that the year will turn out as you have planned it. In early
1985, we didn't imagine that half the year would be spent in Los
Angeles. I didn't know that my life would become so very different at the end of the year from the way it was at the beginning.

One thing that nineteen years of experience has taught me is not
to become over anxious about how the mind of an actor operates.
We still don't know if Nick Lyndhurst has signed his contract to
make the final ten episodes of 'Goodnight Sweetheart', so we
cannot be certain that we shall even be making this series. This
year, it's me to be the pragmatist, and I tell Maurice that everything usually turns out all right in the end.

The one outstanding FA Cup third-round tie is on TV tonight –
Preston North End v. Arsenal. I switch up the sound to try and
garner the atmosphere inside Deepdale. When I see the team, I
have to admit to wondering once again where Arsenal's goals are

going to come from: Manninger, Dixon, Bould, Keown, Vivas, Parlour, Vieira, Petit, Mendez, Boa Morte and Overmars. Surely they are capable of bringing Preston back to Highbury for a replay, and then perhaps Anelka and Bergkamp will be fit and ready to score the goals to take Arsenal through to the next round. Anyway, one goal is likely to settle this match, and I imagine the goal will be sneaked by Arsenal.

Wrong! After twenty minutes of play the score is Preston 2 Arsenal 0, and even the most fervent Gunners supporters can't see any way their team is going to get out of this mess, for mess it most certainly is. As I sit and watch Arsenal being uncharacteristically mauled, their defence torn apart time and again by an aggressive Preston forward line, I think that if Arsenal can come out of this Cup tie losing only 2–0, it will not be an embarrassment – just the upset of the round.

With a solitary minute to play before half-time, Boa Morte turns very quickly on to Mendez's throw-in and produces a cross shot that seems to take a deflection, spins wide of the goalkeeper's outstretched dive and arm, and the ball finds its way into the corner of the net. A goal just at the exact moment! Arsenal go in 2–1 down at half-time and now I think that they will win this tie. I don't believe they would have if they had walked back to the dressing-room 2–0 down. Boa Morte's goal may well prove to be one of the most important goals of Arsenal's season.

Then three minutes into the second half, the game is nearly all up for Arsenal when Stevie Bould passes the ball slowly back to Manninger, who mis-hits his clearance straight at Kurt Nogan. The goalkeeper is stranded on the edge of his six-yard box as the ball flies past him and just wide of the post. Mr Wenger's heart must be in his mouth. Mine certainly is, and I ask myself, 'Do Arsenal want to win this match?' But this is the turning point, and Arsenal start to come into their own, pushing forward with some smart midfield play.

After one or two threatening runs, Overmars bursts through the middle of the field, skipping past two or three challenges and is moving forward to score an equaliser when David Eyres cuts the flying Dutchman down right on the very edge of the penalty area. Eyres is shown the red card instantly and when the protests and the pushing and shoving die down, Petit curls the resulting free kick straight into the corner of the Preston net. Now at 2–2 it seems to me to be a matter of how many Arsenal will score. Petit puts Arsenal ahead eleven minutes from the final whistle, and Overmars delivers the final blow, sidefooting his shot calmly past David Lucas after a pass from Boa Morte. Post-match, there's some controversy about Arsenal's third goal, for Ryan Kidd seemed to be flattened by the forearm of Fabian Cabellero, Arsenal's sub for Mendez; but if he did send his forearm into Kidd's face, that's no more than Manninger experienced when Preston scored their second goal. Yes, I know two wrongs don't make a right, but there were a lot of flailing arms in this match and it's equalled itself up at the end of the game.

SATURDAY, 9 JANUARY

Arsenal are playing a most important league match against Liverpool, and I've said to Maurice that if we manage to grab the three points, I'll put a bet on Arsenal to retain the championship.

Up in the East Stand it's very cold indeed. I can't remember an afternoon, or evening for that matter, that was as cold last season. The three French players are donning black woollen gloves. The match is played at a furious pace, so much so that midway through the second half some of the midfield players seem to have run out of energy. Arsenal come closest to scoring in the first half of the first half, when a shot from Overmars just scrapes past the Liverpool post, with David James beaten; and Boa Morte fires a shot just wide following a tremendous mix-up in the Liverpool penalty area. But the two finest chances of the half fall to Liverpool.

Michael Owen for once (but he needs only one opportunity to win a match) outpaces Keown and Bould and bears down on Arsenal's goal. Manninger comes off his line and Owen is forced to shoot, thankfully with his wrong foot, and the ball goes into the side netting. It should really have been a goal, and I believe that had Liverpool scored at this moment they would have taken all three points. Then from a Vegard Heggem cross, Steve Harkness connects with a stunning volley from just inside the Arsenal penalty area. Somehow Manninger gets down to the shot, which he really couldn't have seen coming, and parries the ball away; the save of the season, as far as I'm concerned. It could well prove to be the most important save of the season too, especially if Arsenal are able to score the one goal that I think will win this match.

At half-time there's no score, so usual for Arsenal this season. In the second half it seems to be all Arsenal, but there is always the chance that Liverpool will come forward and score. Steve Bould has overstretched himself in the first half, damaging his hamstring, and is replaced by young Matthew Upson, who very nearly puts Arsenal ahead with a free header from about six yards out, but he directed the Petit cross straight to James. Arsenal mount attack after attack, but James doesn't have one save to make and Arsenal create not a chance. There isn't one moment when they find themselves in a clear goalscoring position. Those occasions when we believe they might score come from long-range shots that scrape just past the post, or in the case of Anelka miss it by a mile – his shot from the edge of the penalty box is so far wide that Liverpool gain a throw-in between corner flat and halfway line!

Manninger has to pull off another excellent acrobatic save from a Jamie Redknapp free kick, and a goalmouth scramble at the other end gives Arsenal three chances to score a goal, but none are taken and the match is played out largely in the Liverpool penalty area and in midfield, where once more Vieira and Petit are masterly, and Ray Parlour is completely off form. Overmars is replaced by Remi Garde, and Anelka by Wreh, but it makes no difference and the game finishes goalless. Arsenal have, in my opinion, lost two points rather than gained one. They should have beaten Liverpool this afternoon and failing to do so could prove costly.

FRIDAY, 15 JANUARY

Arsenal have bought Nwankwo Kanu from Inter Milan. Arsenal have been in desperate need of another striker, perhaps since they sold Ian Wright (which, judging by his injury record this season and the few outings he has made for West Ham, was a shrewd sale). Kanu has long been a target for Mr Wenger and, I say to Maurice over a good lunch, wasn't Kanu on my wish list about a season and a half ago? I had seen him play for Nigeria and was as impressed by him as I was with Ronaldo. Around £4.5 million is the purchase price being bandied about, and a six-year contract. There is some doubt about the health and fit-

ness of the twenty-two-year-old striker, who has already won a
European Cup and an Olympic gold medal. I expect Dr Sash has
been hard at work determining whether Kanu is worth the
money or whether Arsenal may be buying a pup. Kanu had a
heart valve operation in America two years ago, and the last
thing anyone wants is the 6ft 5in striker dropping down dead in
front of 38,000 loyal Arsenal fans.

Maurice has the lowdown on Kanu. He led Nigeria to victory in
the 1996 Olympic Games soccer tournament shortly after lifting
the European Cup with Ajax; he has eleven international caps and
has scored twice for his country. He last played for Nigeria in June
in a 4–1 defeat by Denmark in the World Cup finals. His opportunities at Inter, who signed him for £1.3 million in 1997, have been
severely limited because of medical doubts. I wonder what
Arsenal feel they can get from this striker that Inter Milan could-
n't? The months ahead will tell us the whole story. We might just
have in our ranks a bargain buy, for if he is as good as Arsene
Wenger believes he is, Kanu at £4.5 million is a great purchase.
John Hartson went yesterday from West Ham to Wimbledon for
£7.5 million. I wonder when Kanu will make his debut for Arsenal,
and what impact he will have on our feeble strike rate.

SUNDAY, 24 JANUARY

Arsenal go into their FA cup fourth round game against Wolves
with Seaman, Keown, Bould and Vieira either injured or suspended. The prolonged absence of David Seaman is something of
a mystery. His injury, whatever it might be, has not been reported,
he has been out for the past month or longer, and I'm beginning to
wonder whether his absence has something to do with Arsenal
preparing to sell him. Arsenal's line-up this afternoon is:
Manninger, Dixon, Adams, Upson, Winterburn, Petit, Parlour,
Garde, Anelka, Bergkamp and Overmars. On paper, Arsenal
should win this match with something to spare, but all away Cup
ties can prove difficult as we saw at Preston in the third round, and
Arsenal have never been the best team in England to win their
Cup ties at a canter.

However, with the match just eleven minutes old, Overmars
collects a pass from Adams, following a brilliant interception,

and starts his mischievous run at the Wolves defence. They back off, and back off, and back off – which is what you don't do against Overmars – and when the little Dutch winger has run infield and finds himself just outside the Wolves penalty box, he looks up (presumably for someone to whom he may pass the ball), but fires a low, accurate shot past Mike Stowell, the Wolves goalkeeper, into the corner of the net. Arsenal are a goal up and I can't imagine, even though there are only eleven minutes played, Wolves coming back into this game and causing a major upset.

Arsenal had, in fact, put the ball into the back of the Wolves net about five minutes earlier, when Anelka got on the end of a Parlour cross and fired a volley past the Wolves goalkeeper, but the linesman had somewhat hesitantly waved Anelka offside. (When the action replay re-runs the video, it shows that Anelka was not offside. It was the finest goal he has scored all season long.)

Arsenal, now a goal up, dominate the game with their speed and efficient passing, although from where I'm sitting they look less than convincing, seemingly playing in first gear. Bergkamp and Anelka seem well below par, although Garde is excellent, as are Dixon and Winterburn. Upson sometimes looks uncomfortable with the ball, and Manninger, so marvellous last season, makes some rudimentary mistakes, but thankfully not when a Wolves player is in his vicinity. One almost senses that Manninger is going to do something that puts Arsenal in trouble. In one Wolves attack, as Michael Gilkes sends in a diagonal cross, Manninger chooses to leave the ball. It hits the bar and fortunately arrives at the feet of an Arsenal defender rather than a Wolves attacker. I wonder what Manninger was thinking as the ball was floated towards him. Did someone call and ask him to leave the ball? Has his judgement suddenly become impaired?

About ten minutes later, a similar cross comes in from Kevin Muscat (the hard man of the Wolves team). The ball is without question Manninger's to pluck out of the air. Upson, who leaves it for him, presumably because Manninger called him to leave it, watches his goalkeeper come late, attempt to punch the ball but punch nothing more than thin air. Havard Flo, Wolves's latest £750,000 signing from Werder Bremen, gets his head to the ball and it sails off the post into the Arsenal net. Wolves have equalised due to poor goalkeeping, or lack of understanding between two inexperienced Arsenal defenders. Will Wolves become dangerous now, and take the game to Arsenal?

At 1–1 at half-time, it would seem to me, and to Kenny Dalglish and Gareth Southgate in the studio, that Arsenal will get into third gear and win this match, but I have to say that this afternoon Arsenal don't look in the mood to step up any gears. Everyone seems to be doing 'just enough' to get them through the afternoon, as though it's Arsenal's divine right to win this game. But I've seen so many matches like this, when the underdog senses blood, goes for it, gets it, and wins the match. It happened yesterday at Villa Park (Fulham won 2–0) and there's no reason at all it shouldn't happen this afternoon at Molineux.

Ten minutes into the second half it almost does! Again it's Flo who is causing the Arsenal defence unrest. From Muscat's diagonal cross (this cross seems to be Arsenal's undoing), Flo muscles Arsenal defenders out of his path and fires a low cross shot that beats Manninger but hits the inside of the right-hand post before rebounding back into play. This is the moment when Arsenal must either step up their game or lose their grip on the FA Cup.

The winning goal comes in the sixty-ninth minute, and it's Bergkamp, who has been roughly treated all afternoon, who scores it. By the time the goal arrives he has blood running from his mouth, caused by a stray elbow. From Remi Garde's corner (Garde is the best player on the field this afternoon), the ball is half cleared and falls to Bergkamp who volleys it goalward. The volley itself never looks as though it will produce a goal, hard and accurate though it is, but on its way the ball is deflected off Flo and then Keith Curle, and flies past Stowell. Arsenal are 2–1 ahead and I can't see them letting this lead disappear.

The game degenerates into a nasty, bad-tempered affair and I don't know why. I think Muscat's close attention to Bergkamp is what sparks everything off, and near the end a Bergkamp foul on Curle brings retaliation that at one point seems likely to escalate into a violent confrontation. Curle aims a punch at Bergkamp and gets away with it. With just two minutes of play left, and by now Arsenal are looking comfortable winners, Emmanuel Petit is shown a red card for something I didn't see him do. Having already been booked for an eighteenth-minute foul on Carl Robinson, the Frenchman is instantly dismissed for, apparently, foul and abusive language towards a linesman. I wonder if the foul and abusive language was in French.

It's ludicrous that Petit has been dismissed (the second time this season) for saying something while Muscat remains on the field without so much as a yellow card. I believe that Arsene Wenger is a very angry man at the end of this match, and who can blame him? It seems to me, as well as Wenger, that there is some type of media campaign against Arsenal, and referees do not do unto Arsenal as they do unto others.

SATURDAY, 30 JANUARY

When I heard on BBC Radio Four's news this morning the opening words, 'Glenn Hoddle, England's football coach . . .' I expected the next words to be, 'died last night when his car . . .' such was the newsreader's tone. Instead, what he went on to say was, '. . . has come under stinging attack from all quarters for telling *The Times* that it is his belief that the disabled, and others, are being punished for sins in a former life.' This morning's feature on Glenn Hoddle in *The Times* has already, and it's only nine o'clock, stirred up a hornet's nest of controversy. Politicians, people from the sports world, commentators from all walks of life and, of course, the disabled and those associated with them, are screaming from the rooftops about Hoddle's own goal.

It's unnecessary to comment, other than to say you cannot, and should not, take away the man's religious beliefs if that is what he holds dear. He is entitled to an opinion. I wonder whether *The Times* journalist sent to interview him brought up the subject of religious beliefs, or whether Hoddle instigated this off his own bat.

The row has deepened, and people from all walks of life are crying out, almost religiously, for the England coach's resignation – I don't quite know why. I don't see what it has to do with football management. So Hoddle has hit back. I suppose he had to really. He claims his remarks about people with disabilities have been 'misconstrued, misunderstood and misrepresented'.

The Football Association immediately defend Hoddle against the criticism. 'We regard him as an excellent coach [not on results, they can't] and supporter of the disabled,' said the FA's Steve

Double. I think this story has a lot of mileage in it yet, not least because Hoddle also said in his interview with *The Times*, regarding the media critics, 'The gloves are off, and I am ready to throw the first bare-knuckle punch.' The *Sun*, not the newspaper to lie down quietly, will be preparing their back-page retaliation. I look forward to the next few days.

But whatever Hoddle has said, if indeed he meant it as written, is not a resigning matter. It seems that as soon as anyone does anything at all wrong these days, there are screams for resignation. Are we no longer allowed to make mistakes?

SUNDAY, 31 JANUARY

Today could be the match of the season at Highbury, Arsenal v. Chelsea, and in the stadium Maurice and I are keen to know whether Arsenal's new signing, Kaba Diawara, will turn out this afternoon for the injured Dennis Bergkamp. It's not long before we hear over the Tannoy that not only is Bergkamp playing, but David Seaman is returning this afternoon for the first time this year. Our defence is as strong as it can be. It'll need to be to keep out a very good Chelsea attack. Seaman, Dixon, Adams, Keown, Winterburn, Parlour, Garde, Petit, Overmars, Anelka and Bergkamp is the starting line-up, and if we thought we were going to miss the influence of Patrick Vieira we are happily wrong, for Remi Garde plays out of his skin. He is developing into a fine midfield defensive player. This afternoon he has his finest game for Arsenal and seems to be involved in every move going forward.

This match has been billed as some kind of blood bath by the tabloid press and, to avoid it becoming one I suppose, Graham Poll, the referee, takes unnecessary action in booking Franck Leboeuf for a nothing foul after just two minutes, and then Dennis Bergkamp for something I didn't see, after four minutes. Perhaps Poll's tactics work, for after Bergkamp's booking the game calms down a little.

It is a dashing though stalemate sort of midfield battle for the first half an hour. Dan Petrescu's name is added to those already in Poll's book. Neither side make either goalkeeper earn his wages, although Overmars does fire one low and accurate drive forcing

Ed De Goey to stretch to push it around the post. Then in the thirty-first minute, Arsenal score. As one would expect, the pass into the Chelsea penalty area comes from the *magnifique* Emmanuel Petit. His chip forward finds Marc Overmars. Somehow the little Dutchman reaches the high ball before Dan Petrescu and it falls into the Chelsea penalty area just where you would usually find two defenders, but not this time. Bergkamp, striding forward, has time enough to switch feet, and with his stronger right foot fires a low, hard shot past De Goey into the far corner of the net.

Arsenal at 1–0 up are a very hard side to beat, and Chelsea don't look as though they are even going to equalise. This 1–0 half-time lead is made all the sweeter when we learn that Manchester United are being held 0–0 by Charlton Athletic.

The second half is a very different game from the first. Chelsea attack, find space, and stretch Arsenal's superb defence to its limit. Seaman has to make one outstanding save from Di Matteo, which he does with such nonchalance that it's easy to forget how ferocious a shot he has just stopped. Chelsea surge forward, and only last-ditch tackles, usually by Keown, prevent them from scoring the one goal they require for a point. Arsenal have a very good chance to increase their lead. From a superb long pass by Ray Parlour, Dennis Bergkamp brings the ball down and moves into the Chelsea penalty box all in one flowing movement, but just when we all think he is going to score another memorable goal, he seems to get his feet tangled up and doesn't even get in a shot.

Two more players find a place in the referee's notebook – Bjarne Goldbaek (who has come on for the injured Michael Duberry), and Martin Keown, who looked all afternoon as though a yellow card had his name written all over it. Remarkably, no one is sent off, although there are moments when provocation by Dennis Wise makes it seem likely that someone, from either team, might be. And still Chelsea continue to attack, and attack, and all the time Arsenal defend and manage to prevent the Chelsea stars from having a shot on goal. Knowing that we must keep hold of this lead, Arsene Wenger brings off Nick Anelka and replaces him with Nelson Vivas to shore up the midfield, and soon afterwards, when perhaps Mr Wenger believes the game might be won, he takes off Bergkamp and Overmars and replaces them with Matthew Upson, and new boy Diawara, who looks like a giant-sized Christopher

Wreh. Indeed, the man who sits next to me shouts out, 'Are you sure you ain't Wreh and we ain't bought anyone at all!?'

This new French forward, bought on Friday from Bordeaux, looks very strong and quick, and soon after coming on he turns Leboeuf inside out, but is closed down before he can fire in a shot on Chelsea's goal. He does, though, look a little lost upfront on his own, but nobody criticises him for he has been training with his team-mates for less than a week. It's too soon to tell how good a player we have bought, but for now all of our attentions are turned to defence, which is where the ball spends most of the final ten minutes of this match. Our extraordinary back four hold out, and I comment to the chap who sits on my left (same man as last season – still don't know his name) how influential Tony Adams's presence is, and whatever are we going to do when he retires.

The final whistle is blown after ninety-six minutes and Arsenal win 1–0. Unfortunately, Manchester United nick a last-minute winner, through Dwight Yorke, and so take all three points and go top of the Premier League. But Alex Ferguson pronounces on the radio later this evening that once again he expects the Premiership to become a two-horse race, between United and Arsenal. I don't know. I have been impressed by Chelsea, and I wouldn't yet write off Aston Villa, although they seem to be going through a slightly black patch this month.

What is certain is that the Manchester United v. Arsenal battle at Old Trafford on Wednesday fortnight will be as important this season as it was last, and we can but pray for the same result. If Arsenal win there, I believe, and I suspect so does Mr Wenger, that the championship is in the Gunners' hands. We can then only lose it.

Monday, 1 February

The Glenn Hoddle story is still making headlines. This is the biggest story of the year, and were there to be yet another massacre in Kosovo I believe this Hoddle story would push the dead bodies from the front pages. Today it is announced that he will be summoned to the Football Association tomorrow where he will put his side of the story before his future is decided – which usually means he is to lose his job. It seems that he has proclaimed that he will not resign, and this on the morning that Tony Blair gets his tuppence worth. The Prime Minister tells the 'This Morning' programme that if Hoddle's views had been correctly recorded it 'would be very difficult for him to stay'.

Maurice thinks that Hoddle will get the push and that Terry Venables will return to the post. I'm reminded of a conversation last year when someone said the next England manager would be Howard Wilkinson, with David Platt at his right hand. Now that Platt has a job in Europe, I wonder whether he would be prepared to return to England to co-produce the biggest football show in town.

Tuesday, 2 February

At about seven o'clock this evening, it is announced that Glenn Hoddle has been sacked as England's football coach, following thirty-six hours of frantic discussion over his suggestion that the disabled were paying for the sins of a previous life. The Football Association told Hoddle that he had damaged himself and his employers by his remarks in an interview with *The Times*, and that his position had become untenable.

Why has his position become untenable? He's committed no crime. He was fairly good at his job as the England coach, and seems to have let nobody down. He explained some of his beliefs to a reporter, as he was asked to do. Is that a sacking offence? Apparently it is. Hoddle fought desperately to keep his job until five o'clock, but once he had been pushed, he publicly admitted making a serious error of judgement that had caused pain to people, for which he apologised.

He is expected to receive a £500,000 pay-off (I was wondering when money would come into it – no good story these days is complete without the mention of money), representing the remaining eighteen months of his contract. Howard Wilkinson, the former manager of Leeds United, was asked to stand in within an hour of the sacking and promptly accepted.

The Football Association continually choose the wrong man for the job, and are continually let down. Of course, when they do choose someone worthy, a fine manager such as Terry

Venables or Alf Ramsey, what happens to them? They are eventually asked to leave or are sacked. I believe Glenn Hoddle, good manager or bad, is well out of it. Let him go and seek work with a league club, and be out of the continual gaze of mad media people, who feel it is their role in life to bring people down because that makes good copy.

WEDNESDAY, 10 FEBRUARY

Tonight's big match is England v. France, live from a freezing cold Wembley Stadium, but it's warm in the Cattle Shed. This is a significant friendly. England are taking on the world champions in preparation for next month's Euro 2000 qualifying match against Poland, which England *must* win. The team is being coached for the first time by Howard Wilkinson, the temporary manager, and I suppose the result could determine whether the Football Association keep him in the job on a permanent basis, or appoint someone else. Nobody seems able to work out who that might be. I suspect the job will be Howard Wilkinson's win, lose or draw, for he is the solid, unadventurous type of chap who gratifies the grey-suited gentlemen at the FA. Flair is not something that administrators feel comfortable with, not that any English-born managers with flair are queuing up to become the next England coach.

Wilkinson's choice of eleven this evening is: Seaman, Dixon, Adams, Keown, Le Saux, Ince, Beckham, Redknapp, Owen, Shearer and Anderton. On paper, it looks a very good side. The French put out a very strong eleven: Barthez, Thuram, Blanc, Desailly, Lizarazu, Pires, Zidane, Deschamps, Petit, Djorkaeff and Anelka. The French team control the game at the start, but England could and should have gone ahead after two minutes, when a curling free kick from David Beckham finds Tony Adams and from six yards out he heads the ball just past Barthez's right-hand post.

Another golden chance falls to Michael Owen about ten minutes later, but he can't get the whole of his foot to the ball and fires his shot against Barthez's leg. About ten minutes before half-time, another wonderful chance drops to Keown, but unfortunately on his wrong foot, and the Arsenal defender snatches at a volley which goes about two yards over the French bar. Had one of these three chances been accepted, England might have gone on to win the match. As it is, the score is goalless at half-time and Howard Wilkinson must be telling his team to carry on as they have been, for they look solid at the back, inventive in midfield, though without any punch upfront. Perhaps Andy Cole might be introduced.

I don't know what the French head coach says to his players at half-time, but they come out for the second forty-five minutes as if they are a different team. England replace Seaman with Nigel Martyn, the Leeds goalkeeper, and the game resumes with France dominating the half from start to finish. I don't believe England have another shot on goal, and not even when Andy Cole replaces Michael Owen does England's attack look as though it's ever likely to penetrate this French defence. In midfield, Zidane controls everything, and is continually fed by the skills of Petit, who is magnificent, and Desailly, who isn't half bad either. Indeed, all of the French eleven are outstanding in this second half and they play England off the park. I don't think I have ever seen an England team so outplayed at Wembley, and yet as France just take hold of this game and dominate it they have nothing by way of goals to show for it. When they do score, the referee doesn't see it. A fantastic shot from Nicolas Anelka hits the bar and crosses, but the referee waves play on and France are denied the lead.

The shot is almost identical to Geoff Hurst's third goal in the 1966 World Cup final, but today we have the television technology to watch a slow motion playback from several angles, and each one shows that Anelka's shot crossed the line and he should have been credited with scoring France's very first goal against England at Wembley. Never mind. Anelka's next chance comes from a wonderful reverse pass from Zidane. It finds the young Arsenal centre-forward with only Martyn to beat, and Anelka slides the ball into the net – France 1 England 0.

Lee Dixon is carried off soon afterwards with concussion, and when Martin Keown goes off with a pulled hamstring, I begin to wonder how many players will be available when Arsenal travel to Old Trafford in a week's time. Rio Ferdinand comes on for Dixon, and he is turned inside out by Djorkaeff before the Frenchman crosses hard and low for Anelka to score his second – France 2 England 0, and that goal should have been Anelka's hat-trick. Zidane has a very good chance to make it 3–0, but somehow

Martyn makes an excellent save from the Frenchman when he is left in the clear, inside the penalty box.

There is never a moment when I think England are going to pull a goal back. They have been well and truly hammered, out-played, and given a lesson in controlled football. There are no excuses. They are not as good as France in any single department. Anelka is brought off (to save him for Saturday, I hope), and replaced by another Arsenal player, Patrick Vieira, who very nearly scores a goal himself. No, at the final whistle England realise, and particularly Howard Wilkinson realises, that some-thing drastic has to be done between now and the Poland match if England are to have any realistic chances of qualifying for Euro 2000. A very good and confident manager would be a start.

After the game, Arsene Wenger says that while England were outplayed by his compatriots, it was due to lack of confidence. Mr Wenger adds that he knows all the England players, and they are very fine footballers indeed. What has happened over the past weeks has done nobody any good at all, least of all the players, and tonight they looked like a team who had had their confidence removed surgically.

SATURDAY, 13 FEBRUARY

This afternoon's game will go down in FA Cup history as 'The Match That Never Was'. It's fifth-round day and Arsenal are at home to Sheffield United, not an easy match – not that any matches at this stage of the competition are easy. I wander to the stadium, giving Colin Hughes from the *Guardian* the prediction that Arsenal will win 4–1. He says he can't imagine that Arsenal will put four goals past United, neither can he see them scoring a goal against this Arsenal defence. But this Arsenal defence, as he terms it, will not be out there this afternoon. The Arsenal team is somewhat unusual: Seaman, Vivas, Grimandi, Bould, Winterburn, Parlour, Vieira, Garde, Bergkamp, Diawara and Overmars. I can see it on the videotron – a large screen that gives the teams and all the other information, as well as action replays when the action is non-controversial, and nothing else this season is going to be as controversial as what happens in the seventy-seventh minute.

In the first half, the team proves to be extremely well balanced and it's all one-way traffic. Arsenal dominate; the only mystery is how they fail to find themselves in a two-goal lead. I know, and so do those around me, that a goal has to come. Sheffield United have a couple of headers at the Arsenal goal, but these go way over the bar and Seaman is never really troubled.

Coming up to twenty minutes of play, Arsenal are throwing forward legions of attacks. Everything seems to be starting from the cultivated boot of Remi Garde, a player who seems to improve with every game he plays, even if he is not a natural replacement for Emmanuel Petit (who today begins his three-match suspension for being sent off against Wolves).

A quick break down the left-hand side of the pitch, between Winterburn (this afternoon making the fourth most number of appearances for Arsenal), Bergkamp and Overmars ends with the ball finding its way to Diawara, who is bundled off it. From the free kick on the left-hand side of Sheffield United's penalty area, Bergkamp, protecting his eyes from the strong sunlight, loops the ball into the penalty box and Patrick Vieira rises above everyone and heads it into the far corner of the net. Arsenal are a goal up and I think this could well be the start of an avalanche.

I'd been complaining for the duration of the match so far that David Seaman, England's number one goalkeeper, just seems to refuse to come off his goalline to collect any crosses from either wing. This is the cause of the goal he concedes early in the second half. From a quickly taken free kick, Paul Devlin crosses the ball deep into the Arsenal penalty box, Seaman stays put on his line, Grimandi isn't tall enough to reach the ball (Adams and Keown would have been), and Marcello, United's Brazilian centre-forward, gets up and heads a fine ball low to Seaman's left. The Arsenal goalkeeper is neither quick nor agile enough to reach it and the header finds its way into the bottom corner of the net for the equaliser.

At 1–1 Arsenal must go forward, but everyone around me thinks it'll end in a draw. Arsenal don't look as though they are going to score a winner. They have shots on goal, but none really bother the United goalkeeper. Arsenal win many corners too, but nothing seems to come from them. Bergkamp is having a poor second half. Mr Wenger replaces Diawara with another new signing, Nwankwo Kanu. The lanky Nigerian takes the pitch to huge applause, but he will earn a place in FA Cup folklore for all the wrong reasons.

This is the incident as it happens. Sheffield United's Lee Morris runs into the Arsenal penalty box and is heading dangerously goalwards when he is tackled by Gilles Grimandi. Sheffield United appeal for a penalty. It clearly isn't, but Morris is injured and stays down in the Arsenal penalty box. The ball is still in play. It's eventually passed back to United's goalkeeper, Alan Kelly, who kicks it into touch so Morris can receive treatment. After treatment, Morris still can't play and is replaced by Bobby Ford. It's Arsenal's throw-in, and Ray Parlour restarts the game by throwing the ball into the right-hand corner of the United half, as is the custom in such circumstances. Unaware of this tradition and that Parlour is following usual sporting practice, even though the Sheffield United defence is lined up on the halfway line, Nwankwo Kanu sets off after the ball and before it can roll off for a goalkick, crosses low for Overmars to tap into the empty net. This is much as Chris Sutton did the season before last, and from the corner he forced Winterburn to give away, Blackburn Rovers scored the goal that kept Arsenal out of the European Champions Cup.

All hell breaks loose. Everyone leaps to their feet to protest that it is cheating and the goal should not be allowed to stand. Referee Peter Jones is surrounded by fuming Sheffield United players and manager, Steve Bruce, who looks as though he is about to have a fit. The referee seeks his linesman's advice before realising that he has no option but to let the Arsenal goal stand. Bruce comes running on to the pitch, scuffles break out between players, although I have to say that the Arsenal players look acutely embarrassed. Bruce orders his players from the pitch. Captain David Holdsworth starts to follow his manager's orders before his teammate Graham Stuart intervenes. Three policemen attempt to keep order on the visitors' bench; many more attempt to stop fighting breaking out in the south stand, and prevent the Sheffield United fans, who have to be as furious as ever fans have been, from invading the pitch and doing damage to Kanu and Overmars. I have never seen anything like this before at a football match, and even though I'm an Arsenal supporter I realise that either the goal should have been disallowed or, if that isn't in the rules of the game, Arsenal should have given Sheffield United a goal back.

In the centre circle, Nigel Winterburn explains to a bemused Kanu what all the fuss is about, and how what he has done could make him a hated figure at every football ground in England.

After eight minutes' delay, the match restarts with Marcelo kicking the ball right into the Arsenal half, hoping, I imagine, that an Arsenal defender might kick the ball into his own goal. No such event occurs, and the match continues up until the final whistle, with Arsenal winning this fifth-round tie, 2–1. I feel so sorry for Sheffield United.

On the drive back to Clarges Street, Maurice and I hear Arsene Wenger tell a reporter that he has offered to replay the game, and that a fuming Steve Bruce, United's manager, applauds Wenger's gesture and says the goal could have been disallowed for ungentlemanly conduct. Within an hour it's announced that the Football Association have accepted Mr Wenger's desire to replay the match and it will take place at Highbury on Tuesday week. Some £600,000 in gate receipts and TV cash will be split between Arsenal and Sheffield United, with the remaining £400,000 going to the FA. I think that all the money from the rematch should go to charity.

The questions of what happens to the players who scored, received yellow cards or are currently serving suspensions are still to be resolved. Will this game simply be wiped from the record book? I don't see how it can be.

TUESDAY, 23 FEBRUARY

This evening I listen to the 'Fair Play Replay' against Sheffield United on the radio, as we all had to in the days before Sky Sports. I was rather hoping that the match would be televised, but it was only yesterday evening that FIFA, who felt the need to interfere and threaten this match, gave their blessing for the replay to go ahead. FIFA's argument was that nothing against the rules had occurred in the first match. Arsenal had scored two legitimate goals, Sheffield United one, *ergo* Arsenal should go through to the quarter-finals. The fact that nobody involved in the game wanted Arsenal's second goal to stand seemed not to concern FIFA. Dangerous precedents were all that they were worried about. Anyway, tonight the teams will once again take the pitch at Highbury and play out this match as though it had never been played before.

It seems to be taking much the same shape as the last, scrubbed-from-the-records match, with Arsenal dominating the first half. A marvellous chance to open the scoring falls to Marcelo, the United centre-forward, but he muffs it and Arsenal breathe again. As it was described on the radio, Marcelo was twelve yards from Arsenal's goal with only Seaman to beat, and blasted his shot high over the bar. United live to regret this miss for after fourteen minutes who else but Marc Overmars puts the Gunners ahead. From the same distance as Marcelo missed his golden opportunity, Overmars hits a low drive into the net, and Radio Five Live almost miss the goal as they have gone across to Preston to hear how they are doing this evening.

Arsenal were 1–0 ahead at half-time in the first match, so I believe they need another goal to sew up this match, and they get it on thirty-seven minutes, and a wondrous goal it is too from Dennis Bergkamp. It seems that he only scores wonderous goals, and he scores them in abundance when he runs into rich form, as he seems to have done now. Picking up a Ray Parlour cross from the right, he swivels on the ball, loses two players, and from about fifteen yards neatly chips the perfect shot over the advancing Alan Kelly. As the ball drops into the net, I can feel the commentators jumping from their seats and applauding such a masterpiece of a goal. At 2–0, surely Arsenal won't allow this match to come close to being a replay.

In the second half, United abandon their defensive policy and send men forward. Of course, this could well lead to a goal rush by Arsenal, much as happened at Highbury on Saturday when they destroyed Leicester City by 5–0, but that is the risk Steve Bruce and his Sheffield United side must take; otherwise they will just defend a two-goal deficit and go out of the FA Cup. What actually occurs is that although Arsenal push forward, and might have scored another one or two goals, United push forward too, and Arsenal find themselves defending their goal more than they would like. With just four minutes of the game left, Lee Morris pulls one back with a simple tap in and now United go forward to try and force a replay at Bramall Lane, which they must believe they would win, after all they did three seasons ago.

But it isn't to be and Arsenal win by precisely the same result as the 'game that never was' ten days ago. In the quarter-finals, Arsenal will meet the winners of tomorrow night's replay between Huddersfield and Derby County, either of whom Arsenal should beat and thus progress to the semi-finals.

SUNDAY, 28 FEBRUARY

The match is being televised live from a very wet and hideously blustery St James's Park, Newcastle. Kick-off is 4 p.m. Arsenal are nearly back to full strength: Seaman, Dixon, Adams, Keown (back from injury after several weeks), Winterburn, Vieira, Garde, Parlour, Bergkamp, Anelka and Overmars. Short of Petit, who is injured and will be out of action for at least another fortnight, this is Arsenal's first-choice team. On their afternoon, they have the beating of anyone else in the Premier League.

However, the game is just three minutes old when a bad tackle by Nolberto Solano fells Remi Garde and leaves the Frenchman writhing. The diagnosis is a badly sprained ankle and, needless to say, Garde plays no further part in the match. He is replaced by Stephen Hughes (not a bad replacement – no longer reserve substitutions, but first-team squad players) and the game moves at first very much in Newcastle's direction.

Alan Shearer misses a near unmissable opportunity just three yards from the Arsenal goal, when he lunges to reach a perfect cross, but somehow lets the ball roll past his outstretched right leg and off for a goalkick. With so much attacking pressure from Newcastle, it seems inevitable that Arsenal will break away and score. The ball is played cleverly out of defence, following yet another Newcastle attack, lofted forward just inside the Newcastle half, and a very poor clearance that should have been easy meat for Nikos Dabizas falls to Dennis Bergkamp. He threads a ball behind Steve Howey and into the path of the ebullient Nicolas Anelka. The young Frenchman's pace gets him through on goal, and without any other thought, he rounds Shay Given and taps the ball into the empty net. Arsenal are a goal up, and Anelka has just scored his sixth goal in four matches. Perhaps Mr Wenger really did know that this young centre-forward was the perfect replacement for Ian Wright after all.

A goal up at half-time, you must believe that Arsenal will gain the much-needed three points. The defence have let in only twelve league goals all season, not a bad defensive record. I think I'm right in saying that it's the best defensive record in Europe! The truth is Arsenal could have been 3–0 up at half time; certainly 2–0 up had Bergkamp's fierce drive not been deflected just to the left of Shay Given's post.

In the seventy-seventh minute Newcastle score, and such an untypical goal for Arsenal to concede. Following a series of passes that brings Newcastle from just outside their own penalty area well into Arsenal's, and with some sloppy clearances by the Arsenal defence, the ball eventually arrives at the feet of Dietmar Hamann, who dribbles past what seems to be the entire Arsenal defence. By the time the German is very close to the Arsenal penalty box, no Gunner is prepared to bring him down, neither should he, and just maintaining his balance, Hamann scores with what looks like a toe-poke. Actually, it's a much better goal than it seems at the moment of being scored. On reflection, I feel that Newcastle deserve a point this afternoon.

It means, as the game ends 1–1, that Arsenal are now seven points behind Manchester United, although we have a game in hand. If we win that one, we will be four points behind, and need United to lose a match very soon. Arsene Wenger says after the match that he believes the European Champions League will take its toll on United, no matter how large their squad, and it's Chelsea, in Mr Wenger's opinion, who will step up the gear required to take the championship. But nobody is ruling out Arsenal. With eleven matches left play, we stand to take a maximum of 33 points. As we currently have 50, and Arsene Wenger feels that 75 points will win this year's title, we must find 25 points. I think it's possible. Manchester United have 57 points, so they require only eighteen more. It's going to be a hard slog for us to retain our title, but certainly not impossible.

SATURDAY, 6 MARCH

It's supposed to be FA Cup quarter-final day but only Arsenal and Derby are playing. The Barnsley v. Tottenham game was called off at ten o'clock this morning due to the ground being thick with snow.

The Arsenal team is: Seaman, Dixon, Adams, Keown, Winterburn, Ljungberg, Parlour, Hughes, Overmars, Anelka and Bergkamp. Derby always prove to be forbidding opponents and they field an adventurous-looking side, but I think they have really come to defend, and hope to sneak a goal that just might win the match. The team is: Hoult, Laursen, Stimac, Prior, Schnoor, Powell,

Carsley, Burton, Eranio, Wanchope and Sturridge. In the first half, if anyone looks as if they are going to score it's Derby. Paulo Wanchope has a marvellous opportunity following a splendid move involving a cross from Stefano Eranio that was turned back into the Arsenal penalty box by Dean Sturridge, but the ever-dangerous Wanchope mis-hits his shot and Seaman is able to fall on the ball.

Overmars makes two or three thrusting runs, taking him from one end of the field to the other in very quick time, but there's no end product. It's Ray Parlour, playing much better in central mid-field this afternoon than ever he did before Arsene Wenger came to the club, whose shots come closest to giving Arsenal the lead, but each of them goes one or two feet wide of the right-hand post, prompting me to suggest that perhaps Parlour genuinely does need an eye test.

Stephen Hughes seems a little out of his depth this afternoon in this fierce battle, but we later learn that he has a broken arm, so no wonder he's replaced at half-time by Nelson Vivas. Derby's man-to-man marking, not least Lee Carsley on Bergkamp, and Igor Stimac on Anelka, upsets Arsenal players and fans alike. When the usually mild-mannered Anelka is fouled yet again by Stimac, he pushes the Derby central defender. The referee calls him over for a word. Anelka listens and then makes a gesture for which he is booked for the first time in his Arsenal career.

With Anelka and three others booked, and the referee increasingly losing control of the match, the first half continues with neither side looking as though they will score. If I were a betting man I would have a large bet that these teams will meet in ten days' time at Pride Park, Derby, for the replay. The closest to a goal we get all half is when Keown, usually so dependable, in passing to David Seaman, loops the ball over the goalkeeper's head by mistake and has to nip round to redeem his almost costly error. So at half-time the score is Arsenal 0 Derby County 0.

What has become apparent in this first half is that being man-marked doesn't at all suit either Bergkamp or Anelka, and this is thwarting all of the Arsenal attack. Arsenal do step up a gear in the second half. Although they make no clear cut chances, it seems as though Arsenal are intent on attacking and Derby are intent on not letting a goal in, for rarely do they form an attack of note, nor do they trouble Keown and Adams. It means that both

Dixon and Winterburn are allowed to go forward and add to our attack, and on two occasions Dixon finds himself forward with a shooting opportunity, but his shots don't cause the Derby goalkeeper too much concern.

Ljungberg is replaced halfway through this half by Kanu and the shape of the attack radically changes with the Nigerian's skills causing many problems down Derby's left-hand side. Overmars is replaced by the huge Diawara for the last quarter of the half and the Frenchman's presence makes more room for Anelka, who slowly comes into the game.

In the final minute, with many of the Arsenal supporters around us having got up and gone home assuming the match is destined to end goalless, Arsenal win a corner on the right-hand side. Ray Parlour, for me the man of the match, goes across to take it and hits a long corner right into the centre of Derby's penalty area. The ball strikes Tony Adams, and ricochets to Martin Keown who shoots, only for the ball to hit his own player, the gangly Nwankwo Kanu, on the chest before, almost in slow motion, the Nigerian turns and slams home a high shot which beats Hoult and flies into the roof of Derby's net – surely the winner.

Derby appeal in vain for an offside, and Dean Sturridge, Derby's most dangerous forward, continues the debate with the referee as Arsenal celebrate their goal, and earns himself a red card. Derby have a minute to play with only ten men, and in injury time Anelka breaks away on the right, crosses low to Diawara who, with only Russell Hoult to beat, hits his shot low and wide. Will Diawara ever score for Arsenal? The referee blows the final whistle and Arsenal are in the FA Cup semi-final, and keeping a firm grip on the trophy they won last season. But they will have to play very much better than this if they are to beat whoever they meet sometime in April, on a neutral ground.

On 'Six–0–Six' which I listen to on my way home, nearly all the early calls are about the poor display of refereeing at Highbury this afternoon. Nine players were booked in a match that was tenacious but certainly not dirty. The calls are not only from Arsenal supporters either; Derby fans have their say, too, and talk about one of the worst refereeing displays they have witnessed this season. Everyone can't be wrong. David Mellor points out that this isn't meant to be a general attack on referees, but it has to be admitted that the standard has dropped. At least fifty of the calls coming through are to talk about how referees should be professional, he says, and to ask that something, although goodness knows what, be done and done quickly.

TUESDAY, 9 MARCH

I'm inside Highbury at quarter to eight this evening for the Arsenal v. Sheffield Wednesday league match. This is a vitally important game for Arsenal, as each league game is these days. They must win if they are to keep the pressure on Manchester United and Chelsea at the top of the table; a draw would not be good enough. So when this team of mine – Seaman, Dixon, Adams, Keown, Vivas, Vieira, Parlour, Ljungberg, Bergkamp, Anelka and Overmars – take the field, I have every confidence that they will score a good few goals and collect the much needed three points. But life isn't like that and it soon becomes apparent that something is not quite right with the way Arsenal are playing. Passes are going astray. The defence looks shaky. The midfield are winning the ball but not finding players to give it to. It's as if the engine has stuck in second gear and is in need of some fine tuning.

Sheffield Wednesday are not just sitting back and defending. They have come here for victory, unlike Derby County last Saturday. Arsenal should have gone ahead after fourteen minutes but Emerson Thorne clears Nicolas Anelka's shot off the line after Pavel Srnicek spills Tony Adams's wonderful through-ball. Seven minutes later, Benito Carbone turns up in the Arsenal penalty area and, though Seaman sprints out to block, the ball falls loose and Keown (who has had two awful games this week) clears the ball to the unmarked Petter Rudi. The Norwegian is so taken aback by his good fortune that he misses what is undoubtedly the best chance of the half. He should have fired the ball into the unguarded Arsenal net.

It's 0–0 at half-time, and quite honestly I think the score is a fair reflection of the match so far. I keep telling the chap who sits next to me that once Kanu comes on the game will change in our favour. Emmanuel Petit is also on the subs' bench and my neighbour feels that it will be the Frenchman who will turn this game if Mr Wenger brings him on. David Elleray, the referee this evening, is excellent, allowing the game to flow and, best of all, he has had no need to show one yellow card. Has there been one Premier League match this season that finished without a player being booked? Nobody around me can think of one, but it could happen tonight.

For the second half, Ljungberg, who had a shocker of a first half, has been replaced by Diawara, who takes up the left-wing role usually the domain of Overmars. The flying Dutchman moves across to the right side. Diawara nearly scores only eight minutes after the restart (but then Diawara always *nearly* scores) – Bergkamp, coming more and more into the game, breaks on the left of the Wednesday area and back-heels to Anelka. His pass finds Diawara twelve yards from goal, but he hits the post for the third time in his five-match career at Highbury. The game goes on and on and I can't see Arsenal breaking through tonight, or is that just the football supporter in me? Why are all football supporters pessimists? I just hope that Wednesday don't come up our end of the field and nick a goal. To leave this match pointless would be to say goodnight to our changes of retaining the championship title, and I still live in hope that we can pull off our double Double. Unlike other football supporters, I'm trying to be an optimist in the face of adversity.

In the sixty-second minute, Mr Wenger brings off Anelka and brings on Kanu, the wonderfully skilful forward who always seems to make things happen; not tonight, though. Wednesday defend diligently. We do everything we can, but Srnicek is in such extraordinary form that he seems to be saving everything Arsenal fire at him. A brilliant free kick by Bergkamp is pushed out for a corner, and there are other shots that look destined to finish in the net that Srnicek manages to get a hand to. Is it really to be one of those nights?

In the seventieth minute, with time fast running out, Mr Wenger plays his ace card – he brings on Petit and takes off Parlour; not that Parlour has played badly, but perhaps Emmanuel Petit has something special up his sleeve. He is greeted with the same roar that is normally reserved for cup-final-winning goals. With seven minutes to go, a quick and accurate free kick, taken by Petit, finds Bergkamp alone in the penalty box and his low shot at last beats Srnicek and gives Arsenal the goal that will surely win this match. The relief around the stadium is tangible. Well, 1–0 is 1–0, and it is three points.

Having let in the vital goal, Sheffield Wednesday have to change their tactics, come out of defence and try to equalise. This leaves more space at the back, and three minutes later, following an Overmars run, dummy, and low pass, the ball finds Kanu and his quick feet do the rest. He tricks two Sheffield defenders and slams a savage shot into the roof of the net – 2–0! Who would ever have thought it?

Two minutes from time, it's Overmars again who goes on one of his lightning, mazy runs. At the absolutely correct moment, he feeds the ball to Bergkamp, running alongside him, Dennis chips over and past a rushing Srnicek, and the ball finds its way into the corner of the net – 3–0! Had we left the match with seven minutes to go – and I felt like it for I couldn't see Arsenal scoring – we'd have missed all three goals and gone away thinking we'd only got a point. The three points put us above Chelsea and into second place, four points behind United. Perhaps we can catch them up once they become fixture-bound and don't know whether they're coming or going.

THURSDAY, 11 MARCH

In the hospitality lounge, after tonight's recording of 'Goodnight Sweetheart', Vic McGuire (Ron) tells an existential joke: a chicken and an egg are lying post-coitally in bed together, when the egg turns to the chicken and says, 'Well, that's that question sorted'. One of the best jokes I've heard in a long time.

Peter Leaver, the chief executive of the Premier League, and Sir John Quinton, the chairman, resigned today after an investigation by the League into the contract drawn up with Sam Chisholm and David Chance, two former BSkyB executives, to act as consultants in the next round of television negotiations. As reported on Radio Four news, the contracts offered the pair a £1.8 million consultancy fee each, plus massive incentive payments. These were said to feature five per cent commission each on any improvements negotiated to the existing television deal (currently worth £743 million over five years, but expected to pass £1 billion); five per cent each of pay-per-view revenue when it's introduced; and ten per cent equity each if the Premier League floats its own television company up to the business being valued at £1 billion. Thereafter they would receive one per cent of the value.

These two follow Graham Kelly and Keith Wiseman, their FA equivalents, and Jim Farry, the former chief executive of the Scottish FA, in resigning this winter. Football may be enjoying a financial boom but its administration continues to lurch from crisis to crisis.

SATURDAY, 20 MARCH

We get to Highbury five minutes before the kick-off of this afternoon's match between Arsenal and Coventry City, a match once again Arsenal must win to keep the pressure on Manchester United who are still sitting at the top of the Premier League. If Arsenal do win this afternoon, they will be just one point behind, although United don't play until tomorrow afternoon, at home to Everton, and I can't see them dropping those points. The team is Arsenal's strongest: Seaman, Dixon, Adams, Keown, Winterburn, Parlour, Vieira, Petit, Bergkamp, Anelka and Overmars. Dixon is today playing his five hundredth match for Arsenal and is awarded something in silver by Peter Hill-Wood before the kick-off.

Emmanuel Petit, who returned from injury to play against Everton last weekend and was sent off for the third time this season, will not play in the next three matches after this one, one of which is against Manchester United in the FA Cup semi-final. There has been much speculation in the newspapers this week that Petit is so fed up with being booked and sent off by what he believes to be inefficient referees, that he is seriously considering leaving England and going to play in Italy, for Lazio. That would be a tremendous loss to the Arsenal, for Petit remains the finest midfield player in the Premier League, and the perfect partner for Patrick Vieira. The two of them have not only transformed Arsenal's midfield, they have also brought Ray Parlour's game on in leaps and bounds. But Arsene Wenger believes that Petit will be an Arsenal player next season, and that he's just angry and frustrated at being picked on by referees. There were some statistics in this morning's *Daily Mirror* which pointed out that Petit's rate of accurate tackling surpasses any other Premier League midfield player, and that there are grounds to suggest that he has become a target for referees' vindictiveness.

In the game the traffic is one-way, and that way is towards Coventry's goal. Deprived of Noel Whelan and John Aloisi through suspension, and George Boateng through injury, Coventry are forced to play five across the midfield which is always going to make it hard for Arsenal to score. Yet they could so easily have been three goals to the good inside the first quarter of an hour. Overmars, put through by a hurried David Seaman clearance, finds himself up against one defender, whom he beats, and in the Coventry penalty box, only for his low shot to go wide of the near post. Then, from the most elegant Bergkamp flick, Petit finds himself inside the penalty box, but he fires his low shot just a whisker wide of the far post. Finally, Bergkamp makes space for himself in an impossible-looking position, which no other player in the Premier League could have done, and when he's in line to bend a typical curler into the far corner of the net, he misfires his shot and goes about ten yards wide.

We're all asking ourselves whether Arsenal are going to score this afternoon when the goal arrives. Receiving the ball in his usual right-hand-side position, Ray Parlour goes past one Coventry defender. Meanwhile, Nicolas Anelka has made a run taking another defender with him, which leaves Parlour free to continue his run into the penalty box and hit a low, right-foot shot with the outside of his boot past Magnus Hedman.

'He wouldn't have scored like that a year ago,' a proud Arsene Wenger says after the match. As ever, Mr Wenger is correct.

Unfortunately for Arsenal, Lee Dixon injures his ankle when he is tackled heavily for no apparent reason, and struggles for a while before being brought off. Ljungberg comes on in his place and takes up his position on the wide right of midfield, Ray Parlour moves to the right-back position, and Arsenal become disturbingly unsettled. With five minutes to go before half-time, Coventry claim a penalty. (I didn't see it but when I watch it again on 'Match of the Day' there can be no doubt that Coventry should have been awarded the spot kick.) A low cross that should have been col-lected with ease by Seaman is palmed into the path of Steve Froggatt, and as the Coventry forward is about to take the ball for-ward he is tripped by the Arsenal goalkeeper. I really don't understand what Seaman is doing recently. Whatever it is, it's not performing as you would expect of an England goalkeeper. The referee allows play to continue and the Coventry players are furious, as I think I would have been had I been a supporter of their club. Still, perhaps this is the luck required to win the Premier League. At half-time Arsenal are a goal to the good, should have been 4–0 up, and will no doubt spend a nail-biting second half hoping to hold on to their one-goal lead.

In the second half Arsenal continue to attack. Coventry have just one shot on Arsenal's goal, by Darren Huckerby, and that off-target. It's for an incident midway through the half that this match will be remembered. When Roland Nilsson and Emmanuel Petit go up for an innocent-looking cross, Nilsson falls to the ground and doesn't move. Stretchers are called immediately, and so, worryingly, is the Arsenal doctor. It doesn't look like a break, and after the match we learn that Nilsson has been rushed to hospital with two broken ribs and a punctured lung. Apparently he was struggling to breathe and the situation was extremely worrying for everyone; but Petit could not remotely be blamed for what happened.

With ten minutes of play left, Mr Wenger brings on Nwankwo Kanu for Anelka, and now we all expect something to happen. Kanu is, for me, the finest forward we have, with his extremely long legs and very quick feet. Kanu is on the pitch for just five minutes when he embarks on a loose-limbed slalom through the middle of the Coventry defence. He looks as though he's about to fall over, but manages to retain the ball and send it wide to Overmars. The flying Dutchman takes the ball from left foot to right and fires a low cross-shot into the far corner of the Coventry net.

At 2–0 Arsenal are not going to lose any valuable points this afternoon, even though they have played quite poorly for much of the match. Petit has probably had his worst game this season for Arsenal – those around me suggest that perhaps his heart just isn't in it this afternoon. Arsenal will have to raise their game at least four notches for the FA Cup semi-final against Manchester United, if they want to play in the Cup final at Wembley.

TUESDAY, 6 APRIL

This evening, it's Arsenal's home game against their bogey side, Blackburn Rovers. We haven't beaten them at Highbury for five seasons. As Rovers are dangerously situated in the relegation zone and Arsenal need three points to maintain their championship challenge, tonight's match will be hard fought and requires the control and skill of a fine referee. That's rather like suggesting that President Milosevic should personally invite all the Kosovo Albanians back to their homes, and leave flowers and champagne at each front door to welcome them. There seem to be few controlled and skilled referees in the Premier League, just a bunch of well-meaning part-timers. I have no doubt they do their best, but their best is not nearly enough.

Maurice and I take our seats just five minutes before kick-off. Never mind. The team is: Seaman, Dixon, Adams, Keown, Winterburn, Vieira, Vivas, Parlour, Overmars, Diawara and Bergkamp. Surely they are capable of finishing off Blackburn.

The game begins slowly, and the powerful wind that sweeps across the pitch doesn't help matters, but the pattern is quickly set. Arsenal do all the attacking and build skilfully, although their timing still seems not to be running as it did last season. Vivas gives the ball away incessantly throughout the game, but thankfully Rovers cannot capitalise on his profligacy. If Vivas plays on Sunday, against Manchester United, and does what he's doing tonight, I'm sure we'll pay dearly for it. However, it must be said that whenever Vivas gives the ball away, he does retrieve it, rather like a well-trained terrier.

Diawara tries very hard but seems not to have quite settled into the speed of the English game yet. There can be no doubting that he is a good player, and I believe that once he scores his first goal for Arsenal everything will start to click into place. Diawara has been so very unlucky not to have scored in his short time at Arsenal – he must have hit the woodwork four or five times – and it seems that the ball just doesn't wish to go between the posts for him. Tonight he almost opens the scoring after eleven minutes when, following a brilliant and speedily executed move between Bergkamp and Overmars, the little winger crosses the ball into Diawara's path, but from six or seven yards the Frenchman doesn't make good contact with the ball and John Filan, the Blackburn goalkeeper, saves easily.

Shortly after this, with Arsenal *knowing* that they must score tonight, Vieira nearly does so with a long-range shot that rockets straight into the arms of Filan. Then a marvellous chance falls to Tony Adams, who seems to me to be playing slightly under par this evening, but unfortunately it falls to his wrong foot, and although the Arsenal skipper tries to shoot into the net the accuracy just isn't there and the ball flies high over the Blackburn crossbar.

Blackburn really should have taken the lead when, on eighteen minutes, a rare Arsenal defensive mistake lets Ashley Ward in but he hits the cross-shot just wide of Seaman's far post and perhaps the only clear-cut opportunity that falls to Blackburn tonight goes begging. It's the first, and really only, time that Seaman is called upon. Alex Manninger, our excellent reserve goalkeeper, has broken his arm and will probably be out for the rest of the season.

The referee loses control of the game after about ten minutes, but I can't say with any certainty that this referee is the worst I have seen this season at Highbury – indeed, he might well be the best! The standard of refereeing all over England this season has been in reverse ratio to the standard of football being played. Why has the standard dropped so dramatically? Why isn't it in the same league as the refereeing I have seen in Europe? There is much niggling and cheating going on down there tonight. I don't like what I see, neither do the other supporters. Shirt pulling has become almost compulsory these days, as has falling over in agony when slightly brushed by a passing arm in a vain attempt to have one of your fellow professionals sent off and suspended. It all shows a unqualified lack of sportsmanship. This game I love is riddled with deceit, intentional or otherwise.

Arsenal score the only goal of the game about five minutes before half-time. Dennis Bergkamp, who has been described by so many as Arsenal's talisman, scores it. From a free kick following another clumsy challenge by Callum Davidson, and with the Blackburn Rovers wall no more than five yards from the ball (more deceit?), Bergkamp fires a low, fierce, right-footed drive towards the Rovers goal, but it hits the wall and comes back towards him. In what appears to me to be one movement, Bergkamp changes feet and somehow hits a ferociously swerving left-foot drive past the static Blackburn defenders, including Filan, into the far corner of the goal. It is a supreme goal from a supreme player, and hard as I try, I cannot think of another footballer in the Premier League (with perhaps the exception of David Ginola) who possesses the God-given skill to do as Bergkamp has done tonight.

Diawara comes into the game very much more in the second half and starts to look threatening, but it's Bergkamp, a class above everyone else on the field this evening, who looks capable of conjuring something from nothing. Ray Parlour nearly scores a second for Arsenal in the opening minutes of the half, but a magnificent save from Filan prevents Arsenal from doubling their lead. It's a nail-biting match if for no other reason than that the stakes are so high. If Arsenal lose or draw tonight they will have seriously damaged their chance of retaining the championship trophy, and at 1–0 there is always a chance that Blackburn will force a goal from somewhere.

In the seventieth minute Arsenal are reduced to ten men, again! With Chris Sutton crawling all over Keown, the Arsenal defender (already booked once early in the first half) lashes out and slaps Sutton with enough force for it to be heard in the stands. There is no alternative for the referee but to dismiss him, and Arsenal must play out the final twenty minutes a man short. Diawara is brought off for Kanu, Overmars is replaced by Steve Bould, who comes in to shore up the back four and prevent Blackburn from nicking an equaliser.

Ten minutes later, following a mazy dribbling exhibition by Bergkamp, he is tripped inside the Blackburn Rovers penalty area. Arsenal are awarded a penalty, and Keith Gillespie, the culprit, is sent off. Dennis Bergkamp puts the ball on the spot but much to everyone's astonishment hits a poor shot that is easily saved by Filan. And so we have to endure the final ten minutes on the edge of a precipice. Blackburn throw everyone forward in search of the equaliser, and Arsenal hold on for dear life. It's not a very convincing victory, but three points nonetheless, keeping us on track to win a second Double.

The man of the match is Nigel Winterburn, who played as good a ninety minutes as I have ever seen him play. I'm not an immense fan of Winterburn's. I'm bewildered how a one-footed player can make it to such heights in English football, but Winterburn is the exception. He regularly turns in fine performances, even if it does mean that he has to keep the ball on his left foot, no matter what the circumstances.

Friday, 9 April

Today, shopping in Oxford, I am hit by a bus!

Yes, really – I'm hit by a bus! I'm walking on the pavement –

although this area is by and large pedestrianised – but as I go to walk around a van that is coming out of the little turning by Austin Reed's, something hits me and sends me and my plastic bag flying across the pavement in different directions. People run over and ask me if I'm all right, which of course I'm not. The bus hit my upper back and right shoulder and I admit to feeling a little dazed. I can stand up so I compose myself and get on to the bus to talk to the driver. What did he think he was doing? He doesn't say much but he writes down his name, the name of the bus company, the number of the bus and the time the bus hit me and hands me the piece of paper. A woman gives me her name and work number too, in case I need a witness. If this had happened in the United States, I should now be planning my retirement. I could live off the damages claimed from the bus company. But this is Britain, and the bus driver doesn't even bother to apologise or inquire after my health!

WEDNESDAY, 14 APRIL

I suppose I could call this Arsenal day, if only because the football club consume my day one way or another. It culminates in what I think is the most thrilling FA Cup semi-final since Arsenal drew with Stoke City in 1971.

Let me start at the beginning. Jennifer d'Abo arranged a table for lunch at Sheekey's in London. I was to play host to Peter Hill-Wood, the Arsenal chairman. Maurice and I thought, quite naturally, that this would be called off when Arsenal drew with Manchester United last Sunday, but it turned out that Mr Hill-Wood was not going to Birmingham for the replay as he has a business appointment in London very early on Thursday morning. So our lunch was on. It gave me the opportunity to repay him for his kindness in having Jennifer, Maurice and me in the directors' box for the Arsenal v. Chelsea Worthington Cup débâcle earlier this season. Peter is the third generation of Hill-Woods to be on the Arsenal board, and Maurice asked how the family became involved. It seems that Peter's grandfather was a country gentleman from Glossop and after the First World War became interested in football through his local team, who were then a Football League club. Eventually, I'm not sure how, the grandfather became involved with Arsenal, and the family and the football club have been united ever since. Peter's father was the chairman, and now so is Peter, although perhaps one might describe him as a nominal chairman. I think most of the day-to-day working of the club is supervised by David Dein. However, the Hill-Wood family preside over the Arsenal, which has moved in that time from being a nothing club, always just escaping relegation, to becoming the most famous and powerful team in the land, winning all there is to win.

One of the knotty problems facing the club is where to move to. Peter was quite candid about what has happened so far (and knows I'm writing it up in my diary for publication). The club has spent about three-quarters of a million pounds just looking for and investigating the right location. Norman Foster, the famous architect, had made designs for a new stadium for the club situated in Drayton Park, but that seemingly has come to nothing. Then there's King's Cross. The problem there rests with the train service and railway company, as well as the number of listed buildings in the area – I believe the gasometers are listed, would you believe it? – and environmental contamination, all of which would make it nigh impossible for the club to move there in the near future. Peter didn't mention Northolt or Hatfield, but touched on Finsbury Park. For local reasons, the park is really a non-starter. It was so nearly Wembley. The club came close to buying the stadium. It was listed, so rather than knocking it all down and starting again, it was Arsenal's intention to build a 60,000 all-seater stadium *inside* the current one.

So it seems that Arsenal will be forced to stay at Highbury for the immediate future, which means no increase in crowd capacity. They could purchase houses around the ground, at way beyond market value, and move the South Stand back to allow more seating, but this would provide no more than another 5,000 seats and would not make financial sense. Filling in the corners of the current stadium to allow more fans to pass through the turnstiles is also a no-no. The groundsmen are profoundly proud of the pitch, as is everyone at Arsenal; it is without question the finest in the country. The reason for this is that light and wind have access to the grass. The natural weather conditions give us an almost bowling-green-type surface, which in turn helps the players.

'If we were to fill in the corners of the stadium,' said Peter, 'I think the groundsmen would commit suicide.'

So we'll just have to get used to the idea that the location where we have been watching our football for as long as we have been supporters will be where we shall continue to watch Arsenal for a long time to come.

The primary job of any chairman is to choose and secure the right manager. Once that's done, the team is in the hands of the manager, and hopefully the results will follow. This has certainly been the case with Mr Wenger. Peter said he wasn't entirely sure at first but when Bruce Rioch left, he went to Japan to meet Wenger. I'm all ears! 'What happened?' Peter was surprised by this quiet, sophisticated, erudite man and immediately wondered whether he would be able to handle some of the rougher customers who were playing for the club. Arsene Wenger quietly told him that he didn't believe this would be a problem. Man management, although Peter Hill-Wood didn't know it at the time, is Mr Wenger's forte.

So, having heard that the Frenchman could handle Arsenal's rougher elements – and at that time there were behavioural problems in abundance – and having been charmed by Mr Wenger, Peter Hill-Wood agreed that this was the man for Arsenal. Now he probably believes it was the best decision he has ever made as Arsenal chairman. He certainly admitted that last season Arsenal played the finest football he has ever seen an Arsenal side play since he began watching them, which was just after the Second World War.

Peter related a funny story to illustrate Mr Wenger's diplomacy. Earlier this season there was a row brewing, which was inevitably blown up by the tabloid press, that Nicolas Anelka was shouting off about Marc Overmars never giving him the ball during the game. Mr Wenger, who speaks no Dutch, called the players together in the dressing-room to get the problem out into the open. He told Marc Overmars, in English, that to get to the root of Anelka's problem it would be better if he were to speak to him in French, the player's mother tongue. Overmars (who speaks no French) agreed, and Mr Wenger, allegedly, asked Anelka what was his problem and what did he really think of Overmars.

Anelka went on about what a selfish colleague is Overmars, how he dislikes him, and then went into a series of French expletives. Mr Wenger sat perfectly calm, listening to his young forward, and then said in French, 'Do you feel better for having got that off your chest, Nicolas?' Anelka did. Mr Wenger then turned to Overmars and told him in English that Nicolas (who speaks very little English) was extremely sorry to have caused Overmars any problems, that he thought he was a wonderful player, and perhaps he might consider giving him the ball more because Anelka is sure they could play so well together. Overmars was happy. Anelka was relieved and happy. And Mr Wenger when he leaves Arsenal might consider a job at the United Nations. Of course, the story might be apocryphal.

Before we leave I ask Peter about obtaining shares in Arsenal – currently trading at about £4200 each! Peter said that should Maurice and I want any he could get some for us, but that seventy-two per cent of the 56,000 shares are owned by the board members, and one company own quite a chunk of what's left. We would therefore be able to pick up only three or four each – perhaps. Is it worth it? What do I want them for? Most fans have a share to entitle them to attend annual general meetings, to have a go at the chairman. I've just realised that if I want to have a go at the chairman, which I do not, I can invite him to lunch and tell him what I think of him across the table. It's cheaper than buying shares!

Peter said, 'When you're sitting at the AGM surrounded by the league championship trophy, FA Cup, the Charity Shield, the Youth Cup and the Ladies' Team Championship trophy, it's rather difficult for your shareholders to give you a hard time, isn't it?' I acknowledged that it must be, but what happens when the board isn't surrounded by all of this silverware?

'Then you can be sure of a hard time,' he said. Football fans are notoriously fickle, but can they really one season believe you can do no wrong, and the next season think you should be sacked? If Arsene Wenger never wins another trophy, I feel he has given my club more than I could ever have dreamed. In his first full season he won the Double, orchestrating the most beautiful and elegant football I have ever seen Arsenal play. This memory will stay with me forever.

Kick-off for the semi-final replay is at 7.45. Manchester United are not fielding Cole and Yorke upfront tonight, but giving Teddy Sheringham and Ole Gunnar Solskjaer the chance to shine. Both cause the Arsenal defence more problems in the first ten minutes than Andy Cole and Dwight Yorke did for the entire 120 minutes

on Sunday afternoon. Arsenal are nearly at full strength, and line
up as follows: Seaman, Dixon, Keown, Adams, Winterburn,
Parlour, Vieira, Petit, Ljungberg, Anelka and Bergkamp. I comment to Maurice that Bergkamp will have to perform for the whole
match as he did in the final ten minutes of extra time on Sunday,
when he started to dictate the game.

Sheringham finds too much space both from open play and from
dead balls, and nearly opens the scoring early on when he meets a
David Beckham cross, but the glancing header, while beating a static
Seaman, flies past the far post. Manchester United are by far the
sharper team. Vieira and Petit are taking time to settle; they are winning the midfield battle against Roy Keane and Nicky Butt, but
can't make their advantage count. Every time they push the ball forward, Anelka and Bergkamp cannot seem to get behind Ronny
Johnsen and Jaap Stam. Stam, Keane and Beckham are all booked
for silly fouls inside the opening half-hour, and so is Keown.

In the seventeenth minute, United go ahead. Beckham latches
on to Peter Schmeichel's hefty clearance and plays a short ball forward to Sheringham, who shields it from Adams and lays it back
to Beckham. He looks up and curls a fierce drive towards the
bottom right-hand corner, across David Seaman. The goalkeeper
seems to have it covered but, somehow, it eludes his dive and
curls into the back of Arsenal's net. Now they are 1–0 ahead,
United lay into the usually oh so reliable Arsenal defence.

With about ten minutes of the first half left, Arsenal start to look
dangerous. This has something to do with the fact that Petit starts
to stamp his authority on the midfield, and finds space and time to
come forward. Bergkamp gets right into the game and nearly
equalises when he for once escapes the stranglehold of Stam, goes
past the Nevilles, and pokes a shot which Schmeichel at full stretch
manages to get his hand to. Had Arsenal had a forward following
up he would have scored but Johnsen gets to the rebound and
clears the ball.

At the start of the second half, Keane plays Solskjaer in with
only the advancing Seaman to beat, but the Norwegian drags his
shot about ten yards wide of the far post. As United sense that this
game could be won by more than Beckham's goal, Mr Wenger
brings on Overmars for Ljungberg and the game changes direction. Even watching on the television, Maurice and I realise just
how important Overmars is to our success. He operates along the

left wing, and has been on the pitch for just six minutes when Arsenal equalise. Maurice and I jump out of our seats. This is going to be our night. Wembley beckons! What happens is Winterburn takes the ball off the foot of a United player, I can't recall which, and feeds it to Bergkamp, who stands way outside the United penalty area with his back to the goal. In one movement, passing players as though they do not exist, Bergkamp turns and advances towards United's goal before unleashing a right-foot shot that I'm sure Schmeichel has covered. The ball deflects off Stam's outstretched left leg and spins at speed into the far corner of the United goal, well out of Schmeichel's reach.

Now Arsenal are rampant, and we all think we've scored again just four minutes later. Bergkamp fires in a wicked low shot that Schmeichel simply cannot hold. Anelka gets to the rebound first, goes around Schmeichel and slides the ball into the empty net. The crowd go crazy, as do the Arsenal players, but Arsene Wenger has noticed that the same linesman who ruled out Roy Keane's goal last Sunday now has his flag waving for offside. David Elleray consults this linesman for some time before awarding Manchester United a free kick, and the score stays at 1–1 with everything to play for.

Then just to add more spice to this marvellous match, Keane, who was booked in the first half, scythes down Overmars and is first shown another yellow card before David Elleray pulls the red card from his pocket and United are down to ten men – as well as being on their back foot. The crowd, the commentators, the pundits, Maurice and I sense an Arsenal victory and probably inside normal time. Arsenal throw forward attack after attack after attack, and come close to scoring their winner. But as the game comes to its ninetieth minute and extra time looms, there's a further turn to this drama, and it's so dramatic that I doubt whether Maurice and I would have dared to write such a final scene. With Arsenal pushing forward the whole time – Arsenal's defence are now having their quietest time since 12.30 on Sunday afternoon – the ball is fed wide right to Parlour, playing very much more authoritatively in this second half, who beats a player and thrusts into the United penalty box. Phil Neville moves towards Parlour and dives in with a tackle that is badly timed. Parlour is sent sprawling, and Arsenal, quite unbelievably, are awarded a penalty in injury time.

As Bergkamp places the ball on the penalty spot, the commentator reminds us that Bergkamp has missed three of his last five spot kicks. Oh, no. I have the strongest of feelings that Bergkamp will miss his kick, the most important kick he has taken since he came into English football, and, who knows, perhaps the most important penalty he has ever taken in his career. Maurice says that Bergkamp can't miss this kick, for isn't it Bergkamp, more than any other Arsenal player, who wants to play in an FA Cup final? The Dutch genius steps up and hits a low, powerful shot to Schmeichel's left, which is where the goalkeeper expected it to go. He dives the right way and saves the kick. Oh, no! Maurice is out of his seat again, and neither of us can believe what has happened. Thirty seconds later the final whistle blows and Arsenal, who should be running their lap of honour around the Villa Park pitch, are forced to play a further half an hour.

I think that United will win now, despite being out on their feet and playing with ten men. Some mistake or other will occur in Arsenal's usually so-reliable back four. Maurice still thinks a 3–1 Arsenal victory will be the outcome.

The flow of the play is inclined to prove me wrong, and Arsenal carry on in the first half of extra time where they finished at the end of full time, and we nearly score. At full stretch, Schmeichel saves a fierce drive from Bergkamp, who must be feeling sick for making his team-mates play extra time at all. Shortly afterwards, Schmeichel manages an outstanding reaction save from a Ronny Johnsen deflection from a Petit corner.

It's still 1–1 at the end of the first half of extra time, and I start to wonder whether this match will go to penalties. Will Dennis Bergkamp have the chance to redeem himself? United haven't created one attack in this first period of extra time, and look lifeless, with no more energy in reserve. Furthermore, Schmeichel, in saving another shot from Bergkamp, who must want to score more right now than at any other time in his illustrious career, has injured himself. The injury is strapped up, but he can't take a goal-kick or move as freely as he would like. Alex Ferguson can't bring Schmeichel off because he has used his three substitutes. Nevertheless I still think it's United's night.

In the second half of extra time, Arsenal continually press forward and Anelka and Overmars come close to scoring but the ball refuses to go into the net for us. I can honestly admit to dreading a penalty shoot-out, for surely Schmeichel, injured and immobile as he is, will save more than Seaman. Then, in the 108th minute, it happens. Arsenal are mounting yet another attack and the ball is fed to Vieira. He looks up and sends a horizontal pass right across his midfield area but the ball falls to a hovering Ryan Giggs, not at all in any type of dangerous position. But Giggs, with energy he must have been storing up, goes past one man, two men, three men – and by now he's in the Arsenal penalty area – four men, five men, and then, once he's slightly wide of Seaman's goal, he lashes a shot high into the roof of the net. I feel physically sick. I just *knew!* When Schmeichel saved the penalty I *knew!* And now we have seven minutes to equalise and take the match to penalties. We get two chances – one falls to Tony Adams who now starts venturing forward, and the other to Nick Anelka, who finds a good shooting angle but fires well wide – and take neither. The final whistle blows and Manchester United have somehow won the semi-final and will meet Newcastle United at Wembley in May.

As United celebrate, they seem to me to be in a state of disbelief. All I can say, as Maurice gets up to leave, is a Victor Meldrew-ish, 'I don't believe it! I just don't believe it!' Maurice is pragmatic, although as upset as am I. 'It's only a game,' he says. Of course he's right, but it's not what I want to hear at this moment. I want to blame Dennis Bergkamp, largely because I need to blame someone! Yet it was Dennis who kept us in this game tonight, and has on so many occasions pulled a match out of the bag for us. He is exceptional and tonight he is the victim of human error, and we all make errors at critical times in our lives. I just wish Dennis's could have been at another time.

I suppose if a Bergkamp goal wins the league championship for us, which is all we have left to win this season, I'll forget tonight, and forgive him anything at all. Being a football supporter means desperately wanting your heroes to redeem themselves. Believe me, it doesn't make me feel in the least bit better tonight, and I wander back to the house from the Cattle Shed in a semi-dazed state. Not for us a consecutive Double. Perhaps for Arsenal this season nothing at all – except memories. I'm glad I have captured them in my diary, but there have been nights when I just wanted to fall asleep forever, and tonight is one of them. How can Maurice possibly say, 'It's only a game'? Put into perspective, though, that's all it is. Tomorrow is the tenth anniversary of the Hillsborough

tragedy, and that occurred at a semi-final. Ninety-six dead. And all
Arsenal did tonight was lose a football match.

FRIDAY, 16 APRIL

What are Arsenal's realistic chances of retaining the championship,
now that's all we have left to play for? If Arsenal can win their
final six matches, they will win the title, but neither Maurice nor I
believe they will do that any more than Chelsea or Manchester
United will. I don't think the championship will be decided until
the final week of the season. We can only hope that Arsenal pull it
off, and that Dennis Bergkamp can atone for his penalty miss by
being the man who leads us to another championship. Perhaps the
scenario might be Dennis scoring from the penalty spot against
Aston Villa in our last game, and this penalty keeps the trophy at
Highbury.

MONDAY, 19 APRIL

I arrive at Highbury this evening for what is without question
Arsenal's most important match of the season so far. Maurice says
that each next match has been the most important match of the
season so far, but now that Arsenal must win to have a chance of
retaining their league championship title, tonight's game against
Wimbledon takes on such significance. Mr Wenger puts out the
following eleven to face Wimbledon: Seaman, Vivas, Keown,
Adams, Winterburn, Parlour, Vieira, Petit, Bergkamp, Kanu and
Overmars.

It's interesting that Mr Wenger has 'rested' Nicolas Anelka. Is
this because Anelka genuinely needs a rest, or because he has not
been leading the front line as Mr Wenger would have wished him
to do? And how will Kanu play alongside Dennis Bergkamp, and
is Bergkamp really fit for tonight's all-important game? Well, in
front of a not quite packed Highbury – the match is being televised
live on Sky – Arsenal make their intentions evident from the word
go. The very fact that Adams and Keown are constantly moving
up to join the attack means that not only do Arsenal want to win
this match, but they want to win it by a wide margin, thus

improving a goal difference very inferior to Manchester United.

Despite Arsenal's incessant pressure, and having more shots at Neil Sullivan, the Wimbledon goalkeeper, than I can remember Arsenal having against any other goalkeeper this season, they cannot put the ball into the net. There are many near misses – balls that fly *just* over the bar, or *just* around the post, or that Sullivan *just* manages to get his fingertips to – but I never expect it to be *just* one of those nights when Arsenal pressurise for ninety minutes and go away empty-handed. Of course, there's always the chance that Wimbledon will break away down the Arsenal end of the pitch and score a goal, and this nearly happens on a couple of occasions, when the adventurous Arsenal back four go on sorties forward only to find themselves embarrassingly exposed. Nelson Vivas, replacing Lee Dixon this evening, is a fine and strong player when going forward, but he leaves huge holes on the right side of the defence when joining the attack, and it's usually Vivas (at least during this first half) whose inaccurate passing of the ball breaks down moves.

All of this pressure brings Arsenal reward in the thirty-fifth minute when Petit, the architect of all that is excellent in Arsenal's midfield, sends a long and accurate cross-field pass to Overmars, who beats most of the right-sided Wimbledon defence, and pulls a low cross back across the Wimbledon penalty area. Parlour, running from a wide and deep position, reaches the cross and sends a low accurate shot into the corner of the net, just where he seems to be slotting in most of his goals for Arsenal these days, or nights. This cushion relieves all of the fans around me; some of the regulars, though, are away in sunnier climes on their holidays. At half-time I think we are all of us perfectly contented with a 1–0 lead, if we can just increase it in the second half. I firmly believe we can and say out loud that I can see us scoring another three goals. All the others around me find this the wildest of predictions, and the chap sitting behind me says, 'In your dreams!' We all agree that Kanu is a quite magical player, an old-fashioned inside-right schemer. Yes, that's what they used to be called! One of those players who can put his foot on the ball and create openings for all around him; but Kanu is quick, accurate, and can score plenty of goals for himself also.

The second half is just four minutes old when Winterburn breaks down a very promising Wimbledon attack, drives out of defence and runs well forward with the ball. Is Winterburn the most improved player in the Arsenal team this season? And is he the greatest one-footed player of the 1990s? With many options at his disposal, he lays the ball left to Vieira who strides forward and crashes a low, right-footed shot past Sullivan, who really hasn't a hope of keeping the ball out of the net. Arsenal 2 Wimbledon 0. Surely we have gained the three much needed points this evening? But Chelsea lost a two-goal lead inside the last eight minutes yesterday afternoon, although it should be said that Chelsea don't have Arsenal's magnificent defence.

With the two-goal lead comes a confidence that seems to infect Vivas who nearly scores a third with a remarkably powerful header from a Petit corner kick. Just because we disappointingly lost to Manchester United last week does not make us a bad side; indeed we are a good enough side to win this season's championship. After all, we are the champions!

Kanu is the next scorer, when he heads a flicked cross from Petit against the inside of the far post, the rebound hits Ben Thatcher and both defender and ball finish up in the back of the net. Then Dennis Bergkamp, who has threatened to score all evening and come so close with some brilliant long-range shooting, breaks away from one defender after another and fires a low shot past a diving Sullivan. The goalkeeper, to his credit, gets his hand to the ball but the power of the Bergkamp shot is too great, and Arsenal are 4–0 up. We are all of us out of our seats once more, and when Arsenal add a fifth, through the outstanding Kanu (what a difference he makes to this forward line), I honestly believe that we will see a record premier League score tonight. I wonder what the Sky Sports commentary team are making of this Arsenal performance.

So inside the space of seven minutes, we find that we are 5–0 up, and with half an hour left to play I am rather hoping that we might score eight, nine or even ten goals tonight. Goal difference could, come the end of the season, be oh so important.

Arsenal continue to go forward, and every time the ball reaches Kanu all the supporters believe anything is possible, for his skill and touch are just astonishing for such a big man – he moves around the Highbury pitch as if he were a ballet dancer. Wimbledon bring on John Hartson, who cost the club £7.5 million, and when I compare him with Kanu I know that Arsene Wenger got it right again. One is a bruiser, the other an artist, and this artist has made a significant difference to Arsenal tonight.

Dennis Bergkamp is brought off the pitch, and moments after he leaves to tumultuous applause (and I noticed that every single on-field player went across to congratulate him when he scored his goal, and the crowd went wild with chants of 'We've got Dennis Bergkamp'), Wimbledon score a goal. From a Ceri Hughes free kick, Wimbledon's most impressive player by far, Carl Cort, rises above the Arsenal defence, as he had been doing for the entire evening, and glances a header past the static David Seaman. I guess Cort deserves the goal. I don't believe I've seen a forward from any other club, including Dinamo Kiev, make life so hard for the Arsenal defence, both in the air and on the ground, as Carl Cort has done this evening. He's one to watch, and has impressed me tonight almost as much as Kanu.

A match that finishes 5–1 in Arsenal's favour is not to be sneezed at. We now find ourselves just one point behind Manchester United, who on Sunday, following what will be a bruising battle with Juventus on Wednesday night, travel to Elland Road to face an emerging young Leeds United side. If Leeds can take all three points, and Arsenal can win at Middlesbrough (if, if, if), then on Sunday evening Arsenal will be heading the Premier League and the destiny of the championship will be in our hands. All we will have to do is win all our remaining games, none of them easy, some supremely difficult. We have to face Derby County and Aston Villa at Highbury, and travel to Middlesbrough, Leeds United and Spurs.

WEDNESDAY, 21 APRIL

Astonishingly, Manchester United have won 3–2 at Juventus and after thirty-one years are in a European Cup final. They will meet Bayern Munich, who this evening won 1–0 against Dinamo Kiev. Munich are not the bookmakers' favourites, that falls to United at 7–4, although Bayern have hardly lost this season and have some world-class players in their ranks; not that United don't – well, they have one, Peter Schmeichel.

Who will win the final? It would be wonderful for English football if United could pull it off and become the first English team to do so since we were banned from Europe in 1985. Can United win

the Treble? I doubt it. Somewhere along the line they are sure to
fall down. History tells us this, although the United squad is larger
than any that went before, so I suppose it's possible. But they have
Arsenal hunting them down in the football league, Newcastle desperate to win the FA Cup this year, and Bayern Munich, who must
feel confident over one game. We shall see. It's all very exciting. I
have to say well done to United. The European Cup is the one
trophy they wanted and now they have the best opportunity they
will ever have to win it in Barcelona in May – three days after the
FA Cup final.

It would have been spectacular had Manchester United been
meeting Arsenal in Barcelona, ten years to the day after we won
the championship at Anfield. It isn't to be because Arsenal
dropped a point in Lens, and another at Wembley against Dinamo
Kiev. Had we secured those lost points, we would have qualified
to play Real Madrid in the quarter-finals. It would have been hard,
but it would have been possible. I have to admit I don't think we
would have overcome Bayern Munich, but it would have been
delightful to have been there, to have tasted a semi-final of the
European Champions Cup. Perhaps next season.

SATURDAY, 24 APRIL

The Radio Five Live commentary comes from the Riverside
Stadium, home of Middlesbrough football club. The match is three
minutes old when I tune in, just in time to hear Arsenal receive a
penalty. Apparently, Vieira broke through the Middlesbrough
defence and slid the ball into the penalty area. Anelka, so quick,
had latched on to the ball before Steve Vickers had realised Anelka
was in the box, and a vain attempt at a tackle brought Anelka
down. Overmars (in Bergkamp's absence with a groin strain) steps
up to take the kick and sends it past a diving Mark Schwarzer.
Things are looking good but I could not in three months of
Sundays have foreseen what is to happen next.

It's not one-way traffic; Middlesbrough could have equalised,
even taken the lead against the run of play. David Seaman makes
some brilliant saves from Dean Gordon and Brian Deane. But
Arsenal are imperious, and seem to be carrying on where they left
off against Wimbledon.

In the thirty-eighth minute, Gordon is caught in possession by the magnificent Vieira, playing so much better since Petit is back at his side. Vieira sends a through ball to the dashing Anelka. Nobody is going to catch this greyhound once he sets off, and nobody does, which means the young Frenchman is through on goal with only Schwarzer barring his way. Anelka shimmies, goes around the Middlesbrough goalie, and Arsenal are 2–0 up. Two minutes later, it's Anelka again who picks up the ball on the right-hand side of Middlesbrough's penalty box, where you would usually find Ray Parlour, and he sends a low cross into the centre of the box. Kanu is there – that he is surrounded by Middlesbrough defenders matters not a jot. He merely side-steps those in front of him, and sends a low, precision side-foot shot into the corner of the Middlesbrough net. Just before half-time, Robbie Mustoe misses a chance to bring Middlesbrough back into the match, curling his shot just beyond the far post.

At 3–0, Arsenal know that they will win this match, and I'm quite amazed at the ease with which the Gunners are taking Middlesbrough apart. Nobody else has this season. By this time, a group of us has gathered in Maurice's kitchen where we make a pot of tea and listen to the second half. Arsenal dominate the match, almost as if they need to score another five this weekend, which would bring their goal difference level with Manchester United.

In the fifty-eighth minute, Arsenal score the best goal of the afternoon in terms of movement, masterclass, team effort. Vieira picks up the ball in midfield, feeds it low and right to Anelka, and sets off on a ghosting run into the Middlesbrough goalmouth. Anelka, of course, beats anyone who faces him by sheer speed (how can any footballer be so fast?) and he sends in another accurate cross that finds Overmars. Without breaking step, the Dutch winger just taps the ball into the path of Vieira who buries a low shot in the far corner of the net. Two minutes later, it is 5–0. This time Lee Dixon crosses low and accurately from the right wing, and Kanu (the best player on the field this afternoon by a mile – so good is he that Arsenal do not even miss Dennis Bergkamp) produces one of the finest goals I have seen from an Arsenal player in many seasons. It's a back-heel flick on the run, with power, that speeds past a diving Schwarzer and finds its way into the far corner. It's as dramatic a goal as any overhead scissors kick you will see, but it is executed with such subtlety that you wonder what other party pieces Kanu has in his size 15 boots.

Then Arsenal score a sixth goal. This is remarkable! In the seventy-seventh minute, Anelka receives the ball with his back to the goal at the edge of the Middlesbrough penalty area. So what does he do? He spins around two defenders, drags the ball on to his right foot, and hits such a tremendous drive that Schwarzer doesn't move, merely watches the ball flash past him and into the net. And that still isn't the end of the scoring. As Arsenal press forward in search of a seventh goal, Middlesbrough score when Armstrong heads a corner kick past Seaman, off the far post and into the net. The match finishes Middlesbrough 1 Arsenal 6, and what this means is that Arsenal have scored eleven goals in their last two matches, go top of the Premier League (although they have played two more matches than Manchester United) and have closed the goal difference gap to one in United's favour.

With United having a very difficult match at Elland Road tomorrow morning, and the possibility of United dropping three or two points, things are looking up for Arsenal. After the match Bryan Robson, the Middlesbrough manager, and former United captain, says, 'This Arsenal team has got to be up there with Liverpool of the seventies and with Manchester United sides of recent years.' This afternoon Arsenal have given an exhibition of exceptional football played along the ground, and if they had not played more games than United I would predict that on this form they will retain their championship. Whatever happens, I believe Arsenal will return to the European Champions League next season and that will mean more adventures across Europe, and probably at Wembley, too.

WEDNESDAY, 5 MAY

Whatever else happened today is eclipsed by tonight's edition of 'Match of the Day' which features the best array of games to be seen on one night this season – Liverpool v. Manchester United (the game Sky Sports choose to televise live); Chelsea v. Leeds; and, most important of all for Maurice and me, Tottenham Hotspur v. Arsenal. This is *the* match Arsenal cannot afford to lose (I keep saying that, don't I?) or even to draw, for if they do the race for the championship could be all over by ten o'clock tonight.

At ten, Maurice and I return to the Clarges Street flat and settle down to watch the highlights of each match without knowing the scores. While the dreadful opening sequence is playing, I mention to Maurice that if the Spurs v. Arsenal game is shown first, it's either because there has been a major upset, or else it's simply the best of the three matches. Des Lynam introduces tonight's main match – '. . . very exciting, sit back and enjoy this, it comes from White Hart Lane . . .'

'Oh no,' I cry to Maurice.

For the next twenty minutes, we watch Arsenal play their brand of beautiful football, in very difficult weather conditions, for it seems to be pouring with rain in London N17, and the most hostile fans of Tottenham drown out any attempt by the Arsenal supporters to make themselves heard. I don't know how many Arsenal fans travelled to Tottenham this evening, probably only a handful. Arsenal erected big screens inside Highbury for tonight's match, and Ken Friar, to whom I spoke earlier today, told me that as many as 20,000 could be there tonight. If circumstances had allowed, Maurice and I would have been at White Hart Lane this evening. We are kept on the edge of our armchairs as Arsenal throw caution to the wind and start the match with a flurry of attacks.

The match is but eight minutes old when the maestro, Dennis Bergkamp, tonight playing upfront alongside Nicolas Anelka (which means the wonderful Kanu is relegated to the subs' bench, not the stigma it once was), takes the ball between Luke Young and Sol Campbell, draws Steve Carr towards him, and then offers a mouth-watering invitation to Marc Overmars to put Arsenal an early goal in the lead. However, Ian Walker is quickly off his line and Overmars's shot is blocked and runs away for a corner. If each side only manages two opportunities tonight, Arsenal have just wasted one of theirs.

Eight minutes later, Arsenal get their second goalscoring opportunity and this time they take it. As one would expect, the chance comes from the genius of Bergkamp (I wonder what the Spurs fans think of our Dutch virtuoso) who sends a pinpoint pass behind Sol Campbell, who this evening looks decidedly indifferent. Running from deep in midfield, Emmanuel Petit controls the ball with his first touch. With his second, he loops it over the advancing Ian Walker's head and into the Tottenham net. Maurice and I jump for joy and a little relief is evident.

Arsenal create their third goalscoring chance when Bergkamp draws Tottenham defenders towards him and slides a precision pass between Young and Campbell. Before anyone in a white shirt can move, Nicolas Anelka is on to the ball, brings Walker off his goalline, and slides the ball into the net. Arsenal are 2–0 up and surely they will take the three points tonight. I would love to have been inside Highbury this evening instead of inside of Claridges. Slightly different I know, but one cannot compare one with the other. I will always remember the night Arsenal went to White Hart Lane and gave them and George Graham a lesson in superlative football skills.

Three more chances fall to Arsenal before half-time. Anelka has a fine shot saved by Walker, then his header from a Petit corner smashes against the underside of the Spurs crossbar, and Parlour could easily have scored when left alone wide right inside the Spurs penalty area. He is indecisive about whether to pass or shoot, opts for the latter, and the cross shot goes a long way wide. In the forty-third minute Vieira is adjudged to have tripped David Ginola, but to Maurice and me it doesn't look like a foul the first time we see it, neither on the playback. However, Steve Dunn, the referee, gives Spurs a direct free kick about twenty yards from Arsenal's goal, and Darren Anderton's softish shot somehow squirms under David Seaman's dive and into the corner of the net. I can only imagine that Seaman saw it late, wasn't paying attention, or the greasy turf made the ball travel far quicker than it seemed to on the television. Arsenal go in at half-time leading 2–1.

We watch the second half anxiously, as Spurs manage to create a lot of chances, one of which Steffen Iversen should have buried, which in turn might well have buried Arsenal's championship ambitions; but Iversen hurries his fierce shot and it goes wide of Seaman's goal. Arsenal, too, have more chances, two of which are spurned by Overmars, but as Maurice and I are having trouble remaining in our seats – not least when it looks to us as if Winterburn and Keown (back from suspension) bring down Iversen well inside the penalty area, and Mr Dunn thankfully denies Spurs a penalty, which they would have missed anyway – Arsenal score a third goal with just three minutes left to play.

And a remarkable goal it is, too; and if a remarkable goal is scored, only one man could have scored it. Yes, Kanu!

Kanu is brought on for a tired Dennis Bergkamp, who has inflicted enough damage on the Spurs defence. Receiving the ball in the inside-right position (for those who can't remember what that is, it's, well, inside right), Kanu chips it over Luke Young's head, spins around him (à la Pele) and fires the ball past a groping Walker. What a goal! What a win! Three more valuable points, and Maurice and I breathe a sigh of relief as we stretch our weakened bodies. It's a little like the penultimate scene from *Fever Pitch*. I think I felt more nervous tonight than I did the night Arsenal went to Anfield and won 2–0 to take the title, ten years ago. Beating Spurs is important in itself, but winning three points here when they will contribute to Arsenal retaining the title is even more nerve-racking.

Arsenal must play Leeds United away next Tuesday night, and Aston Villa on Sunday week. United play at Middlesbrough on Sunday, at Blackburn Rovers next Wednesday, and at home to Spurs on Sunday week. Wouldn't it be ironic should it be Spurs who hand Arsenal the championship?

FRIDAY, 7 MAY

Today is the read-through of the last ever episode of 'Goodnight Sweetheart' written by Maurice and me It takes Gary Sparrow through an adventure that has Yvonne (his 1999 wife) discovering that there is another woman in Gary's life. She follows him and finds that her husband is able to disappear, but to where? Yvonne discovers that Gary is a time-traveller, but what nobody can expect is that Gary becomes locked into 1945 on the eve of VE night and cannot return to the present day. One could accurately describe this episode as 'all being revealed', and it has a very sad ending.

It is with a glint of sadness that our actors, Nick Lyndhurst, Vic McGuire, Christopher Etteridge, Emma Amos and Liz Carling read for the last time the characters that we created for them. I should imagine that there will be a sombre atmosphere at Teddington Studios next Tuesday night when Gary Sparrow says goodbye to Yvonne to begin a new life in immediate post-war Britain and all that entails. I'm moved, too. I have come to like and really appreciate this series, not least because of the fine balance of characters. We have taken them through six years – in fact, the duration of the Second World War.

As we read this final episode, I think to myself that here is another Marks & Gran creation that has reached its inevitable conclusion, but three series after all the pundits thought it would. That says something for the way that we have revitalised the show, made it grow, made it fascinating; my goodness, it even has its own Web site on the Internet. I think it was always likely to be a series that was going to appeal to what Maurice refers to as 'anoraks', and it most certainly has.

SATURDAY, 8 MAY

At Arsenal's training ground, near St Albans, I'm to be photographed with Arsene Wenger and Tony Adams, by Gemma Levine, and I'm really nervous, which is unusual for me.

When Arsene Wenger arrives, I shake the great man's hand and ask him if it has been an enjoyable season. 'Yes, I think so,' he replies. 'We have played very well in part and have learned much.' I tell him that I hope Tony Adams will be lifting the championship trophy at Highbury on Sunday week, and say that the title is now in our hands. 'But it's not,' he says. 'It must be in Manchester United's hands, they have a game more than us. It could finish up that we have the same number of points and the same goal difference, then it will be decided on who has scored more goals and it will be them. I don't consider this to be fair. We should receive the trophy on the basis that we have taken four from six points from them this season. That's how it should be decided.' I agree with Mr Wenger. We talk, too, about his team and how it appears to be getting stronger all of the time, and why.

'We are always looking to strengthen the squad, but only with the right players. We know who we would like.'

'Who?' I ask.

Mr Wenger smiles and before he can tell me that he doesn't wish to answer my question, we are joined by Tony Adams. Much to my amazement, he and I have an instant rapport. I tell him how much I enjoyed his book and its honesty. He thanks me very much and I'm struck by his politeness. I tell him that I have known alcoholics. Another Tony I knew went on a week-long binge, as he often did, and one morning woke up next to a woman he didn't know. She told him she was his wife and that he had married her a week ago. Tony Adams tells me that the same thing happened to him, and he doesn't at all remember his wedding day.

'I don't remember winning the European Cup-Winners' Cup either,' he says.

We have a long discussion about how he decided that he couldn't go on with the constant drunkenness and continue to play football.

'It would be training and then a bottle of Chablis,' he tells me. 'I just missed so much of my life.'

Tony Adams is unwaveringly honest and explains how he now gives talks to schools and helps fellow alcoholics, 'because you're always an alcoholic'. In the next few months, he's speaking at the Oxford Union and will send me tickets; says he'd like to see me there.

I don't think any pre-conception I have had about a fellow human being could have been more off the mark than the pre-conception I had about Tony Adams. He is everything most people believe him not to be – a kind, caring, sensitive, intelligent man, who has recently realised that life doesn't have to be looked at through the haze of alcohol, and that his great achievements can be cherished by real and not fudged memory.

TUESDAY, 11 MAY

Tonight Arsenal lost their crown as champions of the Premier League. The trip to Elland Road that I believed would result in a victory for Arsenal doesn't turn out that way, and by fifteen minutes to ten tonight I know that Arsenal will need an act of God (the same one that's watching over the Manchester United goalmouth) to retain their title. Leeds United have throughout the season, but especially under the management of David O'Leary, become a force to be reckoned with. Only Old Trafford provides a harder match. In the end Arsenal lose 1–0, but it could so easily have been 2–0.

Maurice decides to stay here at Spring Hill. He says he would much rather watch this all-important match with me than on his own, and I feel much the same way.

Before the match begins, Sky Sports reporters go outside into
Elland Road to ask the Leeds United fans what they want to
happen tonight? They all want Arsenal to win the championship,
much rather than Manchester United, but they also want Leeds to
win tonight's match. Of course, the two are not compatible. If they
were really pushed, would they want their team to lose? It's like
the Spurs supporter who rang up Radio Five Live at lunchtime,
when they were having a phone-in to talk about this year's title
race, to say that he would prefer his team to lose 5–0 at Old
Trafford on Sunday rather than let Arsenal win the title again.
Fans are very mixed up. I remember when the chap who sits next
to me at Highbury told me that he thought it would give him
more pleasure to see Spurs relegated than to see Arsenal win the
championship – and this man is married to a Spurs supporter!

When the game gets under way, it looks as though Arsenal
will manage to score one or two goals on the break, although the
ferocity of the tackling by Leeds United indicates that they are
not going to lie down and allow Arsenal an easy ride. David
Batty nearly scores for Leeds with a wonderful volley after just
two minutes. Then Arsenal have several chances, the closest
being a Bergkamp bending shot that Nigel Martyn manages to
get his fingertips to. Parlour has a wonderful chance to put
Arsenal ahead, as do Overmars, Adams and Anelka, but both
Maurice and I recognise that all is not well with Arsenal's move-
ments this evening. Parlour, Bergkamp and Anelka look way
below par, especially Parlour, who continues to give the ball
away in dangerous positions. Perhaps the greatest disappointment in the side is Emmanuel Petit, who by his own majestic
standards is playing like an average midfield player. Yes, he's
everywhere, and involved in everything, but he seems not to be
firing on all cylinders.

Each side has fifty per cent of the possession in the first half, and
both have exactly the same number of attacking possibilities, the
difference being that Leeds United are awarded a penalty in injury
time. It's an unnecessary penalty, too. Martin Keown heads a
sloppy ball back in David Seaman's direction, and with the ball
looking as though it's running out of play, even though it's being
chased by Alan Smith (not the one in the Sky studio, the young
blond-haired Leeds striker) there seems to be no danger. Even if
Smith recovers the ball, I can't see him going anywhere from the

position in which he finds himself. Then Martin Keown comes clattering into Smith, taking his legs right on the goalline, and the referee, Gary Willard, quite rightly awards a penalty.

Young Ian Harte steps up to give Leeds a half-time lead, or at least so every supporter in the stadium believes, but Harte hammers a shot against the Arsenal crossbar, and from the rebound Jimmy Floyd Hasselbaink rifles a low shot straight at the Arsenal goal and somehow or other Seaman not only saves the shot, but holds on to it. This let-off might be a good omen, but what is certainly not is the manner in which the referee seems intent on booking Arsenal players for precisely the same tackles as the Leeds players are committing and getting away with. Hasselbaink goes into the referee's book and so do Vieira, Petit, Parlour and Dixon, and goodness knows how Keown avoids another booking and being sent off. Perhaps the referee's notebook ran out of space.

In the second half, Arsenal look tired and jaded. I can't remember seeing them quite like this. They create few goalscoring opportunities in the first half of this second half, and it seems to me that Leeds will score, despite the fact that Martin Tyler and Andy Gray are talking about how well a point will suit Arsenal. No, I say to Maurice, someone will score a goal. Arsene Wenger knows it must be Arsenal and so he replaces Ray Parlour with Kanu, and Marc Overmars with Kaba Diawara, and later when Nigel Winterburn has his nose broken on the bridge and is out cold with concussion, Nelson Vivas comes on, too.

So now Arsenal are playing with four forwards, although Bergkamp is below par, and they push forward for the goal that will give them the vital three points. Kanu makes a difference and plays two delightful through balls to Bergkamp, who can do nothing with either as he is being carefully monitored by Jonathan Woodgate, playing very well indeed. Diawara, who has yet to score for Arsenal but has come so close so often, almost scores the goal that Arsenal now desperately require. Oh dear, time is running out.

A Bergkamp cross finds Kanu, who for once just can't reach the ball, but it does break for Diawara. He hits a terrific volley which Woodgate heads off the line. About three minutes later, Diawara has a header hit the bar and bounce out of play. No, I don't believe tonight is going to give us the three points we so desperately desire. And yet I still believe a goal will come, which I suppose means that it will come from Leeds United – and it does.

As Winterburn's injury was so serious and play was held up for five or six minutes, the fact that we have reached the ninetieth minute only means that we have about six minutes of injury time to play. Very early on in this period Leeds score, and I can't help believing it's due to Winterburn's absence. Adams, who has been playing magnificently at the centre of defence, feels it's time to go forward, although other than one volley, he never looks as though he's going to score; and he's forward when the ball reaches Harry Kewell, who breaks down the left-hand side. Kewell sets off on a run, much as Ryan Giggs did in the semi-final replay, and when he beats Dixon, he sends in a cross that evades the Arsenal central defence and Seaman. Jimmy Floyd Hasselbaink, the bane of Arsenal it would seem, dives in to head Leeds into the lead. What is so galling is that Hasselbaink scores from precisely the position Winterburn would have been marking had he been on the field. Vivas, I'm sad to say, is nowhere to be seen!

Arsenal now can at best hope for just the one point. They will not nick the three. Really they haven't deserved three points tonight, even though they have done the bulk of the attacking. Much praise must go to Patrick Vieira, who has played wonderfully well, and to David Seaman, who really has kept Arsenal's chances alive until the goal went in. But Nicolas Anelka was anonymous tonight, and it's apparent to anyone who watches the Arsenal regularly that many players are not fit. Had they been, who knows? But they're not and now United, who must have formed a giant conga along the streets of Manchester tonight, have only to win their final two games against Blackburn Rovers and Tottenham Hotspur to take this year's title. I suppose they will.

I'm not so unhappy, or deeply upset even, as I was the night we lost the FA Cup semi-final replay to Manchester United, for on that night I knew we should have been in the final. Tonight, I can't justifiably say that we should have won. The match was even and we neither played up to our usual standard nor created many goalscoring opportunities. I think a draw would have been a fair result. I don't believe we deserved to lose. But lose we did, and though not gutted, I'm slightly filleted.

Thursday, 13 May

After the final 'Goodnight Sweetheart' there's an end of series party. We have had these in the past, but never one quite so final. Maurice and I always said, even to Nick Lyndhurst the day we met him for the first time, that we wanted to take the series only to the end of the war, May 1945. Of course, that seemed like a lifetime away when we started. Anyway, none of us imagined, only hoped, that the series would take off the way it did and we would actually reach our target, VE night 1945. Yet here we are, having achieved our aim, and now it's time to say goodnight, sweetheart.

Sunday, 16 May

This afternoon as Maurice and I walk to Highbury, we see a poster in a car window that really amuses us. It reads: 'Come on you Spurs . . . Scum!' Fingers crossed for a Spurs win or draw at Old Trafford, but I'm not holding my breath. Everyone's optimistic about this afternoon, except me. The gang around us believe that Spurs will get a draw at Old Trafford and we will win at a canter. I think Manchester United and Arsenal will both win and Arsenal will therefore be second to United and qualify for Europe. They all think I'm way off target.

When the game begins, the atmosphere is tense. It looks as though Arsenal's mind is on only one thing, winning this match. It isn't going to be easy for Villa have crowded nine players back behind the ball, and for the first twenty minutes I can't see a route through. Every move is tense, every player nervous, and it shows, even from my place high in the East Stand. Vieira seems more fearful than most, and gives away the ball in situations where he would usually deliver a telling pass. Anelka seems to be out of sorts, and out of the game, and I'm wondering whether this is the last time I shall see this young and fine centre-forward wearing an Arsenal shirt, despite the claims by Mr Wenger that young Nicolas will not being going anywhere.

Bergkamp and Overmars are creating whatever openings there are to be created, and both come very close to opening the scoring. Villa clear a Vieira header and a Bergkamp free kick off the line, and Overmars should have scored when he broke down the left, through the Villa defence. With only Michael Oakes to beat, he shoots at the goalkeeper's legs and the ball spins away. Last season in such a position, you would have backed Overmars to give Arsenal the lead.

After about twenty-five minutes, the biggest cheer of the afternoon goes around the ground and shakes Highbury almost to its foundations. It is pure euphoria! No, Arsenal do not score, but Tottenham do, through Les Ferdinand, 200 plus miles away from this stadium. Never in all my years as an Arsenal supporter have I heard so much praise and cheering for Spurs as comes from the crowd this afternoon. People who are continually slagging off Spurs and anything to do with them – and that includes George Graham – are now singing their praises, cheering them on, calling them – wait for it, wait for it – magic! Are my ears deceiving me? Manchester United 0 Spurs 1. Who would ever have thought it? But there's a long, long time yet to play, and none of us should forget that not only haven't Arsenal scored yet, as they must, but also Spurs have to hold on to this lead, or at least not let in more than one goal, for about seventy minutes.

The buzz around the stadium is probably better than anything I've heard since we won the title here last May, but this enthusiasm seems not to transfer itself to the Arsenal players, who continue to struggle to find a way through the Villa defence. And there are scares, too. Villa have better chances than we do, and waste all three of them. By half-time, Arsenal have had seventeen shots on goal and yet other than the three I've mentioned I can't remember what others there were.

With only three minutes of the first half left at Old Trafford, and the first half completed at Highbury, David Beckham equalises for United and the crowd go into a silence that can be heard for miles around. The guy in front of me, today wearing a funny red-and-white hat and an earpiece that is connected to his portable radio – there must be 25,000 portable radios inside the stadium this afternoon – turns around and tells us that Beckham has bloody well equalised, and I see this goal as the beginning of a torrent. And still we have yet to score.

We kick off for the second half two minutes before they restart at Old Trafford and immediately charge down on Villa's goal, but I can't help thinking that this afternoon, as on Tuesday night, we have lost our shape and this means we are trying things that we haven't tried or done all season. Four minutes into our second half, the guy in front of me tells us that Andy Cole has put United ahead and I know in my heart that no matter what we do this afternoon we cannot prevent Manchester United from winning this year's title.

Arsene Wenger, who said that he would not be listening to what is happening at Old Trafford, makes some substitutions. He brings off Nicolas Anelka, and rightly so, and replaces him with Kanu, and later brings off a very tired Marc Overmars for Kaba Diawara. Now Arsenal have used all three of their substitutes so let's hope there are no further injuries.

I don't really know how long Kanu is on the field but his appearance makes all the difference to the Arsenal; he gives them so many more options. Almost predictably, Kanu scores the goal that gives Arsenal some hope. I don't know whether they know that Manchester United are 2–1 up, but that doesn't matter. Arsenal are now a goal up and play as though they mean to add to their typical scoreline. We can all of us hope that Spurs equalise. But it isn't to be, not this season. Arsenal win their final league game by 1–0, but Manchester United, two minutes after the final whistle blows at Highbury, remain 2–1 up and win the 1998–99 championship by one point.

We finish with no silverware at all, but for all that it has been a jolly good season, particularly this year when the only two games that we lost were against Manchester United in the FA Cup semi-final (which we really should have won) and against Leeds United, that oh so vital match last Tuesday which we did not deserve to lose.

I think the summer break will fire up the Arsenal and they will return in August all the better for their rest. They will surely present to us fans some new names, new faces, probably players we have not heard of, but that will not make them lesser players. Arsene Wenger knows that he must strengthen his squad if he is to make a greater impression in Europe than he did this season. Without Dennis Bergkamp for European away matches, we will at least have Kanu, and once he is fully fit and playing for us regularly (instead of whom?) I wager he will be our top scorer, if not the top scorer in the Premier League.

And who shan't we see at Highbury next season? Well, there is talk that Anelka will go, and perhaps Emmanuel Petit, but I would rather believe that they will both take the field of play in August and be part of a squad that will regain the championship. I have a feeling that Manchester United won't be quite the same team without Peter Schmeichel, who this afternoon said goodbye to Old Trafford.

So are United a better team than Arsenal? Well, United have won the championship and Arsenal haven't so I suppose statistics speak for themselves. But I don't think there's much between them. Sure United have greater strength in depth and that's the reason they have taken the title, but Arsene Wenger buys only fine players, and he will buy some more between now and August, of that I am certain.

This was Arsene Wenger's second full season, and winning the Double in his first season was a difficult act to follow. Perhaps had the right type of player to suit his system and plans become available much earlier in the season, we should have had a much stronger squad in our European campaign. Perhaps had we not had as many French and Dutch international players (although goodness knows, I'm delighted that we have) we wouldn't have had as many of our first team playing the first game of the season as if it were the last. Fitness was ground out of those who took part in a very lengthy World Cup campaign, and fatigue had set in as early as August. We dropped points that I believe we would otherwise have won, and those points would have been vital come the last weeks of the season.

But it's no good crying over spilt points. We did very well, and I don't believe one Arsenal fan would suggest that there is a better manager to lead us forward into the twenty-first century than Arsene Wenger.

TUESDAY, 18 MAY

Maurice and I are interrupted this morning by Harry Harris from the *Mirror*, whom neither Maurice nor I have seen for many months. Harry wishes to invite Maurice and me to the Football Writers' Dinner at the Royal Lancaster Hotel on Thursday evening. He tells me that among those sitting at our table will be footballers Kevin Phillips and Rio Ferdinand, both full England Internationals.

I ask Harry for news on the Arsenal transfer front. I tell him that I spent some time with Arsene Wenger, and I can guess some of the great man's requirements for next season, but Harry will obviously know more than me. He says that he has been reliably informed (and Harry is more often right than wrong) that Arsenal have bought Oleg Luzhny, a full back with Dinamo Kiev, and has heard, too, that Arsenal will be exchanging Nicolas Anelka for Ronaldo in a straight swap. I gasp. The once best centre-forward in the world for the next best centre-forward in the world? Really? Why would Inter-Milan want to lose Ronaldo for Anelka? And then I consider the possibility that Ronaldo, even at twenty-three years of age, may be past his sell-by date.

Maurice tells me he has read on Ceefax that Arsene Wenger has been reported as saying he would very much like to buy some English players too, for he feels that too many foreign players could well alienate the supporter base. I don't think this will be so, although we shan't know until Arsenal's defence and Ray Parlour leave the club or retire. Then we shall not have one homegrown player in our team. I wonder how we, the fans, shall feel then?

Thursday, 20 May

We take a taxi to the Royal Lancaster Hotel and quickly make our way to the large suite where tonight's Footballer of the Year bash is being held. Harry Harris introduces me to some of those around his table, including Alan Sugar, who does not seem enthused to meet me. There is no Rio Ferdinand or Kevin Phillips to be seen. They have failed to turn up. So the token footballer on our table is Graeme Souness, looking older and not as fit as I remember him. I do not speak to him, although he is, I notice, curious to know who I am. I do speak to Alan Sugar, and it is the subject of cigars that brings us together. He is an OK sort of bloke, and take away the fact that he is chairman of Tottenham Hotspur, and of Amstrad, and what you have is a run-of-the-mill Jewish Chigwell bloke, who is fascinating in small doses but really doesn't appear to have too much dinner-table conversation.

As I browse down the list of winners of the Footballer of the Year prize since the 1947–48 season – before I was born – I can't help but notice two things: the first is that only two recipients have not been internationals, these being Jimmy Adamson in 1961–62 and Tony Book (1968–69); also that since 1993–94 not one homegrown player has been awarded this highest of accolades. After Alan Shearer won it that season, the prize has gone to Jürgen Klinsmann, Eric Cantona, Gianfranco Zola, Dennis Bergkamp, and tonight to David Ginola. What does this tell me about the modern-day British footballer? I suppose it says that he is not as good or as consistent as his European counterpart.

It is a fun evening, and the high point is meeting up again with Bob 'The Cat' Bevan, a very old friend of Maurice and mine. Bob is one of the most popular after-dinner speakers on the soccer circuit, and what must be twelve years ago Maurice and I wrote some material for him for an album (records – that's how long ago it was!) to be released at the time of the 1986 World Cup Finals. Immediately we meet, Bob starts rattling off topical jokes. One of the finest of the night was this: 'I think Robbie Fowler was hard done by when he was suspended by the FA. I've been watching a video of his celebration after scoring against Everton, and I'm not sure that all of his nose was over the line . . . although Geoff Hurst swears it was!'

NOVEMBER, 1999

And so the third season under the reign of King Arsene the First came to its close. Arsenal finished runners-up in the league and semi-finalists in the FA Cup. For any other club this would have been considered a fantastic season, but we Arsenal fans have come to expect the best and settle for little else. I reflect that but for a couple of penalty misses we might have won the Double for the second time in as many seasons . . . but it wasn't to be. And so what if Dennis Bergkamp missed in the semi-final replay? Just to have the privilege of watching him every week is enough for me. I just wish I could have his air miles.

Instead Manchester United won the Treble. An astonishing achievement with more than a soupçon of good luck, and one I reluctantly had to applaud. I don't really like Manchester United, but as Arnold Palmer once said: 'The harder you work, the luckier you get.' So Alex Ferguson's dream came true. Every commentator talked about him being knighted. *Sir* Alex? I couldn't understand why winning one European Cup final warranted a knighthood when Bob Paisley, who won four, was never Sir Robert Paisley. And what about Sir Ron Saunders? Or Sir Brian Clough – although many thought he should have been Saint Brian.

I considered the three Arsenal seasons under Mr Wenger and came to the conclusion that for all Manchester United's success, I still deem Arsenal to be the finest team in England, and the finest team cannot win everything every season. What my diary has taught me is how wrong we football supporters can be. Rarely do we predict a match result or the scorers correctly. Whenever we think we could pick a team better than the manager, it becomes apparent that we cannot. And it has highlighted to me that there is nothing I would rather less be than a football manager. No, I would much rather be a fan. It doesn't matter if you're a fan. Your job is never on the line, and if your team plays badly one week, you just get on with your life. I like my football that way.

And being a football fan was put into clear perspective on the night that Manchester United won the European Cup final, and their third trophy of the season. I switched on my radio to hear the news that Slobodan Milosevic had been indicted for war crimes and a warrant had been issued for his arrest by the International Criminal Tribunal. The indictment was expected to involve alleged war crimes in Kosovo and would be announced the following morning by the tribunal's chief prosecutor, Louise Arbour.

I was elated, for I realised at that moment just what a horrible bastard Milosevic truly is. No wonder Aston Villa got rid of him!